KT-582-979

EXPLORE

UNDERSTAND

Your 2022-23 Handbook cover has been created by renowned English artist and designer **Luke Edward Hall**, and commemorates the 1900th anniversary of Hadrian's Wall. Find out more about our collaboration with Luke at **english-heritage.org.uk/luke-edward-hall**

Luke Edward Hall

MEMBERSHIP

Your membership is helping to care for over 400 historic sites across the country. Every day, you're playing a vital role in keeping the story of England alive for future generations. Thank you for your support.

READ ALL ABOUT IT

The *Members' Magazine** comes out four times a year and is packed with inspiration and ideas for making the most of your membership. Be the first to hear about new Members' Rewards, special events and the latest news by signing up to the Members' e-newsletter at **english-heritage.org.uk/newsletter**

KIDS GO FREE

Every Member can bring up to six children to visit our sites for free. Children must be under 18 and within your family group.

EVENTS

Members enjoy free or discounted entry to a whole host of fantastic days out – see p.10 for details, or visit **english-heritage.org.uk/events**

MEMBERS' AREA

Check out your dedicated Members' Area on our website to find specially curated articles, videos and quizzes – along with back issues of the magazine. Younger Members will love the Kids' Area, which features lots of fun activities and crafts to do at home. Simply visit **english-heritage. org.uk/members** to register and log in.

Visit the Members' Area regularly to check out the latest exclusive content just for you. From quizzes written by expert historians to video series exploring the stories of our sites, we're always adding new pieces for Members of all ages to enjoy.

EXCLUSIVE MEMBERS' EVENTS

As a Member, you can delve far deeper into our sites. Our experts will invite you behind the scenes, let you handle artefacts, lead you in workshops and take you on walking tours. We have events across the country every year. Look out for these in your magazine and in your Members' Area.

MEMBERS' REWARDS

Our Members' Rewards programme gives you access to a wide range of exclusive competitions, deals and special offers, which are updated throughout the year at **english-heritage.org.uk/ rewards**

MORE DAYS OUT

Your membership card opens doors to many other associated attractions and properties – either at no extra charge or for a discounted rate. See p.298 or check the online Members' Area.

SHARE YOUR EXPERIENCE

Follow us on Facebook, Twitter and Instagram – we love to hear about your days out, as well as your recommendations and general tips for making the most of your membership.

Subscribe to our YouTube and TikTok channels to watch history being brought to life. From a Victorian cookery series with world-renowned Mrs Crocombe to our kids' interviews with characters throughout history, you'll find plenty of videos to keep you entertained and inspired.

　　　*The *Members' Magazine* is mailed directly to UK Members, and to Life Members overseas.

Welcome

As ever, your English Heritage handbook is a real treasure trove of all the key facts and information you need to plan a wealth of wonderful days out in England's past.

Whether you want to make a beeline for a certain site, browse what's on offer in a particular region or revisit an old favourite, your handbook will be an indispensable companion as you head out to explore the places where history really happened.

This year marks the 1900th anniversary of Hadrian's Wall in AD 122. It's one of England's most famous historic monuments, and we are incredibly privileged to care for a number of sites along the ancient Roman frontier. To celebrate, we're planning a year of special Roman-themed events and activities across the country. You can find out more about our plans throughout the year in your *Members' Magazine* and e-newsletter.

We're also excited to be reopening Clifford's Tower, one of York's best-loved landmarks. After years of careful planning and months of intensive building work, a sensitive new internal structure and an immersive new interpretation scheme has given the tower a new lease of life.

As ever, a huge range of conservation work is taking place across the country – much of it supported by our Members. Our project to revive the park and house at London's Marble Hill is very nearly complete, and a major programme of repair is well under way at Belsay Hall in Northumberland.

You can keep up to date with all our latest news by signing up to the newsletter and following us on Facebook, Twitter, Instagram, YouTube and TikTok. We'll also continue to bring you inspiration for days out, in-depth articles and unmissable offers in the Members' Area of the website and the *Members' Magazine*, which is published four times a year.

Lastly, I'd just like to say thank you for being part of English Heritage, and for giving us your support. Without you, we simply wouldn't be able to protect our country's past for the benefit of future generations.

Kate Mavor CBE
Chief Executive

Stonehenge, Wiltshire

Beeston Castle & Woodland Park, Cheshire

Planning
your visit

This section contains important information about planning your visit and helpful contact details.

Access

Our handbook listings indicate accessible areas of our properties with the use of the ♿ symbol. If you have a disability, your carer or companion is always admitted free. Many of our sites have accessible parking.

For more detail on access for families and visitors with disabilities at our sites, please call us on 0370 333 1181.

Email us at customers@english-heritage.org.uk, or visit **english-heritage.org.uk**

Book your visit online

You don't need to book your ticket in advance, but you'll always get the best price and guaranteed entry by booking online ahead of your visit. You can however still turn up without a booking, unless otherwise stipulated.

We can't take bookings over the phone, but please get in touch if you have difficulties booking online.

Tintagel Castle, Cornwall

Home of Charles Darwin, Down House, Kent

If you have booked a time slot for a free visit you can no longer make, please cancel it online. This will free up the space for someone else to visit. If you have booked for an event with an additional charge or paid for a non-member friend, please note that we are unable to cancel and refund your payment.

Remember to bring your membership card with you, along with a copy of your ticket confirmation email – either as a print out or on your phone.

We will follow the government's guidance on Covid-19 and have appropriate measures in place. Please visit the website for the latest advice.

To avoid disappointment, please continue to check for any local restrictions before you book or start out for your visit. You can find the latest information at **english-heritage.org.uk/plan-your-visit/**

Catering and picnics

Many of our properties offer delicious home-made food and drink. You're welcome to picnic in the grounds of most of our properties.

Dogs

We welcome dogs on leads wherever possible, but please see individual property listings and look out for the dog symbol. Assistance dogs are welcome at all sites.

Families and children

With towering castles and underground passages, tales of royal revels and wartime heroes, our sites provide endless adventures for children. From gardens to coastlines, we offer spectacular outdoor locations for fun, exploration and picnics. Alongside our events, exhibitions and interactive displays you'll also find fantastic family-friendly resources at many of our properties. To ensure everyone is safe while having fun, children visiting sites must be accompanied by an adult. For larger groups, please ensure there is a sensible ratio of adults to children.

Educational visits

Visiting an English Heritage property is an inspiring way to discover more about the past. We offer free self-led educational visits to all our sites, and excellent value hands-on expert-led Discovery Visit workshops at selected sites. These support the National Curriculum across a range of subjects and all key stages. We also provide a wide range of free downloadable teaching resources to support your visit and help with school trip planning. Find out more at **english-heritage.org. uk/education**

Guides and tours

You'll find guidebooks, audio tours and multimedia guides at many of our sites. We also provide audio guides and trails for children (some available in different languages). All of our paying sites, and a few of our free-to-enter sites, have guidebooks – almost 100 of these are 'Red Guides', with their distinctive red spines. Written by experts, all of our guidebooks feature a tour of the site together with an in-depth history of the people who lived and worked there. Packed with plans, reconstruction drawings, eyewitness accounts and beautiful photography, they make essential reading as well as brilliant souvenirs of your visit. Many of our sites provide guided tours, please speak to a member of staff to see what is available on the day. Short histories and descriptions of our free-to-enter sites are also available on our website. Dive deeper into the hidden histories of our sites with the *Speaking with Shadows* and weekly English Heritage podcasts, both available for free on major podcast platforms.

Photography

In some properties we don't allow photography, due to the sensitive nature of some materials. Non-commercial photography is welcome in the gardens and grounds of all our sites.

Safety and smoking ⚠

Due to their historic nature, some of our sites have potentially hazardous features – please pay attention to all safety notices on site. If you have any doubts, our staff can always advise on safety issues. Please wear suitable footwear to avoid accidents, and do not climb on walls or monuments. In areas of woodland deer pasture there may be a slight risk of ticks, so keep vulnerable parts of your body covered and/or use insect repellent. Smoking or vaping is not permitted inside any of our properties.

Travel and transport

Where possible in the property listings, we have provided local train information. For bus travel, please visit **traveline.info** where you can search for our sites and get the most up-to-date times and routes. Alternatively you can call Traveline on 0871 200 22 33 (calls cost 12p plus your phone company's access charge). For cycle routes, call 0300 303 2604 or visit **sustrans.org.uk**. OS Landranger/Explorer map references have also been supplied for each property.

Please note

All of our sites have uneven surfaces due to their historic and/or outdoor nature, so please wear appropriate footwear. Please observe site signage, barriers and staff instructions. Please supervise children closely. Metal detecting, smoking, fires, BBQs and unauthorised commercial photography and drones are prohibited at all our properties. Damage to our sites is a crime.

Free parking

Members enjoy free parking at the majority of our sites by displaying a current car sticker. Free parking does not apply at sites that are not managed by English Heritage. Full details of parking can be found in the individual listings in this handbook.

Pricing

If you're planning to take a visitor who isn't a Member to a site, here's all the information they will need about the price of entry.

Admission prices

Prices shown are for tickets booked online in advance and include a small voluntary donation (where applicable). You don't need to book your ticket in advance, but you'll always get the best price and guaranteed entry by booking online ahead of your visit.

Seasonal pricing applies at some of our properties, with peak, standard and off-peak prices depending on season and day of the week. This helps us to manage visitor numbers and allows us to offer off-peak tickets at quieter times.

Admission categories: Adult; Concession (over 65s, Jobseekers and students with relevant ID); Child (age 5-17, under 5s go free); Family tickets admit one or two adults and up to three children (ticket categories may vary at properties not managed by us).

We offer a 15% discount (10% for Stonehenge) for groups of 11 or more paying together. Call 0370 333 1181 or visit english-heritage.org.uk/visit/group-visits

In addition to access to our sites, we offer a variety of events that are either free or reduced cost to our Members. This varies by the scale of the programme, and whether there is external involvement. Please see the website for the latest details.

Overseas Visitors Pass

Visitors from overseas planning to visit a number of properties may save money with an Overseas Visitors Pass (OVP). These provide admission to all English Heritage properties marked with the OVP symbol over a 9- or 16-day period. Call 0370 333 1181 or visit english-heritage.org.uk/ovp

Gift Aid

UK taxpayers choosing a 'with donation' ticket and Gift Aiding their admission allow us to claim an additional 25p for every £1. This helps us to look after the historic places in our care, and keep the story of England alive for future generations. Admission tickets 'without donation' are also available; the same right of admission applies. Please also remember to Gift Aid your membership; it really does make a big difference to our work. Call 0370 333 1181 or visit english-heritage.org.uk/giftaid

Events

Welcome to an exciting year of events to inspire the whole family. As well as jousts and historical reenactments, this year we are introducing some new activities to bring even more stories to life, such as our brand-new pirates events at some of our seaside sites. Also don't miss our programme of exclusive Members' events.

Sign up for events updates

Get regular events updates sent straight to your inbox. Just visit **english-heritage.org.uk/ newsletter** to register. You can also keep up to date with our events programme at **english-heritage.org.uk/events** or check the latest copy of your *Members' Magazine*.

Old favourites

Thrills and spills are back. Once again, you'll be able to enjoy the sight of knights clashing at a joust or tournament. Romans will patrol **Hadrian's Wall** and the Second World War guns will fire at **Dover Castle**. The content of events may change depending on the restrictions in place, but there'll still be plenty of action to enjoy.

Events for all the family

Learn what it takes to be a pirate, try your hand at archery, enjoy Victorian pastimes and join historical characters in a medieval court. Take part in games, crafts and activities that will fire the imagination.

Easter adventure quests

Join us on a legendary quest during the Easter holiday. Intrepid adventurers who complete their mission will get a certificate to prove it, and there may even be a chocolate treat too!

Anniversaries

From celebrating 1900 years of **Hadrian's Wall** to reflecting on 125 years of **Whitby Abbey's** association with *Dracula*, you can enjoy a host of events marking a variety of anniversaries in 2022/23.

Fighting knights

Our brave medieval knights will take on the ultimate challenge at our fiery series of Knights' Tournaments and Jousts this summer.

Halloween events

Get into the spirit of Halloween and hunt for ghosts as darkness descends on a ruined castle. Discover spine-tingling tales of ghostly apparitions, dastardly deeds and ghoulish goings-on, or kick up crackling leaves with the kids and get creative with creepy crafts, fancy dress and spooky trails.

Christmas adventure quests

Enjoy some festive fresh air and all-new surprises as you join our fun adventure quests at sites across the country. Hunt for clues to reveal quirky tales, or sit back and enjoy a hot chocolate or mulled wine in beautiful surroundings. It's a great way for the whole family to get out and about in Christmas week.

Exclusive events for Members

Every year we put on over 150 events exclusively for Members. Meet the experts, find out what it takes to care for our sites and discover the histories of some of England's most fascinating places. Visit the Members' Area of the website or check your *Members' Magazine* for full details. In April 2022 we will be holding our Members' Week, with a special programme of events around the country just for you.

Shop with us

From traditional treats like ginger wine and lemon curd to artisan gifts inspired by our sites, our shops offer an inspiring, imaginative and unusual alternative to the high street, with ideas that cover all ages and all interests.

Each of our shops has a unique range of products inspired by the stories of our sites – expect art deco cups **Eltham Palace** (p.38), commemorative Battle of Britain pocket watches at **Dover Castle** (p.66) and Victorian kitchenware at **Audley End** (p.154). Whichever site you visit, you can expect a warm welcome from our staff and a wide selection of items, with everything from jewellery to homeware, history books to memorabilia, and food and drink to toys, games and fancy dress.

Our shops are the perfect places to pick up one of our famous Red Guides. These beautifully illustrated guidebooks feature maps, reconstructions and historical images, taking you on an expert tour of each site and telling fascinating stories along the way.

You'll also find our range of award-winning food and drink. Our alcoholic drinks are a particular highlight, with traditional fruit wines and a wide selection of meads. Mead is the world's oldest alcoholic drink, and we sell more of this delectable nectar than anyone else. Many of our sites offer free tastings of all our wines and meads – the perfect way to get a flavour of the past.

Find out more

Our online gift shop features an extensive range of products and online exclusives at **english-heritageshop.org.uk**

Boscobel House and The Royal Oak, Shropshire

Gainsborough Old Hall, Lincolnshire

Eat with us

Whether you are looking for a cup of tea, slice of cake or a more substantial lunch, we have over 30 cafés and tearooms across the country to choose from.

Stonehenge, Wiltshire

Walmer Castle and Gardens, Kent

Audley End House and Gardens, Essex

Marble Hill, Twickenham

Our cafés, tearooms and kiosks can be found at sites across the country. At each, you'll find plenty of tasty treats and refreshing drinks to help fuel your adventure. And, whether you're taking in the view at **Tintagel's** Beach Café (p.110), relaxing in the Walled Garden at **Wrest Park** (p.148) or enjoying a Roman burger at **Birdoswald Roman Fort** (p.270) on **Hadrian's Wall** (p.266), you can relax in the knowledge that all the money we raise from our food and drink helps care for England's story.

We seek out high-quality ingredients from local producers, and hold all our suppliers across the country to strict welfare and environmental standards. And wherever we can, we use ingredients grown on site – visit **Audley End House** (p.154) or **Walmer Castle** (p.80), for instance, and you could find yourself tucking into that day's harvest from the kitchen garden.

Check the website before you visit to find out the latest information.

A few of our favourites

- Tuck into fish and chips, crab sandwiches or a Cornish pasty at **Tintagel Castle's** Beach Café
- Treat yourself to high tea in **Osborne's** Terrace Bistro – set within what was once Queen Victoria's private chapel
- Admire the grand Riding House from **Bolsover Castle's** tearoom with a cake and a cuppa
- Enjoy alfresco eating at **Eltham Palace**
- Savour a proper Sunday lunch in the Brew House Café at **Kenwood**
- Soak up the stunning views of **Rievaulx Abbey** from inside its imaginatively designed café
- Keep watch over **Hadrian's Wall** during your lunch break at **Birdoswald Roman Fort**
- Try a locally sourced dish in the baronial setting of **Framlingham Castle's** atmospheric café

Handy tip
When using your handbook look out for these icons in the site information panels:

🍽 Café

☕ Tearoom

Osborne, Isle of Wight

Stay with us

Unlock the doors of an English Heritage holiday cottage and enjoy a unique perspective of some of England's most iconic sites. Steeped in history but equipped with modern comforts, our cottages will be sure to make your holiday a memorable one.

Dover Castle, Kent

St Mawes, Cornwall

Mount Grace Priory, House and Gardens, North Yorkshire

Lindisfarne Priory, Northumberland

Why stay with us?

One of the great benefits of a stay in our cottages is that you have access to the grounds once the public have gone home. Relax in the peace of **Rievaulx Abbey** (p.238), take an evening stroll along the beach at **Osborne** (p.92) or watch the sun rise over the parade ground at **Pendennis Castle** (p.108). You can also enjoy watching the sunset from **St Mawes** (p.112) as you look out to sea, or take a quiet walk through the serene gardens at **Walmer Castle** (p.80), **Audley End** (p.154) and **Mount Grace Priory** (p.234). Get away from the everyday by crossing the dramatic causeway to stay in the Coastguard's Cottage at **Lindisfarne Priory** (p.292), or command fine views of the English Channel at **Dover Castle** (p.66) as you wake up within the walls of the 'Key to England'.

The cottages also make excellent bases from which you can explore the local area, though with our sites literally on the doorstep you won't need to go far to make some magnificent memories.

Find out more

Book or browse the brochure at
english-heritage.org.uk/holidaycottages
or call 0370 333 1181

South East
Battle Abbey South Lodge

Carisbrooke Castle
The Bowling Green Apartment

Dover Castle The Sergeant Major's House
& Peverell's Tower

Osborne Pavilion Cottage
& No. 1 & No. 2 Sovereign's Gate

Walmer Castle The Garden Cottage
& The Greenhouse Apartment

South West
Pendennis Castle The Custodian's House
& Callie's Cottage

St Mawes Fort House

East of England
Audley End House Cambridge Lodge

Wrest Park Gardener's House

East Midlands
Hardwick Old Hall East Lodge

Kirby Hall Peacock Cottage

West Midlands
Witley Court Pool House

Yorkshire
Mount Grace Priory Prior's Lodge

Rievaulx Abbey Refectory Cottage

North East
Lindisfarne Priory Coastguard's Cottage

Osborne, Isle of Wight

Hiring a property

For a historic celebration

From iconic London landmarks to medieval castles, an 18th-century villa to Queen Victoria's seaside retreat, host your event in the places where history happened.

Our rich historical settings are perfect for everything from corporate away-days and business meetings to lavish dinners and spectacular showcases. Whether you are looking to host a small private event or a large-scale extravaganza, we have a range of venues guaranteed to make your event unique and memorable.

For a memorable wedding day

Your wedding day is everlasting. It's the start of the next chapter of your story. It's a moment captured in time – through pictures that stand for a lifetime and memories re-lived for years to come.

English Heritage's historic wedding venues share this unique sense of the everlasting. With castles rising above the sea, royal retreats and sweeping views of age-old gardens, our venues give you a connection to the past and an inspiring setting for your future.

Properties for hire

Properties available for hire are marked with a ⊺ throughout the handbook. Those also licensed for civil ceremonies are marked with a ▲.

East
▲ **Wrest Park** Bedfordshire

London
▲ **Eltham Palace**
▲ **Kenwood**
▲ **Ranger's House**
Wellington Arch

South East
▲ **Osborne** Isle of Wight

South West
▲ **Old Wardour Castle** Wiltshire
▲ **Pendennis Castle** Cornwall

Find out more

T. 0300 020 0017
W. english-heritage.org.uk/venuehire
E. hospitality@english-heritage.org.uk

SAVE 20% ON GIFT OF MEMBERSHIP

A GIFT TO TREASURE ALL YEAR

Share your love of history and give your friends and
family unlimited access to hundreds of historic places
with an English Heritage Gift of Membership.

**BUY ONLINE NOW AT ENGLISH-HERITAGE.ORG.UK/GIFT
USING CODE: GIFT127**

ENGLISH HERITAGE

Birdoswald Roman Fort, Cumbria

Kenilworth Castle and Elizabethan Garden, Warwickshire

Highlights of our collection

English Heritage manages hundreds of the most inspiring and beautiful places in England. They provide a unique encounter with the events that have shaped our history.

Stonehenge, Wiltshire

Whitby Abbey, North Yorkshire

Prehistoric sites

Stonehenge (p.138) is the world's most famous prehistoric ritual site. Its 'henge' and standing stones were developed over many centuries, and it is surrounded by many other prehistoric monuments.

At **Grime's Graves** (p.168), Neolithic miners used antler picks to excavate flints for tools, weapons and ritual objects. You can descend one of the pits and view underground galleries.

Chysauster Ancient Village (p.105) is a fascinating Iron Age settlement of sophisticated 'courtyard houses' of a type unique to west Cornwall and the Isles of Scilly.

Roman sites

Birdoswald Roman Fort (p.270) was a major fort along Hadrian's Wall, which for centuries marked the northern frontier of the Roman Empire. The fort is close to the best-preserved section of the Wall.

Lullingstone Roman Villa (p.74) was a fine country house set in a secluded Kent valley. Wall paintings found on the site provide rare evidence of the introduction of Christianity to Roman Britain.

Wroxeter Roman City (p.210), or Viroconium, was one of Roman Britain's largest towns and the final destination of Watling Street. The 7-metre-high wall known as 'The Old Work' was once part of a magnificent municipal baths complex, but much of the city lies buried beneath the fields.

Castles

Dover Castle (p.66) is one of the greatest fortresses in Europe, with a history spanning the centuries from the Iron Age to the Cold War. At its heart is the majestic Great Tower, a luxurious palace designed to receive royal visitors.

The Midlands stronghold of **Kenilworth Castle** (p.212) seamlessly combined military strength with aristocratic sophistication. The castle became an Elizabethan palace, with the finest buildings and gardens of its age.

In Cornwall, a powerful medieval baron recreated the world of King Arthur and his knights at the atmospheric clifftop castle of **Tintagel** (p.110).

Monasteries and abbeys

The ruined church of **Whitby Abbey** (p.242) is seated majestically on the cliffs above the town. The grand medieval ruins are on the site of an important Anglo-Saxon monastery.

Battle Abbey (p.86) is a beautiful Benedictine monastery built by William the Conqueror on the very spot where, in October 1066, he defeated Harold and won the English crown.

Furness Abbey (p.260) is a vast and magnificent abbey complex in the early Gothic style. Its secluded woodland setting still reflects the wish of the Cistercian monks to install themselves 'far from the concourse of men.'

Country houses

Audley End House (p.154) is a palatial mansion set in an outstanding landscaped park. Its fortunes and those of its owners rose and fell – and its fascinating story is still visible in its architecture, furnishing and decoration.

Brodsworth Hall (p.246) provides a unique insight into the twilight years of a Victorian country house. Its interiors and furniture are conserved just as they were found when English Heritage acquired the site.

Italianate **Osborne** (p.92) on the Isle of Wight provided Queen Victoria and Prince Albert with a peaceful home in which they could raise their nine children – and rule a growing empire.

Historic gardens

Wrest Park (p.148) is an exuberant French-style mansion with outstanding gardens created by the de Grey family. Today they trace over three centuries of English garden history.

Witley Court (p.216) retains the atmosphere of a magnificent country house, despite being gutted by fire in 1937. Its recreated Victorian gardens include an elegant parterre and the Perseus and Andromeda Fountain – one of the grandest in Europe.

The grounds of the Greek Revival **Belsay Hall** (p.288) contain a medieval castle as well as exceptional gardens. The unusual Quarry Garden was inspired by an owner's travels in the Mediterranean.

Prehistory

BEFORE AD 43

The earliest known humans came to England nearly a million years ago, but continuous settlement began only after the end of the last Ice Age, some 12,000 years ago.

The first farmers

Nomadic 'hunter-gatherer' people left few visible traces, but with the arrival of farming in the Neolithic (New Stone Age) period, people began constructing monuments. Among the earliest are ritual enclosures like **Windmill Hill** and communal tombs like **West Kennet Long Barrow**.

Monuments and metal-working

Circular earthwork 'henges' appear from about 3000 BC, when **Stonehenge** was begun. The later Neolithic and early Bronze Ages saw massive stone circles like **Castlerigg Stone Circle** and **Avebury Stone Circle** raised, sometimes becoming elements of 'ritual landscapes' like that including mysterious **Silbury Hill**. **Grime's Graves** flint mines were in use by 2600 BC, but the working of bronze was known in England before **Stonehenge** was completed in about 2000 BC.

Round barrows, villages and hillforts

Individual burials in Bronze Age 'round barrows' (like **Flowerdown Barrows**) meanwhile replaced communal tombs. From about 1500 BC landscapes were divided up by great field systems, with dwellings grouped into villages such as **Grimspound** and **Chysauster Ancient Village**. New iron-working technology from around 750 BC coincided with the spread of hillforts like **Maiden Castle**. Then town-like tribal power centres such as **Lexden Earthworks** developed – a process interrupted by the Roman Conquest.

Stonehenge, Wiltshire

We care for 57 sites within this period, including:

- Avebury Stone Circle
- Castlerigg Stone Circle
- Chysauster Ancient Village
- Grime's Graves
- Lexden Earthworks
- Maiden Castle
- Mayburgh Henge
- Silbury Hill
- Stonehenge
- West Kennet Long Barrow
- Windmill Hill

Romans

AD 43-C. 410

Roman Britain lasted for over three and a half centuries, leaving an indelible mark on the nation's landscape. English Heritage's Roman sites reflect the era from its violent beginning to its obscure close.

Conquest

Though Julius Caesar raided Britain in 55 and 54 BC, full-scale conquest began when Roman forces landed near **Richborough Roman Fort** in AD 43. Despite resistance by Boudica (Boadicea) and others, Roman armies had reached northern Scotland by AD 84, before eventually retiring to the permanent frontier of **Hadrian's Wall**. Incomparably the most impressive Roman monument in Britain, the Wall's defensive system includes major forts like **Birdoswald**, **Chesters** and **Housesteads**.

Civilisation

Away from the frontiers, Roman Britain was for long periods peaceful and prosperous. 'Country houses' like **Lullingstone Roman Villa** flourished, bath-houses and amphitheatres were built, and many towns were founded – including large **Silchester** and **Wroxeter** and smaller **Aldborough** and **Corbridge** – often at existing British tribal centres. Most were later walled against increasing external threats.

The Saxon shore

Towards the end of the 3rd century, attacks by seaborne Germanic raiders prompted the creation of 'Saxon Shore' coastal fortifications like **Burgh Castle Roman Fort**. Further trouble saw the system strengthened in the next century, and **Pevensey Castle** added. Garrisons were by now mainly British-born, and little distinguished 'Romans' from 'Britons' when imperial rule petered out. There was no clearly definable end to Roman Britain.

Corbridge Roman Town, Northumberland

We care for 58 sites within this period, including:

- Birdoswald Roman Fort
- Burgh Castle Roman Fort
- Chesters Roman Fort
- Corbridge Roman Town
- Hadrian's Wall
- Housesteads Roman Fort
- Lullingstone Roman Villa
- Pevensey Castle
- Portchester Castle
- Richborough Roman Fort and Amphitheatre
- Wroxeter Roman City

c. 410-c. 425	c. 550-c. 650	597-625	787-789	871-899	927	1066
End of Imperial Roman rule in Britain	Anglo-Saxons conquer lowland England	Principal Christian missions	Viking raids begin	Alfred the Great reigns	Aethelstan becomes first king of all England	Norman Conquest begins

Early Middle Ages

C. 400-1066

This momentous era between the end of Roman Britain and the Norman Conquest, when Britons, Anglo-Saxons and then Vikings struggled for dominance, saw the gradual emergence of a unified English nation.

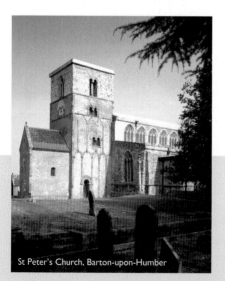

St Peter's Church, Barton-upon-Humber

The English conquest

Post-Roman Britain was assailed by seaborne Germanic peoples – Angles, Saxons, Jutes and Frisians. Though delayed by Romano-British resistance (perhaps the origin of myths around 'Arthur') these 'Anglo-Saxon' invaders conquered most of lowland England by the mid-600s, establishing several independent kingdoms. Tantalising hints about this shadowy period come from sites like **Birdoswald Roman Fort**, **Tintagel Castle** and **Wroxeter Roman City**.

Christian culture blossoms

Increasingly called 'English', the pagan conquerors were converted to Christianity by missionaries from Rome and Ireland. Christian culture blossomed: **Lindisfarne Priory** produced its illuminated Gospels, while Bede's writings at **St Paul's Monastery, Jarrow** fostered the concept of an English nation. The architecture and craftsmanship of **St Peter's Church, Barton-upon-Humber** and **Sandbach Crosses** likewise reflect the English Church's vitality.

The Viking threat

Towards the end of the 8th century, soon after **Offa's Dyke** defined its western boundary, England's development was imperilled as Viking raids became invasions. King Alfred of Wessex turned the tide, and his descendants reconquered Viking-held lands: his grandson Aethelstan became the first ruler of a unified English state. But Danish pressure was revived by King Cnut, and it was a weakened England which faced the Normans in 1066.

We care for 19 sites within this period, including:

- 1066 Battle of Hastings, Abbey and Battlefield
- Lindisfarne Priory
- Lydford Castle and Saxon Town
- Offa's Dyke
- St Augustine's Abbey
- St Paul's Monastery, Jarrow
- St Peter's Church, Barton-upon-Humber
- Sandbach Crosses
- Tintagel Castle
- Whitby Abbey

Medieval

1066-1485

Nearly half of all English Heritage sites date from the 'medieval' centuries between the battles of Hastings in 1066 and Bosworth in 1485. Their variety mirrors the era's developing character.

The land filled with castles

Earthwork and timber 'motte-and-bailey' castles were the instruments and symbols of the Norman Conquest. Many, like **Clifford's Tower** and **Totnes Castle**, were later refortified in stone. The great stone keeps of the Norman and Angevin kings and their barons formed the core of major early fortresses like **Dover Castle**, **Conisbrough Castle** and **Richmond Castle**. The focus then shifted to many-towered enclosure walls with powerful gatehouses, as at **Framlingham Castle** and **Goodrich Castle**. Equipped with halls, chapels and many domestic buildings, some strongholds like **Beeston Castle** or **Kenilworth Castle** were immense in scale. More compact fortresses – including **Farleigh Hungerford Castle** and **Nunney Castle** – developed towards the end of the era, with some (like **Berry Pomeroy** and **Kirby Muxloe** castles) equipped for artillery defence.

Town and country

Only a tiny minority of medieval people lived in castles. English Heritage's collection also includes lightly fortified or undefended manor houses like **Stokesay Castle** or **Old Soar Manor**, and urban houses like **Gainsborough Old Hall**. Country life is represented by **Wharram Percy Deserted Medieval Village** and farm buildings such as the imposing **Leigh Court Barn**.

Clifford's Tower, North Yorkshire

We care for 203 sites within this period, including:

- Beeston Castle
- Carisbrooke Castle
- Carlisle Castle
- Castle Acre Priory
- Clifford's Tower
- Conisbrough Castle
- Dover Castle
- Framlingham Castle
- Goodrich Castle
- Kenilworth Castle
- Leigh Court Barn
- Old Wardour Castle

Medieval (cont)

1066-1485

Cleeve Abbey, Somerset

Stokesay Castle, Shropshire

Oases of peace

Whether in castle, town or country, medieval life was dominated by the Church: in the 14th century about one in fifteen Englishmen were clergy of some kind. English Heritage cares for parish churches such as **St Mary's Kempley** with its impressive wall paintings, bishops' mansions including **Lincoln Medieval Bishops' Palace**, and the evocative remains of many monasteries, from big, prosperous **Castle Acre Priory** to tiny **Mattersey Priory**.

Each reflects the characteristics of the monastic order which inhabited it: 'mainstream' Benedictines at **Binham Priory** and **Whitby Abbey**; solitude-seeking Cistercians at **Furness Abbey** and **Rievaulx Abbey**; decoration-loving Cluniacs at **Wenlock Priory**; Augustinian canons at tranquil **Lanercost Priory**; hermit-like Carthusians at **Mount Grace Priory, House and Gardens** or the urban friars of Gloucester's **Blackfriars** and **Greyfriars**.

Memories of conflict

Many of English Heritage's medieval sites, by contrast, recall the foreign or internal wars of medieval England. Some – like **Carlisle Castle** – guarded land borders against Scots or Welsh, or like **Carisbrooke Castle** and **Dartmouth Castle**, defended coasts against seaborne invasion and raiding. Others, including **Rochester Castle**, endured conflicts between monarchs and barons, or like **Dunstanburgh Castle** or **Warwarth Castle**, witnessed the dynastic Wars of the Roses, ended by the Battle of Bosworth, which began the Tudor age.

We care for 203 sites within this period, including:

- Aydon Castle
- Cleeve Abbey
- Longthorpe Tower
- Middleham Castle
- Mount Grace Priory, House and Gardens
- Muchelney Abbey
- Old Sarum
- Rievaulx Abbey
- St Mary's Church, Kempley
- Scarborough Castle
- Stokesay Castle
- Warkworth Castle and Hermitage

Tudors

1485-1603

The pivot of medieval and modern history, the Tudor era saw strong royal government established, England transformed from a Catholic to a Protestant nation, and the flowering of a distinctively English culture.

The triumph of monarchy

Ending the Wars of the Roses, Henry VII curtailed aristocratic power and castle-building, and his successors strengthened the grip of monarchy. Henceforth fortresses would be raised only by the crown, most notably Henry VIII's coastal artillery forts – the first co-ordinated system of national defence – including **Deal Castle**, **Pendennis Castle** and **Portland Castle**.

Religious upheavals

Henry's new-style forts defended England against European Catholic reaction to the religious changes he initiated: English Heritage's outstanding collection of monastic ruins bear witness to his Dissolution of the Monasteries. After swinging from Edward VI's radical Protestantism to Mary's revived Catholicism, the nation settled down to religious compromise under Queen Elizabeth I.

The flowering of English culture

Elizabeth's long and glorious reign witnessed the expansion of English sea power (reinforced by her defeat of the Spanish Armada) and the flowering of English culture epitomised by Shakespeare. It also saw the burgeoning of the great English country house. Some were converted monasteries or adapted medieval fortresses like **Kenilworth Castle and Elizabethan Garden**, but most were built from new, like **Kirby Hall**. All these developments expressed a new-found English self-confidence.

Kirby Hall, Northamptonshire

We care for 50 sites within this period, including:

- Berwick-upon-Tweed Ramparts
- Deal Castle
- Hailes Abbey
- Hardwick Old Hall
- Kenilworth Castle and Elizabethan Garden
- Kirby Hall
- Norham Castle
- Pendennis Castle
- Rushton Triangular Lodge
- St Mawes Castle
- Titchfield Abbey

Stuarts

1603-1714

Following a long peace, the intense political and religious conflicts of the Stuart era transformed England's government. Developments in architecture and living standards are reflected in this era's English Heritage sites.

Boscobel House and The Royal Oak, Shropshire

Gracious living

The earlier ('Jacobean') part of the period saw many lavish mansions like **Audley End House** and **Bolsover Castle** built, and fine interiors created in more modest dwellings like **Great Yarmouth Row Houses**.

The English revolution

The Civil Wars between Charles I and Parliament (1642-51) brought much devastation; epic sieges of **Pendennis Castle** and many other places; and (after his imprisonment at **Carisbrooke Castle**) the king's execution and the creation (1649-53) of the Commonwealth, the only republic in English history. Young Charles II narrowly escaped capture near **Boscobel House**.

Restoration and new styles

Epitomised by Pepys's diary, the reign of the restored Charles II brought continuing scientific advances, but also plague and fire in London and humiliating Dutch attack, provoking the building of defences like **Tilbury Fort**. The 'English Baroque' style of Christopher Wren and **Abingdon County Hall** came increasingly into fashion towards the end of the period.

England and Britain

The era's long-simmering religious disputes were addressed in 1689, after the Catholic James II was deposed by the Protestant William and Mary. Under Queen Anne, the Acts of Union with Scotland made England part of 'Great Britain'.

We care for 40 sites within this period, including:

- Abingdon County Hall
- Audley End House and Gardens
- Berry Pomeroy Castle
- Bolsover Castle
- Boscobel House and The Royal Oak
- Carisbrooke Castle
- Great Yarmouth Row Houses
- Langley Chapel
- Pendennis Castle
- Tilbury Fort

Georgians

1714-1837

An age of contrasts, counterpointing elegant aristocratic mansions with grimy, overcrowded mills and the horrors of the slave trade, the Georgian era saw Britain become the world's first industrial nation, at the hub of a rapidly growing empire.

Elegant mansions

Our outstanding collection of Georgian and Regency mansions reflect a progression of fashionable styles, from the Palladian of Chiswick House via Robert Adam's Kenwood to the 'Regency' Greek Revival of Belsay Hall and The Grange at Northington. Extravagant or tasteful interiors (as at Marble Hill) were matched by formal or 'landscaped' gardens often adorned (as at Audley End House and Wrest Park) with charming garden architecture.

Industrial Revolution

The wealth which financed these mansions was increasingly the product of England's pioneering Industrial Revolution, itself founded on entrepreneurial enterprise and new developments like canals, the 'factory system' and steam power. The Iron Bridge was the world's first of its kind, and the world's first steam trains ran in England in 1825.

War, empire and slavery

International trade, including the transatlantic slave trade, boomed alongside an expanding empire, particularly in India and the Americas. Britain's involvement in the slave trade ended in 1807, but slavery itself was not abolished in the British empire until 1833. Meanwhile, as Dover Castle and Dymchurch Martello Tower demonstrate, Britain's growing military and especially naval power did not go unchallenged, notably during the long wars with Revolutionary and Napoleonic France. The Duke of Wellington, the greatest military hero of these wars, is remembered at Apsley House, Walmer Castle and Wellington Arch.

Belsay Hall, Castle and Gardens, Northumberland

We care for 41 sites within this period, including:

- Apsley House
- Belsay Hall, Castle and Gardens
- Chiswick House
- Derwentcote Steel Furnace
- Iron Bridge
- Kenwood
- Marble Hill
- The Grange at Northington
- Walmer Castle and Gardens
- Wellington Arch
- Wrest Park

Victorians

1837-1901

The long reign of Queen Victoria saw Britain at the zenith of its international power and status, and the greatest manufacturing nation in the world.

Masters and servants

Queen Victoria's strong personality is reflected at **Osborne**. Her wealthier subjects also continued to build great mansions like **Brodsworth Hall** and **Witley Court**, operated by armies of servants – as **Audley End's** kitchens, nursery wing and stables demonstrate.

A hive of industry

J.W. Evans Silver Factory and **Stott Park Bobbin Mill** recall Victorian England as a hive of manufacturing industry. Rural life was also transformed by machinery, as seen in English Heritage's collection of windmills.

Doubt and certainty

The publication of Charles Darwin's ideas on evolution (developed and written at **Down House**) shook Victorian religious certainty, but did not stem the period's flood of chapel- and church-building – the latter almost always in the ubiquitous 'Gothic Revival' style. **St Mary's Church, Studley Royal** is a glittering example.

An imperial power

Despite the 1860s French invasion scare, which produced new fortifications like **Fort Brockhurst** and the updating of older defences like **Dartmouth Castle**, Britannia's fleets continued to rule the waves and her armies to fight far-flung colonial wars. The Indian Mutiny of 1857 and the Boer War of 1899-1902 dented 'Imperial' confidence, but at the queen's death the British Empire was still rapidly expanding.

Brodsworth Hall and Gardens, North Yorkshire

We care for 28 sites within this period, including:

- Audley End House
- Brodsworth Hall and Gardens
- Home of Charles Darwin, Down House
- Fort Brockhurst
- Mount Grace Priory, House and Gardens
- Osborne
- Saxtead Green Post Mill
- St Mary's Church, Studley Royal
- Stott Park Bobbin Mill
- Witley Court

Modern

1901-PRESENT

During a century of rapidly developing technologies, the two World Wars which dominate the modern age of British history acted as catalysts for previously unimaginable social changes.

Two World Wars – and a third?

The First World War, with its terrible carnage, and the Second World War – whose far greater impact on civilian life is underlined at **Great Yarmouth Row Houses** – are both reflected in English Heritage properties. Old fortresses like **Tynemouth Priory and Castle** were updated for new types of warfare, and the Secret Wartime Tunnels beneath **Dover Castle** played a crucial role in saving the nation in 1940. The dead of both wars are remembered by the London war memorials cared for by English Heritage, including the poignant **Royal Artillery Memorial** at Hyde Park Corner. But **York Cold War Bunker** is a chilling reminder that the threat of even greater mass destruction remained ever-present.

Social transformation

Both World Wars transformed the social structure of England: **Brodsworth Hall** tracks the decline of the country house and its servant-dependent lifestyle – though remodelled **Eltham Palace** displays the stylish living still enjoyed by the millionaire few.

An ongoing revolution

The post-Second World War creation of the Welfare State made life easier for the many. The advent of radio and TV and more recently of affordable computer technology fostered a still greater (and still continuing) revolution in lifestyles.

Dover Castle, Kent

We care for 22 sites within this period, including:

- Brodsworth Hall and Gardens
- Calshot Castle
- Dover Castle (Secret Wartime Tunnels)
- Eltham Palace
- Great Yarmouth Row Houses
- Portland Castle
- Royal Garrison Church
- Tynemouth Priory and Castle
- York Cold War Bunker

WELCOME TO

LONDON

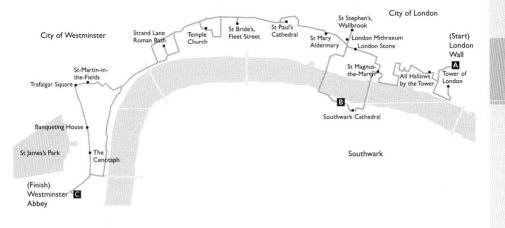

The London Royal Route

5 miles | 1 day

Walk the ancient royal processional way between the commercial City of London and the political City of Westminster. The route links martyrdom, holy wells, ancient power stones, places of peace, the tombs of saints and the haunts of sinners. With stories of fire, conquest, rebellion and Reformation, this walk takes you into the heart of England's history.

In partnership with

the British Pilgrimage Trust

Discover English Heritage sites along the pilgrimage route

A London Wall *(p.44)*

B Winchester Palace (see diversion) *(p.44)*

C Chapter House & Pyx Chamber *(p.44)* and Jewel Tower *(p.45)*

View more details and a downloadable version of this route at **english-heritage.org.uk/pilgrimage**

APSLEY HOUSE

HYDE PARK – W1J 7NT

Revel in the dazzling interiors, glittering treasures and fabulous art collections of the Duke of Wellington's Apsley House. Enjoy the multimedia guide, and find out how the 'Iron Duke' entertained in the grandest style.

Home of the first Duke of Wellington and his descendants, and popularly known as 'Number 1 London', Apsley House stands right in the heart of the capital at Hyde Park Corner. It is London's only surviving aristocratic townhouse open to visitors today. Originally designed by Robert Adam for Baron Apsley – from whom it takes its name – it was lavishly and fashionably remodelled for Wellington by Benjamin Wyatt between 1819 and 1829.

Wellington is most famous for defeating Napoleon at the Battle of Waterloo in 1815, the culmination of a brilliant military career. But he was also a major politician, becoming Prime Minister in 1828. Reflecting the duke's rising status, Apsley House's magnificent interiors provided the perfect backdrop for entertaining, particularly at the annual Waterloo Banquets, which commemorated the great victory.

Other highlights include the grandiose Dining Room, with its breathtaking crystal chandelier and gilt Portuguese tableware service, one of many treasures presented to Wellington by grateful nations.

The mansion's interior also displays Wellington's outstanding art collection. Paintings by many famous artists – including Velázquez, Rubens, Goya, Titian and Breughel – hang throughout the first-floor rooms, and a colossal nude statue of Napoleon by Canova dominates the stairwell at the centre of the house.

When the seventh Duke of Wellington gave the house to the nation in 1947, the family retained the private rooms, which they still use today. This makes Apsley House the only property cared for by English Heritage in which the owner's family still lives.

Apsley House offers multimedia guides for adults and children.

Complete your experience by crossing the road to Wellington Arch, one of London's most iconic landmarks, which also honours the famous duke.

Please note: Photography in the house is not permitted.

NEW FOR 2022

WOMEN OF INFLUENCE: WELLINGTON AND HIS FRIENDS

This exhibition explores Wellington's relationships with the women in his life. Portraits and letters reveal intimate aspects of the duke's life for the first time ever. Runs from the 1 April until 30 October.

OPENING TIMES

1 Apr-23 Dec, Wed-Sun & Bank Hols	11am-5pm
2 Jan-31 Mar, Sat-Sun	10am-4pm
24 Dec-1 Jan	Closed

Last entry 30 mins before closing

Exterior Café

Summer	5pm
Winter	4pm

VISIT US

Address: Apsley House, 149 Piccadilly, Hyde Park Corner, London W1J 7NT

Direction: Adjacent to Hyde Park Corner tube station, next to the entrance to Hyde Park

Train: Victoria ½ mile

Bus: Visit traveline.info or tfl.gov.uk/plan-a-journey

Tube: Hyde Park Corner

Tel: 020 7499 5676

NON-MEMBERS

Adult **£12.80** | Concession **£11.50**
Child **£7.60** | Family 2 Adults **£33.20**
Family 1 Adult **£20.40**

Joint ticket with Wellington Arch
Adult **£16.00** | Concession **£14.50**
Child **£9.60** | Family 2 Adults **£41.60**
Family 1 Adult **£25.60**

Pre-booked guided tours are available for groups. Visit english-heritage.org.uk/visit/places/apsley-house/plan-your-visit/group-visits/ or call the site on 020 7499 5676

 ACQ.1947 OVP

Disabled access very limited. Please phone property for information.

MAP PAGE 326 (3E)
OS MAP 176, 161/173: TQ284799

ELTHAM PALACE AND GARDENS

GREENWICH – SE9 5QE

At Eltham Palace you'll discover what 1930s millionaires could achieve when they built and furnished a mansion regardless of expense. It's a triumph of style, taste and ahead-of-the-time home comforts, with wonderful gardens and a children's play area. Come and experience a unique art deco extravaganza.

Stephen and Virginia Courtauld created a uniquely memorable masterpiece when they built their mansion adjoining the Great Hall of medieval Eltham Palace. Completed in 1936, the exterior of the new house was built in sympathy with the old hall. But its interior is an outstanding showcase of 1930s high fashion.

An introductory film uncovers the history of the palace, how it was created, and how the Courtaulds lived in it. Multimedia handsets draw you into 1930s society, and help you experience what it was like to be a guest here. Visual guides to each room help you admire the mansion's striking art deco design details.

What impresses most is the house itself. The dining room is an art deco tour de force, with bird's-eye maple veneered walls, a shimmering aluminium-leaf ceiling and black-and-silver doors portraying animals and birds. Still more exotic is Virginia Courtauld's bathroom, with onyx bath and sink and gold-plated bath taps.

You can also take a look into her walk-in wardrobe, next to her bedroom. It displays glamorous period dresses based on those she wore, and you can try on replica 1930s clothes and accessories. Explore her nephews' bedrooms and bathroom, complete with an innovative shower. It's one of a pioneering range of ultra-modern conveniences you'll find in this lavishly 'high-tech' home, including underfloor heating, a centralised vacuum cleaner and a built-in audio system.

Admire the 1930s Map Room, reflecting the Courtaulds' exotic holidays, often involving pioneering travel by air. Also on view are a luxury wartime air-raid shelter and a billiard room, with a mural featuring the family's pet lemur, Mah-Jongg.

For a complete contrast with the 1930s rooms, step into the Great Hall – the only substantially remaining part of the medieval royal palace of Eltham. It has a magnificent hammer beam roof, built for Edward IV in the 1470s. Henry VIII spent much of his childhood at Eltham.

Be sure to leave time to wander the palace's beautiful gardens, including the fragrant sunken Rose Garden and the Rock Garden with its cascade. They've been replanted and re-presented in the style commissioned by the Courtaulds.

Eltham Palace also has a stylish visitor centre with a shop and café, as well as play areas for children.

🎬 *Bright Young Things* (2003); *Revolver* (2005); *Brideshead Revisited* (2008); *Poirot – Three Act Tragedy* (2010); *The Crown; Trust; Stan & Ollie* (2018); *Misbehaviour* (2020); Florence and The Machine's *'Shake it Out'* music video; Jessie Ware's *'Alone'* music video.

🔲 Available for corporate and private hire

🔲 Licensed for civil wedding ceremonies

OPENING TIMES

1 Apr-30 Oct, Mon-Sun	10am-5pm
31 Oct-23 Dec, Sat-Sun	10am-4pm
2 Jan-10 Feb, Sat-Sun	10am-4pm
11-19 Feb, daily	10am-4pm
20 Feb-31 Mar, Wed-Sun	10am-4pm
Christmas Opening	
24-25 Dec	Closed
26 Dec-1 Jan, daily	10am-4pm

Last entry 30 mins before closing

VISIT US

Address: Court Yard, Eltham, London SE9 5QE

Direction: Off Court Rd SE9, Jct 3 on the M25, then A20 to Eltham. Please use satnav postcode SE9 5NP to help direct you straight to the car park

Train: Mottingham ½ mile walk (best for visitor centre entrance). Eltham Station is also ½ mile walk

Bus: Visit traveline.info or tfl.gov.uk/plan-a-journey

Tel: 0370 333 1181

NON-MEMBERS

Adult £17.60 | Concession £15.80
Child £10.60 | Family 2 Adults £45.80
Family 1 Adult £28.20

Members may be charged for special events

Pushchairs and large rucksacks need to be left at the entrance of the house.

Parking: charges apply to non-members, free for Members with valid English Heritage car sticker.

Some restrictions on photography in the house.

MAP PAGE 327 (4F)
OS MAP 177, 162: TQ424740

CHISWICK HOUSE & GARDENS

CHISWICK – W4 2RP

Chiswick House is a neo-Palladian villa designed and built by Richard Boyle, 3rd Earl of Burlington, in the 18th century. After travelling to Italy in his youth, Burlington was inspired to bring the grandeur of ancient Rome home to London. His close friend, the architect and gardener William Kent, not only played a huge role in decorating the interior of the house but also designed the grounds.

Today Chiswick House & Gardens covers 65 acres in west London, from the manicured Italian Garden to the untamed Wilderness. Explore the fine Gallery Rooms in the house, restored to their 18th-century grandeur, and learn about the people who shaped Chiswick House over the last 300 years. After visiting the heritage camellia collection in the Conservatory, make your way to the historic Kitchen Garden, now open at all times when the house is open. This is where Chiswick House grows its own organic produce, available to buy from the Kitchen Garden Cart on Thursday and Saturday mornings.

After exploring the house and gardens, treat yourself in the gift shop before heading over to the café, which offers an ever-changing menu of delicious fresh food and drink. The café is next to the children's play area – perfect for using up a little energy before heading home.

Check the Chiswick House and Gardens website to find out what's on.

Managed by Chiswick House & Gardens Trust in partnership with English Heritage. chgt.org.uk

> ⊤ Available for corporate and private hire – contact Chiswick House & Gardens Trust 020 3141 3351
>
> ⚑ Licensed for civil wedding ceremonies

OPENING TIMES

House and Kitchen Garden

1 Apr-30 Oct, Mon and Wed	11am-3pm
Sat-Sun	11am-4pm
31 Oct-31 Mar	Closed
Last entry 30 mins before closing	
Gardens, daily all year round	7am-dusk

Please see website for the conservatory opening times

Occasionally the house or conservatory is closed for private events – please check chgt.org.uk prior to visiting

House is available for private tours and group bookings on Tue, Thu and Fri, Apr-Oct and daily, Nov-Mar

VISIT US

Direction: Burlington Lane, Chiswick, London W4 2RP

Train: Chiswick ¼ mile walk (10 mins)

Bus: Visit traveline.info or tfl.gov.uk/plan-a-journey

Tube: Turnham Green 1 mile then bus E3

Tel: 020 3141 3352

NON-MEMBERS

House
Adult **£4.50** | Concession **£2.25** | Child **£2.25**
Family 2 Adults **£10.50** | Family 1 Adult **£6.50**

Kitchen Garden
Adult **£8.50** | Concession **£4.25** | Child **£4.25**
Family 2 Adults **£21.00** | Family 1 Adult **£12.50**

Combined House and Kitchen Garden
Adult **£12.50** | Concession **£5.50** | Child **£5.50**
Family 2 Adults **£23.60** | Family 1 Adult **£16.00**

Free guided tours – see website for details

Entry to the gardens is free; donations welcome

National Art Pass holders free entrance to the house

Members may be charged for special events

Disabled access to ground floor only.

Dogs on leads (most areas of the garden only). Assistance dogs allowed inside the house.

Parking (charges apply – disabled bays available) – off Westbound A4. Satnav: W4 2RP.

No photography allowed inside the house.

Caution: deep water, steep stairs.

MAP PAGE 326 (3E)
OS MAP 176, 161: TQ210775

KENWOOD

HAMPSTEAD – NW3 7JR

Kenwood is among the finest of all the great houses in our care. Its breathtaking interiors and fabulous world-class art collection are free for everyone to enjoy. The neo-Classical villa and its tranquil parkland are favourites with visitors seeking relief from the bustle of central London, and there's plenty here for families to discover together.

Crowning Hampstead Heath, Kenwood House was remodelled by Robert Adam between 1764 and 1779 for William Murray, first Earl of Mansfield, creating the imposing mansion that greets visitors today.

Most striking of all Kenwood's glories is its suite of magnificent Robert Adam rooms: the Entrance Hall, Great Staircase, Anteroom, and his masterpiece, the Great Library, lavishly redecorated as they originally appeared over two centuries ago.

Kenwood also famously displays the Iveagh Bequest, an internationally renowned art collection assembled by brewing magnate Edward Guinness, Earl of Iveagh, and bequeathed to the nation, along with the Kenwood estate, in 1927. It features paintings by Rembrandt, Van Dyck, Vermeer, Gainsborough, Reynolds, Turner and Constable. A lift to the first floor provides full access to all our collections, including the Suffolk Collection of Stuart portraits, with full-length paintings of extravagantly dressed Jacobean courtiers. Ask our volunteer explainers about the house and its paintings.

Integrated interpretation helps you discover the story of Kenwood and its people, from Lord Mansfield and his mixed-race great-niece, Dido Belle, to Lord Iveagh, Kenwood's great benefactor.

'Growing Space', an activity base in the Orangery, tempts families to stay and play together. Our explorer backpacks are perfect for families with under fives; Mac and his doggy paw prints lead you to hands-on activities.

Kenwood's 112-acre parkland, landscaped by Humphry Repton, is renowned for its fine views over London. There's plenty to explore and admire: sculptures by Henry Moore and Barbara Hepworth, lakeside walks and paths meandering through ancient woodland, a Site of Special Scientific Interest. Don't miss the conserved ornamental 18th-century dairy, which once both supplied the mansion with fresh produce and allowed the ladies of the house to take tea or fashionably play at dairymaids (please check with the site for opening details).

You can also download our free app before visiting: **english-heritage.org.uk/kenwood**

🎬 *Notting Hill* (1999); *Mansfield Park* (1999); *Scenes of a Sexual Nature* (2006); *Venus* (2006).

🍽 Available for corporate and private hire
🔔 Licensed for civil wedding ceremonies

OPENING TIMES

House

1 Apr-30 Oct, daily	10am-5pm
31 Oct-31 Mar, daily	10am-4pm
24-26, 31 Dec & 1 Jan	Closed

Brew House Café*

1 Apr-30 Sep, daily	9am-6pm
1-30 Oct, daily	9am-5pm
31 Oct-31 Jan, daily	9am-4pm
1 Feb-31 Mar, daily	9am-5pm
24-25 & 31 Dec	Closed

Garden House Shop*

1 Apr-30 Oct, daily	10am-5pm
31 Oct-31 Mar, daily	10am-4pm
24-25 & 31 Dec	Closed

Estate open from 8am to dusk
(see park entrance for closing time)

Entry to the House and grounds is
free; donations welcome

*Correct at time of printing but
please see website for latest updates

Last entry 30 mins before closing

VISIT US

Address: Kenwood, Hampstead
NW3 7JR

Direction: Hampstead Lane

Train: Gospel Oak or Hampstead
Heath (both London Overground)

Bus: Visit traveline.info

Tube: Golders Green or Archway
then bus 210

Tel: 0370 333 1181

NON-MEMBERS

Pre-booked guided tours may be
available for groups, please email
bookings@english-heritage.org.uk
or call 0370 333 1181 for latest
information

Disabled access (lift to all floors for visitors
with a disability or mobility requirements;
toilets).

Dogs on leads (restricted areas only).

Parking: charges apply to non-members,
free for Members with valid English Heritage
car sticker. Disabled bays available.
Mobility service available on request.

MAP PAGE 326 (3E)
OS MAP 176, 173: TQ271874

CHAPTER HOUSE AND PYX CHAMBER

WESTMINSTER ABBEY – SW1P 3PA

Built in 1250, the Chapter House was used for monks' daily meetings, and sometimes by medieval parliaments. A beautiful vaulted building, it displays a medieval tiled floor and spectacular wall paintings.

Under the care and management of the Dean and Chapter of Westminster.

OPENING TIMES

1 Apr 2022–31 Mar 2023, Mon-Fri	10am-4.30pm
Sat	10am-4pm
2 Apr, 24-25 Dec & 1 Jan	Closed

May be closed at short notice on state and religious occasions

VISIT US

Direction: Within Westminster Abbey. Members who do not wish to visit the rest of the Abbey: enter Dean's Yard from Broad Sanctuary and turn left across the square to find the cloisters. All other visitors should use the normal visitor entry point for the Abbey

Train: Victoria and Charing Cross

Bus: Visit traveline.info

Tube: Westminster and St James's Park

Tel: 020 7222 5152

NON-MEMBERS

Buy ticket from Westminster Abbey or online

ACQ.1872 Chapter House

ACQ.1901 Pyx Chamber

MAP PAGE 326 (3E)
OS MAP 176/177, 161/173: TQ299795

COOMBE CONDUIT

KINGSTON UPON THAMES – KT2 7HE

Two brick-walled chambers, connected by an underground passage. Part of a system collecting spring water and channelling it to Hampton Court Palace.

Managed by the Kingston upon Thames Society.

COOMBE CONDUIT

OPENING TIMES

Apr-Sep, 2nd Sun of month   2-4pm

VISIT US

Direction: Coombe Lane West close to corner with Lord Chancellor Walk

Train: Norbiton ¾ mile or Raynes Park 1 mile then bus 57

Bus: Visit traveline.info

Tube: Wimbledon then bus 57

Tel: 020 8549 4586

ACQ.1978 Caution: deep water.

Disabled access (exterior only).

MAP PAGE 326 (4E)
OS MAP 176, 161: TQ204698

HARMONDSWORTH GREAT BARN

HILLINGDON – UB7 0AQ

Medieval timber-framed barn, built 1426-27. One of the largest barns ever built in England, and among the least altered medieval buildings in Britain. Managed by the Friends of the Great Barn at Harmondsworth.

OPENING TIMES

1 Apr-30 Oct, 2nd and 4th Sun of the month	11am-4pm
31 Oct-31 Mar	Closed

VISIT US

Direction: Located in High Street, Harmondsworth Village

Train: West Drayton 2 miles

Bus: Visit traveline.info

Tube: Heathrow Terminals 1, 2, 3 – 2 miles

Tel: 0370 333 1181

ACQ.2012

MAP PAGE 326 (3E)
OS MAP 176, 160: TQ056778

LONDON WALL

TOWER HILL – EC3N 4DJ

The best-preserved remnant of the Roman wall which formed part of the eastern defences of Roman Londinium. Built c. AD 200.

OPENING TIMES

Any reasonable daylight hours

VISIT US

Direction: Located outside Tower Hill Underground station, EC3

Train: Fenchurch Street ¼ mile or London Bridge 1 mile

Bus: Visit traveline.info

Tube: Tower Hill

DLR: Tower Gateway

Tel: 0370 333 1181

ACQ.1953

Caution: falling masonry.

MAP PAGE 327 (3F)
OS MAP 176/177, 173: TQ336807

WINCHESTER PALACE

SOUTHWARK – SE1 9DG

Part of the 12th-century great hall of Winchester Palace, London mansion of the Bishops of Winchester, including a striking rose window.

Managed by Bankside Open Spaces Trust.

OPENING TIMES

Any reasonable daylight hours

VISIT US

Direction: On Clink Street close to corner with Stoney Street (between *Golden Hinde* replica ship and the Clink Prison Museum)

Train/Tube: London Bridge ¼ mile

Bus: Visit traveline.info

Tel: 0370 333 1181

ACQ.1967

MAP PAGE 327 (3F)
OS MAP 176/177, 173: TQ325803

JEWEL TOWER

— WESTMINSTER – SW1P 3JX —

Tucked away between the Houses of Parliament and Westminster Abbey, the Jewel Tower is an easily overlooked but precious fragment of English history. It also offers you magnificent views of the Houses of Parliament.

The Tower was built in c. 1365 as the 'Jewel House' to safeguard Edward III's silver plate and royal treasures. It's the sole surviving remnant of the 'Privy Palace', the private royal apartments within the great medieval Palace of Westminster. It's also the only part of the palace complex which survived the disastrous fire of 1834 and is regularly open to the public.

Displaying a finely carved medieval vault, its 14th-century architecture remains largely unaltered, with an anti-clockwise spiral staircase. You can still see the excavated remains of its original moat. The tower later became a royal Tudor lumber room, whose contents included dolls discarded by Henry VIII's daughters. Subsequently it housed the House of Lords records and then the National Weights and Measures Office, determining the value of weights and measures for Britain and its empire.

You can explore the Tower's history and changing roles over the centuries across three floors of displays. Outstanding among its collection are the Westminster Capitals, eight rare and beautifully carved early Norman sculptures made in the 1090s, which once adorned William Rufus's Westminster Hall. Admire the Palace of Westminster Sword, part of a richly decorated Anglo-Saxon weapon. A screen offers you digital reconstructions of Westminster Hall, St Stephen's church and the Palace of Westminster before the 1834 fire.

Light refreshments are available.

⊞ Available for corporate and private hire

OPENING TIMES

1 Apr-30 Oct,
Wed-Sun   10am-5pm

31 Oct-31 Mar, Sat-Sun   10am-4pm

25-26 Dec & 1 Jan   Closed

Last entry 30 mins before closing

VISIT US

Direction: Located on Abingdon Street, opposite the southern end of the Houses of Parliament (Victoria Tower)

Train: Victoria and Charing Cross ¾ mile, Waterloo 1 mile

Bus: Visit traveline.info

Tube: St James's Park and Westminster ¼ mile

Tel: 020 7222 2219

NON-MEMBERS

Adult £6.60 I Concession £5.90
Child £4.00 I Family 2 Adults £17.20
Family 1 Adult £10.60

ACQ.1938 ♿ 🏠 ☕ Ⓜ 🛍 OVP

New café with indoor and outdoor seating.

Disabled access (limited).

MAP PAGE 326 (3E)
OS MAP 176/177,
161/173: TQ301793

MARBLE HILL

TWICKENHAM – TW1 2NL

A beautiful Palladian mansion set in riverside parkland, Marble Hill is the last complete survivor of the elegant 18th-century villas which bordered the Thames between Richmond and Hampton Court.

It was begun in 1724 for Henrietta Howard, Countess of Suffolk, a remarkable woman of letters and friend of some of England's greatest writers. The house and gardens were planned by fashionable connoisseurs, including the poet Alexander Pope.

Marble Hill was intended as an Arcadian retreat from crowded 18th-century London. There can be few places in England which better evoke the atmosphere of Georgian fashionable life.

 Nanny McPhee Returns (2010); *Vanity Fair* (2018); *Harlots* (2019).

NEW FOR 2022

Revived and transformed, Marble Hill will reopen in spring 2022. It will be open to the public, free, five days a week for seven months of the year. Thanks to generous grants from the National Lottery Heritage Fund and Community Fund, and the help of local people and volunteers, we've conserved, redisplayed and re-interpreted the house's furnishings, hangings and art collections, and installed lift access to the first floor. We've opened up more areas in the park and enhanced its biodiversity. So there are new gardens to visit, with a free family trail and a play area for children. The Coach House Café reopened in 2021.

OPENING TIMES

House

Spring 2022-30 Oct, Wed-Sun	10am-5pm

See website for latest opening information

31 Oct-31 Mar	Closed

Park
7am-dusk
Please be aware some areas of the park may be temporarily closed for restoration work

Coach House Café

1 Apr-30 Sep	8am-6pm
1 Oct-23 Dec	8am-4pm
24 Dec	8am-2pm
25 Dec	Closed
27 Dec-31 Mar	8am-4pm

Entry to the House and grounds is free; donations welcome. Pre-booked group tours may be available

Last entry 30 mins before closing

VISIT US

Direction: Richmond Road, Twickenham, London

Train: St Margaret's, Twickenham or Richmond

Bus: Visit traveline.info for the latest bus timetables and routes

Tube: Richmond 1 mile

Tel: 020 8892 1900

Café: please check website for details.

Disabled access (exterior, ground floor and first floor only; toilets). There are hard paths throughout the park, but some areas have uneven ground.

Dogs: in certain areas within the grounds can be let off leads. Only assistance dogs are allowed inside the house.

Parking: charges apply to non-members, free for Members with valid English Heritage car sticker.

New guidebook.

MAP PAGE 326 (4E)
OS MAP 176, 161: TQ173736

RANGER'S HOUSE THE WERNHER COLLECTION

GREENWICH PARK – SE10 8QX

The Wernher Collection is one of the greatest private art collections ever assembled in Europe. Enhanced interpretation guides you through its diverse wonders, displayed within a mansion which doubled as the exterior of the *Bridgerton* home in the Netflix series.

Gathered by fabulously wealthy diamond magnate Sir Julius Wernher (1850-1912), the collection is showcased in an elegant Georgian villa, once the official residence of the 'Ranger of Greenwich Park'. It includes nearly 700 varied works of art, including early religious paintings and Dutch Old Masters, fine Renaissance bronzes and silver treasures, and the life-sized erotic statue, *The Love of Angels*. You'll also see Botticelli's *Madonna of the Pomegranate*, recently discovered to be from the painter's own workshop.

The 120 pieces of medieval and Renaissance jewellery – the largest collection in England – feature pendants set with a galaxy of precious stones. There are tapestries with scenes of Chinese life, a mechanical travelling cabinet whose drawers pop out, and rarely seen paintings by famous artists.

Sir Julius developed his keen eye for fine craftsmanship while assessing diamonds. He could afford to buy the very best, and his passion was for what he called the 'splendidly ugly' – tiny, unusual artworks expertly crafted in rich materials. So you'll discover an enamelled gold skull pendant, a minute boxwood coffin with intricate contents, and a 2nd-century BC Greek gold earring of the goddess Victory. Everyone will have their favourite. What will yours be?

Explore a preview of highlights from the collection on our website english-heritage.org.uk/visit/places/rangers-house-the-wernher-collection/history-and-stories/

🎬 *Belle* (2013); *Bridgerton* (2020).

🎦 Available for corporate and private hire

🔺 Licensed for civil wedding ceremonies

OPENING TIMES

1 Apr-30 Oct,
Wed-Sun   11am-4pm

31 Oct-31 Mar   Closed

VISIT US

Address: Chesterfield Walk, Blackheath, London

Direction: Ranger's House is on Chesterfield Walk and overlooks the junction of General Wolfe Road and Shooters Hill Road

DLR: Deptford Bridge then bus 53, or 20 min walk from Cutty Sark

Train: Blackheath ¾ mile

Bus: Visit traveline.info for the latest bus timetables and routes

River: Greenwich Pier

Tel: For enquiries, please call Eltham Palace on 020 8294 2548

NON-MEMBERS

Adult **£11.20** | Concession **£10.10**
Child **£6.60** | Family 2 Adults **£29.00**
Family 1 Adult **£17.80**

No photography allowed inside the house.

MAP PAGE 327 (4F)
OS MAP 177, 161/162: TQ388769

WELLINGTON ARCH

HYDE PARK – W1J 7JZ

Walk into this famous landmark to gain wonderful views over Royal London from the balconies, and see the Household Cavalry riding past. Enjoy four floors of fascinating exhibitions within and discover the vital part played by the Royal Artillery in the First World War.

Set in the heart of the capital at Hyde Park Corner, opposite Apsley House, Wellington Arch is one of London's most iconic monuments. It's crowned by the largest bronze sculpture in Europe, depicting the Angel of Peace descending on the 'Quadraga' – or four-horsed chariot – of War.

The balconies just below the sculpture offer you glorious panoramas over the Royal Parks and central London. It's a unique spot from which to view the Household Cavalry passing beneath, to and from the Changing of the Guard at Horse Guards Parade.

On the first floor within the arch, you'll discover a display revealing its fascinating and sometimes surprising story. Originally intended as a grand outer entrance to Buckingham Palace, it later took on the role of a victory arch proclaiming Wellington's triumph over Napoleon, and once housed London's smallest police station. By 1883, however, the arch was causing traffic bottlenecks. So it was moved, stone by stone, some 100 metres (328 feet) to its current position. The great bronze Quadriga sculpture, by Adrian Jones, was added in 1912. Jones had been a cavalry veterinary officer, and the sculpture's horses reflect his deep knowledge of equine anatomy.

On the second floor, you'll find a display about the Royal Regiment of Artillery, 1914-1918. Mounted in partnership with the Royal Artillery, it commemorates the wartime sacrifice of over 49,000 artillerymen, and considers how they were remembered by the nearby Royal Artillery Memorial, controversial because it was the first war memorial in Britain to depict a fallen soldier. The exhibition also focuses on the human aspect, highlighting the story of Gunner Stone, VC, and includes rarely seen artefacts from the Ypres battlefields.

Combine your trip to Wellington Arch with a visit to the Duke of Wellington's London residence, Apsley House, just opposite.

From April 2022, come and see a series of exhibitions by some of Britain's leading contemporary artists.

⊤ Available for corporate and private hire

DON'T MISS

The exhibition on the first floor, which gives you some fascinating insights into the history of Wellington Arch. Find out how and why the arch was moved from one side of Hyde Park to the other. Did you know that it once had a huge statue of the Duke of Wellington on top, provoking violent controversy? Wellington Arch may be small, but it has a big history.

OPENING TIMES

1 Apr-30 Oct, Wed-Sun	10am-5pm
31 Oct-31 Mar, Wed-Sun	10am-4pm
24-26, 31 Dec & 1 Jan	Closed

Last entry 30 mins before closing

May close due to corporate or private hire

VISIT US

Address: Wellington Arch, Apsley Way, Hyde Park Corner, London W1J 7JZ

Direction: Hyde Park Corner, W1J

Train: Victoria ½ mile

Bus: Visit traveline.info or tfl.gov.uk/plan-a-journey

Tube: Hyde Park Corner, adjacent

Tel: 020 7930 2726

NON-MEMBERS

Adult **£6.60** | Concession **£5.90** | Child **£4.00**
Family 2 Adults **£17.20** | Family 1 Adult **£10.60**

Joint ticket with Apsley House
Adult **£16.00** | Concession **£14.50** | Child **£9.60**
Family 2 Adults **£41.60** | Family 1 Adult **£25.60**

Prices include entry to exhibitions

Pre-booked guided tours are available for groups. For group visits, go to english-heritage.org.uk/visit/places/wellington-arch/plan-your-visit/group-visits/ or call Apsley House on 020 7499 5676

ACQ.1999 ♿ E ⌂ T ⊗ ⌖ ⚠ OVP

MAP PAGE 326 (3E)
OS MAP 176, 161/173: TQ284798

BLUE PLAQUES

Blue plaques commemorate famous people and interesting buildings – and, most often, mark the link between the two. They offer an accessible introduction to the inspiring stories of personal achievement that lie behind the brick, stone and stucco of our streetscape.

London's blue plaques scheme, founded in 1866, is believed to be the oldest of its kind in the world – and has inspired many similar programmes across the UK and abroad. English Heritage has run the scheme since 1986, and there are now over 970 official plaques in Greater London.

The London plaques celebrate all areas of human endeavour and reflect London's past and present as an international city of enormous diversity and talent. Plaques put up in recent years have commemorated an exciting range of figures – from sporting greats such as footballer Bobby Moore, to modern musical legends like John Lennon, Bob Marley and Freddie Mercury, as well as the suffragettes Emmeline and Christabel Pankhurst, and stars of the stage and screen, including Ava Gardner, Margaret Lockwood and Sir John Gielgud.

Sometimes historical events or groups of people are commemorated, rather than individuals. Examples are the plaque that marks the house in which the artists of the Pre-Raphaelite Brotherhood gathered in Gower Street, Bloomsbury, and the blue roundel at Alexandra Palace – from where the world's first regular high-definition television broadcasts were transmitted.

Among those awarded plaques in 2021 were six women who blazed a trail in different ways. Diana, Princess of Wales, is commemorated at the flat in Earl's Court where, as Lady Diana Spencer, she lived as a young woman. Caroline Norton, the 19th-century author whose campaigning led to married women being permitted to own their own property, is also now memorialised, as is the pioneering barrister Helena Normanton. With her husband William, Ellen Craft escaped from slavery in the American South and then campaigned to end it; a roundel marks the Hammersmith house where they found refuge. The fashion designer Jean Muir and the crystallographer Dame Kathleen Lonsdale are also now commemorated, as are the playwright John Osborne, the broadcaster and art historian Sir Kenneth Clark and the man behind the Muppets, Jim Henson.

FIND OUT MORE

Our guidebook, *The English Heritage Guide to London's Blue Plaques*, is available at the English Heritage online shop and in all good bookshops. A map-linked blue plaques app may be downloaded at the app store for both Apple and Android phones and tablets, and each official London plaque has its own page on the English Heritage website.

GET INVOLVED

The scheme relies entirely on private donations and almost all plaques originate from a proposal from a member of the public. To be considered for a blue plaque, a person must have been dead for 20 years, and an authentic building holding strong associations with them must survive in London. If you would like to nominate someone for a blue plaque in London, go to **english-heritage.org.uk/propose-a-plaque**

Help us continue this work by making a donation today: **english-heritage.org.uk/support-the-scheme**

LONDON STATUES AND MONUMENTS

Explore central London to discover over 45 statues and monuments which honour famous historical figures from all over the world, from monarchs and generals to explorers and nurses. They also include some outstanding 20th-century war memorials, including the iconic Cenotaph.

The statues and monuments in English Heritage's care include masterpieces of sculpture and architecture. Many depict monarchs and aristocrats, generals and statesmen, nurses and explorers. These reflect the values of the times in which they were made and unveiled. These values may not align with those some people hold today, particularly when commemorating Britain's history as an imperial power. Only four women are commemorated – two queens and the nurses Florence Nightingale and Edith Cavell. The monuments include the famous Cenotaph and the Royal Artillery Memorial, still the settings for ceremonies of remembrance each year.

Find out more at **english-heritage.org.uk/ london-statues-and-monuments**

THE CAPITAL'S STATUES AND MONUMENTS

Belgian Gratitude Memorial
Victoria Embankment, WC2N

Captain Scott
Waterloo Place, SW1

Carabiniers' Memorial
Chelsea Embankment, SW3

Cenotaph
Whitehall, SW1

Chindit Memorial
Victoria Embankment, SW1

Christopher Columbus
Belgrave Square, SW1

Duke of Cambridge
Whitehall, SW1

Duke of Devonshire
Whitehall, SW1

Duke of Kent
Crescent Gardens (locked), Portland Place, W1

Duke of Wellington
Apsley Way, W1

Earl Haig
Whitehall, SW1

Edith Cavell
St Martin's Place, WC2

Field Marshal Bernard Montgomery
Whitehall, SW1

Florence Nightingale
Waterloo Place, SW1

General de Gaulle
Carlton Gardens, SW1

General de San Martin
Belgrave Square, SW1

General Gordon
Victoria Embankment, SW1

George Washington
Trafalgar Square, WC2

Guards Crimean War Memorial
Waterloo Place, SW1

King Charles I
Whitehall, SW1

King Edward VII
Waterloo Place, SW1

King George II
Golden Square, W1

King George III
Cockspur St, SW1

King James II
National Gallery, Trafalgar Square, WC2

Cenotaph © Sterling Images/Shutterstock Edith Cavell

HUMANITY

Thomas Cubitt Captain Scott

Dover Castle, Kent

WELCOME TO THE

SOUTH EAST

South East

All footpaths lead to Canterbury

Each route takes 1 day

Canterbury has welcomed pilgrims for over a thousand years, attracted by the city's many ancient churches, saints, holy springs and, latterly, Chaucer's tales.

Ⓐ Old Way to Canterbury
(Patrixbourne start, 8 miles)
See *St Augustine's Abbey & Conduit*

Ⓑ North Downs Pilgrims Way
(Chilham start, 7 miles)
See *St Augustine's Abbey & Conduit*

Ⓒ Augustine Camino
(Faversham start, 12 miles)
See *Faversham Stone Chapel, Maison Dieu, St Augustine's Abbey & Conduit*

Ⓓ Via Francigena in England
(Shepherdswell start, 11 miles)
See *St Augustine's Abbey & Conduit*

*An extra day is recommended to fully explore and enjoy Canterbury.

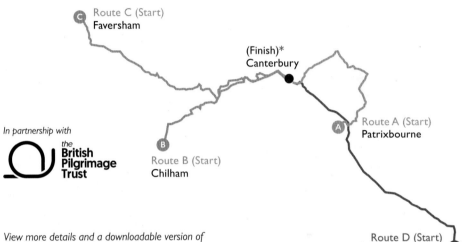

Ⓒ Route C (Start) **Faversham**

(Finish)* **Canterbury**

Ⓐ Route A (Start) **Patrixbourne**

Ⓑ Route B (Start) **Chilham**

Ⓓ Route D (Start) **Shepherdswell**

In partnership with
the **British Pilgrimage Trust**

View more details and a downloadable version of this route at english-heritage.org.uk/pilgrimage

DONNINGTON CASTLE

BERKSHIRE – RG14 2LE

The striking, twin-towered, 14th-century gatehouse of this castle, later the focus of a Civil War siege and battle, survives amid impressive earthworks.

OPENING TIMES

Any reasonable daylight hours, exterior viewing only

Car park open daily	7am-7pm

VISIT US

Direction: 1 mile N of Newbury, off B4494

Train: Newbury 1¼ miles

Bus: Visit traveline.info for the latest bus timetables and routes

ACQ.1952   👤 🐕 P ⚠

Disabled access (Caution: steep slopes within grounds).

Parking: charges apply to non-members, free for Members with valid English Heritage car sticker.

> MAP PAGE 326 (4C)
> OS MAP 174, 158: SU461692

BISHOP'S WALTHAM PALACE

HAMPSHIRE – SO32 1DH

The ruins of a medieval palace used by the bishops of Winchester. Much of what survives is the work of William Wykeham, bishop from 1367. The ground floor of the farmhouse, adapted from the palace's lodging range, houses the Bishop's Waltham Town Museum.

BISHOP'S WALTHAM PALACE

Download a free audio tour from our website.

OPENING TIMES

Grounds

1 Apr-30 Oct, daily	10am-6pm or dusk if earlier
31 Oct-31 Mar, daily	10am-4pm
25 Dec	Closed

Farmhouse Museum

1 May-26 Sep, Sat-Sun	12pm-4pm

VISIT US

Direction: In Bishop's Waltham

Train: Botley 3½ miles

Bus: Visit traveline.info for the latest bus timetables and routes

Tel: 0370 333 1181

ACQ.1952 🎧   🐕 🖼 P 🖼 ⚠

Disabled access (grounds only).

Dogs on leads (restricted areas only).

Museum (limited opening hours).

Caution: deep water, unguarded drops.

> MAP PAGE 326 (5C)
> OS MAP 185, 119: SU552174

CALSHOT CASTLE

HAMPSHIRE – SO45 1BR

This Tudor artillery fort, built to defend the approaches to Southampton, later saw service in both World Wars.

Managed by Hampshire County Council.

OPENING TIMES

Please see website for details

VISIT US

Direction: On spit, 2 miles SE of Fawley, off B3053

CALSHOT CASTLE

Train: Beaulieu Road 10 miles, Southampton 15 miles

Bus: Visit traveline.info for the latest bus timetables and routes

Tel: 023 8089 2023; when castle is closed, please call 023 8089 2077

NON-MEMBERS

Please see website for details

ACQ.1964   E 👤 🛒 ⊗ P
🖼 ⚠

Disabled access (part of the Courtyard, toilets and some exhibtion space).

Parking charges apply.

Caution: deep water, steep stairs.

> MAP PAGE 326 (6C)
> OS MAP 196, OL22/OL29/119: SU489025

FLOWERDOWN BARROWS

HAMPSHIRE – SO22 6PS

Three Bronze Age burial mounds, including two bowl barrows and the largest and finest disc barrow in Hampshire.

OPENING TIMES

Any reasonable daylight hours

VISIT US

Direction: Off B3049, out of Winchester to Littleton; at crossroads in centre of village

Train: Winchester 2 miles

Bus: Visit traveline.info for the latest bus timetables and routes

Tel: 0370 333 1181

ACQ.1972 🐕

> MAP PAGE 326 (5C)
> OS MAP 185, 132: SU459320

FORT BROCKHURST

HAMPSHIRE – PO12 4DS

One of the best surviving of the artillery forts built to protect Portsmouth's vital harbour during the 1850s-60s, when invasion by Napoleon III's France was expected. It's largely unaltered, and you can still see the moated keep, parade ground and emplacements for formidable heavy guns.

OPENING TIMES

Exterior:
Any reasonable daylight hours

Interior: Apr-Oct, 2nd and
4th Sat of the month   11am-3pm

Due to occasional operational changes, we advise visitors to check website in advance

Additional opening times during Gosport Heritage Open Days – please check website

VISIT US

Direction: Off A32, in Gunner's Way, Elson; on N side of Gosport

Train: Fareham 3 miles

Bus: Visit traveline.info for the latest bus timetables and routes

Tel: 0370 333 1181

ACQ.1963 👤🐕🅿🖼⚠

Disabled access (grounds and parts of ground floor only).

Dogs on leads (grounds only).

Parking: charges apply to non-members, free for Members with valid English Heritage car sticker.

Caution: deep water, unguarded drops, steep stairs.

MAP PAGE 326 (6C)
OS MAP 196, OL29/119:
SU596021

THE GRANGE AT NORTHINGTON

HAMPSHIRE – SO24 9TG

Set like a lakeside temple in a landscaped park, the Grange at Northington is among the foremost examples of the Greek Revival style in England, remodelled after 1808.

🎬 *Onegin*, with Ralph Fiennes.

OPENING TIMES

Exterior only:
1 Apr-31 May, daily	10am-6pm
1 Jun-31 Jul, daily	9am-2pm*
1 Aug-30 Sep, daily	10am-6pm
1 Oct-31 Mar, daily	10am-4pm

*Closes early for Opera evenings in June and July

24-26 Dec & 1 Jan	Closed

VISIT US

Direction: Located 4 miles N of New Alresford, off B3046 along a farm track – 450 metres (493 yards)

Train: Winchester 8 miles

Bus: Visit traveline.info for the latest bus timetables and routes

Tel: 0370 333 1181

ACQ.1975 ♿🐕🛡🖼☕🔔🅿 🖼⚠

Disabled access (with assistance, steep steps to terrace).

Caution: unguarded drops, steep stairs.

MAP PAGE 326 (5C)
OS MAP 185, 132: SU562362

HURST CASTLE

HAMPSHIRE – SO41 0TP

HURST CASTLE

Among the most advanced of Henry VIII's artillery fortresses, later strengthened by immense 19th-century gun emplacements, Hurst Castle helped defend the Solent up until the Second World War. You can now visit the Tudor keep, where Charles I was imprisoned in 1648, but the east and west wings are undergoing conservation.

Managed by Hurst Marine.

OPENING TIMES

1 Apr-30 Sep, daily	10am-5.30pm
1-31 Oct, daily	10am-4pm

1 Nov-31 Mar
See **hurstcastle.co.uk** for details

Opening times are weather dependent throughout the year. Call 01590 642500 to check before you visit

VISIT US

Direction: 2 mile walk on shingle spit from Milford on Sea. Best approached by ferry from Keyhaven. Ferry departs 10am then approx. every 20 minutes, charges apply – see hurstcastle.co.uk

Train: Lymington Town 6½ miles

Bus: Visit traveline.info for the latest bus timetables and routes

Tel: 01590 642500

NON-MEMBERS

Adult **£4.50** I Concession **£4.00**
Child **£2.50**

ACQ.1933 🏖🐕🇪🏰🚶🚻🖼 🐶⚠

Dogs on leads.

Castle Café open 1 Apr-31 Oct (not managed by English Heritage).

Parking (charge payable)
Keyhaven SO41 0TP.

Caution: deep water, unguarded drops, steep stairs.

MAP PAGE 326 (6B)
OS MAP 196, OL22/OL29:
SZ318897

KING JAMES'S AND LANDPORT GATES, PORTSMOUTH

HAMPSHIRE – PO1 2EJ

Two ornamental gateways, formerly part of Portsmouth's defences. King James's Gate (1687) has been moved, but Georgian Landport Gate (1760), once the principal entrance to Portsmouth, remains in its original position.

OPENING TIMES

Exterior from roadside only:
Any reasonable daylight hours

VISIT US

Direction: King James's Gate forms the officers' entrance to United Services Recreation Ground, Burnaby Rd; Landport Gate as above, men's entrance on St George's Road

Train: Portsmouth Harbour ¼ mile

Bus: Visit traveline.info for the latest bus timetables and routes

Tel: 0370 333 1181

ACQ.1930

Caution: beware of traffic.

MAP PAGE 326 (6C)
OS MAP 196, OL29/119
KING JAMES'S GATE: SZ636999
LANDPORT GATE: SZ634998

MEDIEVAL MERCHANT'S HOUSE, SOUTHAMPTON

HAMPSHIRE – SO14 2AT

Among the oldest surviving merchant's houses in England, this partly timber-framed combination of home, shop and warehouse was originally built in about 1290. Now vividly recreated as it looked in the mid-14th century, with replica furnishings.

OPENING TIMES

1 Apr-30 Sep, Sat-Sun	11am-4pm
1 Oct-31 Mar	Closed

VISIT US

Direction: 58 French St, ¼ mile S of city centre, just off Castle Way (between High St and Bugle St)

Train: Southampton ¾ mile

Bus: Visit traveline.info for the latest bus timetables and routes

Tel: 023 8022 1503

Local Tourist Information:
Southampton: 023 8083 3333

NON-MEMBERS

Adult **£5.60** | Concession **£5.00**
Child **£3.40** | Family 2 Adults **£14.60**
Family 1 Adult **£9.00**

ACQ.1973 OVP

Disabled access (two steps).
Ground floor only.

MAP PAGE 326 (6B)
OS MAP 196, OL22: SU419112

NETLEY ABBEY

HAMPSHIRE – SO31 5FB

The most complete surviving Cistercian monastery in southern England, with much of its big 13th-century church, cloister and monastic buildings still standing. Later converted into a Tudor mansion, now largely vanished. The abbey's Romantic Gothic ruins inspired many artists and writers, including Constable, Turner and Jane Austen. Download a free audio tour from our website.

OPENING TIMES

1 Apr-30 Oct, daily	10am-4pm
31 Oct-31 Mar, Sat-Sun	10am-4pm
25 Dec	Closed

VISIT US

Direction: In Netley; 4 miles SE of Southampton, facing Southampton Water

Train: Netley 1 mile

Bus: Visit traveline.info for the latest bus timetables and routes

Tel: 0370 333 1181

ACQ.1922 P

Gravel car park, limited spaces.
Caution: falling masonry.

MAP PAGE 326 (6C)
OS MAP 196, OL22: SU453090

ROYAL GARRISON CHURCH, PORTSMOUTH

HAMPSHIRE – PO1 2NJ

The roofed and furnished chancel of a church constructed c. 1212 and damaged by 1941 bombing.

OPENING TIMES

The church will be closed for conservation work until summer 2022. Please check website for latest information and opening times once reopened

VISIT US

Direction: In Portsmouth; on Grand Parade S of High St

Train: Portsmouth Harbour ¾ mile

Bus: Visit traveline.info

Tel: 0370 333 1181

[ACQ.1970] 🚻 ⊗ P

Parking (charged on Grand Parade).

MAP PAGE 326 (6C)
OS MAP 196, OL29/119:
SZ633992

SILCHESTER ROMAN TOWN WALLS AND AMPHITHEATRE

HAMPSHIRE – RG7 2HP

An Iron Age tribal centre, Silchester became the important Roman town of Calleva Atrebatum. The complete circuit of its walls, 1½ miles long, can be traced, although no buildings within survive. Outside are remains of a Roman amphitheatre. Download a free audio tour from our website.

OPENING TIMES

Any reasonable daylight hours

Car park	
1 Apr-30 Sep, daily	8am-7pm
1 Oct-31 Mar, daily	8.30am-4pm

VISIT US

Direction: On a minor road, 1 mile E of Silchester

Train: Bramley or Mortimer, both 2¾ miles

Bus: Visit traveline.info for the latest bus timetables and routes

Tel: 0370 333 1181

[ACQ.1965] 🚻 🏛 P ⚠

There is no parking at the amphitheatre, visitors should park at the main car park for the Roman Town. Prior notice of tall vehicles (i.e. coaches and minibuses) wishing to park in the car park is needed. Car park operated by Hampshire County Council – please contact 0118 970 0132 to open height barrier.

Caution: unguarded drops, steep stairs.

MAP PAGE 326 (4C)
OS MAP 175, 159: SU639624

SOUTHWICK PRIORY

HAMPSHIRE – PO17 6EB

Remains of a wealthy Augustinian priory, originally founded at Portchester: once a famous place of pilgrimage. Only part of the refectory wall survives.

OPENING TIMES

Any reasonable daylight hours

VISIT US

Direction: Access via footpath from Priory Road, opposite village car park

SOUTHWICK PRIORY

Bus: Visit traveline.info for the latest bus timetables and routes

Tel: 0370 333 1181

[ACQ.1970] 🚻 P ⚠

Parking in village car park.

Caution: falling masonry.

MAP PAGE 326 (6C)
OS MAP 196, 119: SU629084

TITCHFIELD ABBEY

HAMPSHIRE – PO15 5RA

The ruins of a 13th-century abbey of Premonstratensian canons, later converted into a Tudor mansion. The church was rebuilt as a grand turreted gatehouse. Download a free audio tour from our website.

OPENING TIMES

1 Apr-30 Sep, daily	10am-5pm
1 Oct-31 Mar, daily	10am-4pm
25 Dec	Closed

VISIT US

Direction: Located ½ mile N of Titchfield, off A27, along Mill Lane, opposite Fisherman's Rest pub

Train: Fareham 2 miles

Bus: Visit traveline.info for the latest bus timetables and routes

Tel: 0370 333 1181

[ACQ.1923] 🚻 P ⚠

Disabled access (with assistance, steep steps to terrace).

Car park accessed via narrow entrance through high wall.

Parking: charges apply to non-members, free for Members with valid English Heritage car sticker.

Caution: steep stairs.

MAP PAGE 326 (6C)
OS MAP 196, 119: SU542067

PORTCHESTER CASTLE

—— HAMPSHIRE – PO16 9QW ——

Set within the most magnificently complete Roman fort walls in northern Europe, this medieval castle became a crowded prisoner of war camp. Our dramatic displays immerse you in the story of the African-Caribbean soldiers held here during the Napoleonic wars.

Much the best-preserved of the Roman 'Saxon Shore' forts, Portchester retains most of its Roman defences, including 16 towers. During the 12th century a Norman castle with a powerful keep was built in one corner, developing into a 14th-century royal palace.

Later, the castle was transformed into a vast prisoner of war camp. During the Napoleonic Wars up to 8,000 captives were held here. Our displays examine how they fought poverty and boredom and retained their national identity.

On the keep's ground floor, you'll find a representation of the theatre where French prisoners performed plays. On the upper floors, surround sound effects evoke the prisoners' sea journey to Britain.

Another arresting installation highlights Portchester's most surprising prisoners, around 2,000 African-Caribbean soldiers captured while fighting for the French on St Lucia in the Caribbean. You'll discover how they encountered kindness as well as cruelty and prejudice. Find more about them at **english-heritage.org.uk/black-prisoners**

Climb to the roof of the 30-metre (100 feet) high keep for breathtaking views of the Roman fort, with the great sweep of Portsmouth harbour beyond.

OPENING TIMES

1 Apr-30 Oct, daily	10am-5pm
31 Oct-10 Feb, Sat-Sun	10am-4pm
11-19 Feb, daily	10am-4pm
20 Feb-31 Mar, Sat-Sun	10am-4pm
24-25 Dec	Closed

VISIT US

Direction: On the S side of Portchester off A27; Junction 11 on M27

Train: Portchester 1 mile

Bus: Visit **traveline.info** for the latest bus timetables and routes

Tel: 023 9237 8291

NON-MEMBERS

Adult **£9.00** | Concession **£8.10**
Child **£5.40** | Family 2 Adults **£23.40**
Family 1 Adult **£14.40**

[ACQ.1926] 🎧 ♿ 🍽 ■ E 💷 ⬚ 🚹 🚼 P
🚗 📷 [OVP]

Caution: relatively steep stairs to the exhibitions on upper floors of the keep.

Disabled access (grounds and lower levels only).

Dogs on leads (outer grounds only).

Toilets (facilities are in the car park, operated by Fareham District Council).

MAP PAGE 326 (6C)
OS MAP 196, OL29/119: SU625046

WOLVESEY CASTLE (OLD BISHOP'S PALACE)

HAMPSHIRE – SO23 9NB

An important residence of the wealthy bishops of Winchester since Anglo-Saxon times, standing near to Winchester Cathedral. The extensive surviving ruins date largely from the 12th century. Download a free audio tour from our website.

OPENING TIMES

1 Apr-30 Sep, daily	10am-6pm
1-30 Oct, daily	10am-4pm
31 Oct-31 Mar, Sat-Sun	10am-4pm
25 Dec	Closed

VISIT US

Direction: 600 metres SE of Winchester Cathedral, next to the Bishop's Palace; access from College St

Train: Winchester ¾ mile

Bus: Visit traveline.info for the latest bus timetables and routes

Tel: 0370 333 1181

ACQ.1962

Please do not climb on the walls.

No access to the adjacent garden (private property).

Caution: deep water, falling masonry.

MAP PAGE 326 (5C)
OS MAP 185, 132: SU484291

BAYHAM OLD ABBEY   KENT – TN3 8LP

One of southern England's finest monastic ruins, Bayham Abbey was founded in the early 13th century by Robert de Thurnham for the Premonstratensian 'white canons'. Renowned for the quality and richness of their architecture, these impressive ruins include much of the church, chapter house and picturesque 14th-century gatehouse. The secluded nature of the site is enhanced by views of the picturesque landscape designed by Humphry Repton, creating a beautiful and tranquil experience.

OPENING TIMES

1 Apr-30 Oct, daily	10am-5pm or dusk if earlier
31 Oct-31 Mar	Closed

VISIT US

Direction: 1¾ miles W of Lamberhurst, off B2169

Train: Frant 4 miles then bus 256

Bus: Visit traveline.info

Tel: 0370 333 1181

ACQ.1961

Parking: charges apply to non-members, free for Members with valid English Heritage car sticker.

Caution: deep water, unguarded drops.

MAP PAGE 327 (5G)
OS MAP 188, 136: TQ650365

DEAL CASTLE

KENT – CT14 7BA

Lively storytelling, displays and activities help you explore every corner of Deal Castle, the biggest and most elaborate of all Henry VIII's coastal artillery forts.

As you enter this formidable fortress, you'll be faced by a replica Tudor cannon. It's a reminder that Deal was one of the revolutionary new-style artillery castles built from 1539 by Henry VIII to counter a threatened invasion by European Catholic powers. Flanked by neighbouring Walmer Castle and now-vanished Sandown Castle, all linked by defensive earthworks, it was the crucial centrepiece of three forts whose heavy guns commanded the vital sheltered anchorage between the hazardous Goodwin Sands and the shore. Its distinctive multi-lobed design provided all-round firepower from a total of over 140 guns, arranged in five tiers.

On its squat rounded bastions – intended to minimise the effect of incoming cannonballs – you'll find 'Guarding the Downs', one of the displays which vividly illustrate how the castle worked.

Within the round keep, the core of the fortress, you'll find 'Henry VIII's Castle of War', opening windows on the world of 1539 and how Deal fitted into it. A huge illustrated jigsaw-style map of Europe lays out the international situation when the castle was built. Sit on the thrones of Henry, his nervous fourth wife, Anne of Cleves, or his opponents the Pope, the Emperor and the King of France; pick up the earphones and you'll hear each one's thoughts. Nearby, there's a 3D jigsaw model of the castle to assemble. In neighbouring rooms you'll discover site-finds of Tudor weaponry from Camber Castle, another of Henry's forts, including pike heads, armour-piercing arrows, and equipment for cannons and muskets.

If you want to try defending the castle yourself, go down to the castle basement to 'Explore and Defend the Rounds'. This dark, narrow and winding passage encircles the whole castle, and is equipped with 53 ports for handguns to mow down any attackers who reached the dry moat. If you dare to venture into the Rounds, you can borrow wellies (the passage floor can be wet after rain) and a replica musket from racks near the entrances. Look out for the wind-up listening devices, which let you eavesdrop on two soldiers during the Civil War siege of 1648, when the castle saw hard fighting. Don't get lost!

To find out more about the fort's later history, climb the spiral stairs to the Georgian panelled rooms of the keep's upper floor. Here the 'Captains of Deal' display tells you about the commanders and garrison soldiers of the castle from Tudor times until the 20th century. You can read 'conversations' between contrasting captains, and hear the thoughts of others. Don't miss the room highlighting the graffiti written or scratched on the castle roof over the centuries, where you can leave your own mark on paper to add to Deal Castle's fascinating history.

The castle stands right next to Deal's attractive beach, and there are fine sea views from the ramparts. A cycle path links Deal and Walmer Castles (p.80) along the beachfront.

OPENING TIMES

1 Apr-30 Oct, daily	10am-5pm
31 Oct-23 Dec, Sat-Sun	10am-4pm
2 Jan-10 Feb, Sat-Sun	10am-4pm
11-19 Feb, daily	10am-4pm
20 Feb-31 Mar, Wed-Sun	10am-4pm

Christmas Opening

| 24-25 Dec | Closed |
| 26 Dec-1 Jan, daily | 10am-4pm |

VISIT US

Address: Marine Road, Deal, Kent CT14 7BA

Direction: SW of Deal town centre

Train: Deal ½ mile

Bus: Visit traveline.info for the latest bus timetables and routes

Tel: 01304 372762

NON-MEMBERS

Adult **£9.00** | Concession **£8.10**
Child **£5.40** | Family 2 Adults **£23.40**
Family 1 Adult **£14.40**

ACQ.1904

Disabled access (courtyards and ground floor only, parking available).

Parking: charges apply to non-members, free for Members with valid English Heritage car sticker and free ticket from the machine (3 hours maximum stay). See signs on arrival for details.

MAP PAGE 327 (4J)
OS MAP 179, 150: TR378522

DOVER CASTLE

KENT – CT16 1HU

Crowning the White Cliffs high above the Channel, Dover's majestic fortress offers visitors an unparalleled journey into the past, from Roman times via medieval sieges to the Second World War and beyond.

Renowned as 'the Key to England', Dover Castle boasts a long and immensely eventful 2,000-year history. Its spectacular site still displays a Roman lighthouse and an Anglo-Saxon church. Begun soon after 1066, it became a medieval royal castle-palace of immense strength. In the labyrinthine tunnels beneath it, Vice Admiral Ramsay planned the miraculous rescue of the British Army from Dunkirk in 1940. It later concealed a secret Cold War bunker – now echoed in a thrilling Escape Room experience.

MEDIEVAL ROYAL PALACE

Dover Castle is first and foremost the strongest medieval fortress in England, created by King Henry II and his Plantagenet successors in the 12th and 13th centuries. Mutually supporting circuits of towered walls made it the very first 'concentric' castle in Europe. At its heart stands the mighty keep – the Great Tower. Built between 1180 and 1185, this symbol of kingly power was also a palace designed for royal ceremony.

The interior of the Great Tower palace has been recreated as it might have appeared when newly completed. Entering the Great Tower, you'll find projected figures, which bring to life your journey round the vibrantly recreated and colourfully furnished rooms of the palace, from kitchens and royal bedchambers to the impressive King's Hall.

You can follow the dramatic story of Henry II and his turbulent brood in an introductory exhibition, 'A Family at War', and a virtual tour reveals the Great Tower to those unable to explore it.

EPIC SIEGES

Climb to the Great Tower's roof for panoramic views over the castle's immense complex of medieval fortifications. These saw desperate fighting during the epic sieges of 1216-17, when the castle resisted ten months of attack by a French army. Intrepid visitors can descend into the Medieval Tunnels, burrowed beneath the castle during and after the siege.

THE FIRST WORLD WAR

During the First World War, Dover was officially designated as a Fortress, with the castle as its military headquarters. The Fire Command Post recreates this dramatic chapter in its history. Explore what it was like to work here, try communicating in Morse code, learn semaphore and discover how to spot enemy or friendly ships.

To counter the new threat of aerial attack, the fortress mounted pioneering anti-aircraft guns. Now it's home to the only working British 3-inch anti-aircraft gun in the world, which performs regular firing demonstrations on selected weekends in summer.

Exploring the maze of intriguing and sometimes eerie tunnels beneath Dover Castle, burrowed at times of crisis both for the fortress and the nation it defended. The atmospheric Medieval Tunnels were cut during and after the epic sieges of 1216-17. When French invasion threatened during the Napoleonic Wars, they were enlarged into 'bomb proof' underground barracks for up to 2,000 defending troops.

When even greater danger to castle and nation loomed in 1940, the extended Secret Wartime Tunnels became the nerve-centre of Operation Dynamo – the rescue of the British army from Dunkirk. Witness the drama of the evacuation in the very place where it was planned, and relive the tension in the Underground Hospital. Later still, and right up until 1984, the tunnels housed a secret Cold War government bunker; experience the imminent horror of nuclear war in the immersive Bunker Escape Room.

THE SECOND WORLD WAR: RESCUE FROM DUNKIRK

Dover Castle's defences were even more sorely tested in the darkest days of the Second World War, when tunnels deep beneath the castle became Vice Admiral Bertram Ramsay's bomb-proof naval headquarters.

On 26 May 1940, Ramsay began the rescue of the British Army and its allies, trapped at Dunkirk and fighting for their lives. The task of rescuing them – 'Operation Dynamo' – demanded sending a huge improvised fleet of ships across the Channel, under attack from air, sea and land. The British Army in France depended upon it.

Make the adventurous journey into the Wartime Tunnels and immerse yourself in the drama of the daring evacuation that followed. Film presentations vividly recreate the run-up to Dunkirk. Then, in the very place where Operation Dynamo was planned, witness the astounding rescue from the eastern breakwater and beaches happening all around you.

You can also take a fascinating guided tour of the Underground Hospital within the tunnels, reliving the tension as a surgeon battles to save an injured pilot. Find out more about the 'Miracle of Dunkirk' in the 'Wartime Tunnels Uncovered' exhibition, featuring the recorded voices of many who actually took part.

OPENING TIMES

1 Apr-30 Jun, daily	10am-5pm
1 Jul-31 Aug, daily	10am-6pm
1 Sep-30 Oct, daily	10am-5pm
31 Oct-23 Dec, Sat-Sun	10am-4pm
2 Jan-10 Feb, Sat-Sun	10am-4pm
11-19 Feb, daily	10am-4pm
20 Feb-31 Mar, Wed-Sun	10am-4pm
Christmas Opening	
24-25 Dec	Closed
26 Dec-1 Jan, daily	10am-4pm
Last entry 1 hour before closing	

VISIT US

Address: Dover Castle, Castle Hill, Dover, Kent CT16 1HU

Direction: E of Dover town centre

Train: Dover Priory 1½ miles

Bus: Visit traveline.info for the latest bus timetables and routes

Tel: 0370 333 1181

Local Tourist Information:
Dover: 01304 205108

NON-MEMBERS

Peak (28 May-31 Aug, Sat-Sun and Bank Holidays)
Adult **£28.00** | Concession **£25.20**
Child **£16.80** | Family 2 Adults **£72.80**
Family 1 Adult **£44.80**

Standard (1 Apr-27 May and Sep-Oct, Sat-Sun and Bank Holidays; 28 May-31 Aug, Mon-Fri)
Adult **£26.00** | Concession **£23.40**
Child **£15.60** | Family 2 Adults **£67.60**
Family 1 Adult **£41.60**

Off-peak (1 Apr-27 May and Sep-Oct, Mon-Fri and Nov-Mar)
Adult **£24.00** | Concession **£21.60**
Child **£14.40** | Family 2 Adults **£62.40**
Family 1 Adult **£38.40**

STAY WITH US

Peverell's Tower was at one time a prison. Today it makes a perfect romantic castle tower for two.

The *Sergeant Major's House* is surrounded by hundreds of years of history. This spacious four-storey Georgian residence sleeps six. Great for families, it even has its own secret games room.

See p.16 for details on staying at Dover and our other holiday cottages.

After Dunkirk, the tunnels played a leading role in the elaborate deception which fooled the enemy about the true target of the D-Day invasions. Later still, during the 1960s Cold War, they hosted a top-secret government bunker.

Both the Great Tower Café and the NAAFI Restaurant have been reinvigorated. Menus in the Great Tower Café include more family-friendly options, and the NAAFI has enhanced takeaway and sit-down meal options.

All this, and very much more, makes it well worth enjoying a whole day of discovery at Dover Castle.

🎬 *The Other Boleyn Girl* (2008); *Into the Woods* (2014); *Avengers: Age of Ultron* (2015); *Wolf Hall* (2015); *The Crown* (2016); *King Lear* (2018)

Additional charges for Members and non-members apply for the Bunker (discount for Members) and may apply on event days.

ACQ.1965

Please see the Dover Castle website for information on accessibility. Mobility scooters are available and should be booked in advance.

Dogs are welcome on a lead at all times, although not permitted in the Great Tower and Secret Wartime Tunnels (apart from assistance dogs).

We advise you to wear comfortable shoes.

MAP PAGE 327 (5J)   OS MAP 179, 138: TR325419

The Great Tower is free-flow and self-guided. Stewards in the tower are always on hand to answer any questions. Access to the Operation Dynamo experience in the Secret Wartime Tunnels is by guided tour only. Due to the immersive nature of these visits, no independent guiding is allowed in these areas. However, tour leaders of groups of younger visitors must stay with their parties at all times. Access to the Underground Hospital (separate access from Operation Dynamo) is by guided tour only (limited to 30 people and lasting approximately 20 minutes). At peak times, there may be queues at the popular tunnel experiences. Groups of 11+ can call and book ahead for a group discount on admission. Car parks open at site opening time. Last tunnel tours depart one hour before closing.

HOME OF CHARLES DARWIN, DOWN HOUSE

KENT – BR6 7JT

Experience the Victorian country house where the world was changed. Explore the home of Charles Darwin and his family at your own pace.

A delightful place in itself to visit, Down House is a site of outstanding international significance. Here the famous naturalist Charles Darwin lived with his family for 40 years, worked on his revolutionary theories, and wrote *On the Origin of Species by Means of Natural Selection* – the book which shook the Victorian world and has influenced thinking ever since.

You'll find Darwin's work and personality vividly reflected throughout the house and grounds. The handheld tour, narrated by Sir David Attenborough and Andrew Marr, guides you round the family rooms as well as the garden. It includes commentaries by experts, animations, film footage and games for all the family.

The ground floor rooms have been recreated as they appeared when he lived here with his indefatigably supportive wife, Emma, and their many children. They include the 'Old Study' where Darwin wrote his most famous books, still displaying his chair, writing board and many personal items. You can also visit the family's drawing room – with Emma's grand piano – billiard room and dining room. Upstairs, his bedroom has been recreated as when he rested there. It gives a detailed insight into Darwin's personal side – from the non-scientific books he enjoyed reading to his taste for Old Master prints. A refuge when

he was suffering from poor health, it also enabled him to keep an eye on his garden experiments from the room's large bay windows. A soundscape lets you listen in on Emma reading to her husband, and both children and adults can step into the dressing closet to dress up as Charles and Emma.

'UNCOVERING ORIGIN' EXHIBITION

The award-winning exhibition on the house's first floor covers Darwin's life, his scientific work, and the controversy that it provoked. Beginning with an introduction to Darwin and the impact of his theories, the displays continue with his famous five-year voyage aboard the *Beagle* in 1831-36, including a full-scale recreation of his on-board cabin. You'll discover how Darwin's observations of wildlife during the voyage influenced his thinking, and how an insect bite may have triggered the ill-health which plagued him all his life. Further displays highlight *On the Origin of Species*, which immediately sold out its first edition and consolidated Darwin's international recognition and notoriety.

The Darwin children's schoolroom celebrates family life at Down House. There's also an education room available for family learning, and a resources room for those interested in delving deeper includes digitised versions of Darwin's journals and notebooks.

EXPERIMENTS IN THE GARDENS

By no means the stereotypically stern Victorian father, Darwin involved his children in his practical experiments in the extensive gardens of Down House. This was his 'outdoor laboratory' and the place where he made many of his discoveries. You can now follow these via the multimedia guide, beginning with Darwin's 'weed garden' illustrating the struggle for existence in nature.

The sundial amid pretty flowerbeds highlights Emma Darwin's role as a gardener, a surviving mulberry tree recalls family traditions, and a 'lawn experiment' investigates proliferation of plant species. Visit the nearby hothouse to see some of Darwin's most fascinating experiments, and the working observation beehive in the laboratory. Explore our new interactive panels in the gardens and the laboratory, which help to bring Darwin's experiments to life.

After a tour of the extensive kitchen gardens, you reach what is for many a place of pilgrimage: the wooded Sandwalk. This was Darwin's famous 'thinking path', which he paced for five laps a day while working out his theories.

Stop off at the tearoom, in Darwin's kitchen area, for a refreshing break before exploring the grounds.

Please note: No photography is allowed inside the house.

HELPING BUTTERFLIES

Many butterfly species are in serious trouble. To help them, partners including the London Wildlife Trust have begun to create a Butterfly Bank at Down House. Wild flowers seeded on this chalk bank will support existing local butterfly populations and attract new species. But it will take some time to establish, so watch that space…

OPENING TIMES

1 Apr-30 Oct, daily	10am-5pm
31 Oct-23 Dec, Sat-Sun	10am-4pm
2 Jan-10 Feb, Sat-Sun	10am-4pm
11-19 Feb, daily	10am-4pm
20 Feb-31 Mar, Wed-Sun	10am-4pm

Christmas Opening

24-26 Dec	Closed
27 Dec-1 Jan, daily	10am-4pm

VISIT US

Address: Down House, Luxted Road, Downe, Kent BR6 7JT

Direction: Luxted Road, Downe; off A21 or A233

Train: Orpington 3¾ miles, Bromley South 5½ miles

Bus: R8 and 146 service Down House, for more information visit **traveline.info**

Tel: 01689 859119

NON-MEMBERS

Peak (28 May-31 Aug, Sat-Sun and Bank Holidays)
Adult £18.90 | Concession £17.00
Child £11.40 | Family 2 Adults £49.20
Family 1 Adult £30.30

Standard (1 Apr-27 May and Sep-Oct, Sat-Sun and Bank Holidays; 28 May-31 Aug, Mon-Fri)
Adult £17.60 | Concession £15.80
Child £10.60 | Family 2 Adults £45.80
Family 1 Adult £28.20

Off-peak (1 Apr-27 May and Sep-Oct, Mon-Fri and Nov-Mar)
Adult £16.30 | Concession £14.70
Child £9.80 | Family 2 Adults £42.40
Family 1 Adult £26.10

Audio tour is the multimedia tour.

Dogs (except assistance dogs) are not allowed on site at any time and must not be left unattended in the car park.

Parking available but can be limited at busy times. Coach parking available for one coach, must be booked in advance.

MAP PAGE 327 (4F)
OS MAP 177/187,147: TQ431611

DYMCHURCH MARTELLO TOWER

KENT – TN29 0NU

One of 103 ingeniously designed artillery towers built between 1805 and 1812 at vulnerable points around the south and east coasts, to resist threatened Napoleonic invasion. It's been re-equipped with its single roof-mounted cannon, which could be rotated to fire in any direction. The small garrison occupied 'bomb-proofed' rooms within.

Open in partnership with the Friends of Martello 24.

OPENING TIMES

Exterior only:
Any reasonable daylight hours

Interior:
1 Apr-31 Oct, Sat-Sun
& Bank Hols   2pm-4pm

Bespoke visits for groups of 10 or more by appointment, please email theromneymarsh.net/ visitmartello24#bespoke

VISIT US

Direction: Access from Dymchurch High Street

Train: Sandling 7 miles; Dymchurch (Romney, Hythe and Dymchurch Railway) ¾ mile

Bus: Visit traveline.info for the latest bus timetables and routes

Tel: 01787 366604

ACQ.1959 **E** 🚫 ⚠

Caution: steep stairs.

MAP PAGE 327 (5H)
OS MAP 189, 138: TR102292

EYNSFORD CASTLE

KENT – DA4 0AA

The substantial walls of a very early Norman 'enclosure castle', begun c. 1085-87 and unusually little altered. In an attractive village setting.

OPENING TIMES

1 Apr-30 Sep, daily	10am-6pm
1 Oct-31 Mar, daily	10am-4pm
25 Dec	Closed

VISIT US

Direction: In Eynsford, off A225

Train: Eynsford 1 mile

Bus: Visit traveline.info

Tel: 0370 333 1181

ACQ.1948 ♿ 🚫 **P** ⚠

Caution: deep water, steep stairs.

MAP PAGE 327 (4F)
OS MAP 177, 162: TQ542658

FAVERSHAM STONE CHAPEL (OUR LADY OF ELVERTON)

KENT – ME13 0TB

Ruins of a small Anglo-Saxon and medieval chapel, incorporating the remains of a pagan Romano-British mausoleum. Near the probable site of the Roman town of Durolevum.

OPENING TIMES

Any reasonable daylight hours

VISIT US

Direction: In field immediately N of A2 just W of Ospringe and opposite Faversham Road

Train: Faversham 1½ miles

Bus: Visit traveline.info for the latest bus timetables and routes

Tel: 0370 333 1181

ACQ.1972 🐕 ⚠

Access is across a field.

Caution: beware of traffic.

MAP PAGE 327 (4H)
OS MAP 178, 149: TQ992613

HORNE'S PLACE CHAPEL

KENT – TN26 2AL

Rare survival of a domestic chapel, built for William Horne in 1366 and attached to his manor house, which was attacked during the Peasants' Revolt of 1381. (House and chapel are privately owned.)

OPENING TIMES

By appointment only. Please phone Customer Services on 0370 333 1181

Open for the 1st and 2nd weekends of Heritage Open Days

VISIT US

Direction: 1½ miles N of Appledore

Train: Appledore 2½ miles

Bus: Visit traveline.info for the latest bus timetables and routes

Tel: 0370 333 1181

ACQ.1950 🚫 ⚠ OVP

Caution: steep stairs.

MAP PAGE 327 (5H)
OS MAP 189, 125: TQ958309

LULLINGSTONE
ROMAN VILLA

—— KENT – DA4 0JA ——

Among the most exciting Roman villa survivals in Britain, Lullingstone Roman Villa's vivid displays and interpretation give you a unique insight into Roman domestic life over three centuries.

The villa was begun in about AD 100, and developed to suit successive wealthy owners. These may have included the family of Pertinax, Roman Emperor for just 87 days in AD 193. Additions included a heated bath suite and a remarkable underground pagan 'cult room', including a wall painting of water deities, by far the oldest painting in English Heritage's care.

The villa reached its luxurious zenith in the mid-4th century, when a big new dining room was added. This displays spectacular mosaics, including Europa and Jupiter, and Bellerophon killing the Chimera. By now Christians, the owners also created a 'house-church' above the pagan cult room: wall paintings discovered here are among the earliest evidence of Christianity in Britain, but pagan worship may also have continued, suggesting a relaxed relationship between the old and new faiths.

All this is clearly interpreted in the galleries overlooking the excavated remains, where you'll see finds including adult and infant skeletons. Modern children and adults can play Roman board games, handle original building materials and try on Roman costumes. See the villa come to life in a film and light show that illuminates excavated areas and reveals how they were once used.

OPENING TIMES

1 Apr-30 Oct, daily	10am-5pm
31 Oct-10 Feb, Sat-Sun	10am-4pm
11-19 Feb, daily	10am-4pm
20 Feb-31 Mar, Sat-Sun	10am-4pm
24-26 Dec & 1 Jan	Closed

VISIT US

Direction: ½ mile SW of Eynsford, off J3 of M25, A20 towards West Kingsdown, A225 to Eynsford

Train: Eynsford 2 miles

Bus: Visit traveline.info for the latest bus timetables and routes

Tel: 01322 863467

NON-MEMBERS

Adult £10.00 | Concession £9.00
Child £6.00 | Family 2 Adults £26.00
Family 1 Adult £16.00

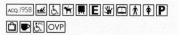

Dogs on leads (restricted areas only).

Parking: charges apply to non-members, free for Members with valid English Heritage car sticker.

MAP PAGE 327 (4F)
OS MAP 177/188, 147/162: TQ530651

RICHBOROUGH ROMAN FORT AND AMPHITHEATRE

———— KENT – CT13 9JW ————

Evocatively sited amid the East Kent marshes, Richborough Roman Fort is the most symbolically important of all Roman sites in Britain, witnessing both the beginning and almost the end of Roman rule here.

Here the invading Roman forces first came ashore in AD 43. Later the main port of entry to Roman Britain, it became the site of one of most important 'Saxon Shore' forts, long sections of whose stone walls still stand high. It was also one of the last Roman forts to be regularly occupied: there was still a large Roman population here in the early 5th century.

NEW FOR 2022

In summer 2022 a major new project will transform the experience of visiting Richborough, highlighting its leading role in the history of Roman Britain. We're creating an upgraded site museum, displaying the most fascinating site finds and a new exhibition telling the story of Richborough and its people. New information panels, family trail and audio guide and new accessible paths will make the fortress easier to explore for more people. We're also building a simulation of a Roman timber gateway, tower and rampart, as constructed by Roman soldiers when they first arrived here. There'll be an exploratory excavation of the nearby amphitheatre, and a programme of activities for local schools and the wider community.

OPENING TIMES

Fort: Please see website for details

Amphitheatre: Any reasonable time in daylight hours, access across grazed land from footpath; please call 01304 612013 for details

VISIT US

Direction: At the A256/A257 roundabout, head for Sandwich then turn left onto Richborough Road and proceed for approx. 1 mile

Train: Sandwich 2 miles

Bus: Visit traveline.info for the latest bus timetables and routes

Tel: 01304 612013

NON-MEMBERS

Adult £9.00 | Concession £8.10 | Child £5.40
Family 2 Adults £23.40 | Family 1 Adult £14.40

ACQ 1912

Dogs on leads (restricted areas only).

New guidebook.

MAP PAGE 327 (4J) OS MAP 179, 150
FORT: TR324602
AMPHITHEATRE: TR321598

KIT'S COTY HOUSE AND LITTLE KIT'S COTY HOUSE

KENT – ME20 7EZ

The remains of two megalithic burial chambers. Impressive Kit's Coty has three uprights and a massive capstone. Little Kit's Coty House, alias the Countess Stones, is now a jumble of sarsens.

OPENING TIMES

Any reasonable daylight hours

VISIT US

Direction: W of A229, 2 miles N of Maidstone

Train: Aylesford 2½ miles

Bus: Visit traveline.info for the latest bus timetables and routes

Tel: 0370 333 1181

ACQ.1883 🐕 ⚠ Caution: beware of traffic.

MAP PAGE 327 (4G)
OS MAP 178/188, 148
KIT'S COTY HOUSE: TQ745608
LITTLE KIT'S COTY HOUSE: TQ744604

KNIGHTS TEMPLAR CHURCH, DOVER

KENT – CT17 9DP

Foundations of a small medieval chapel with a distinctive round nave, a feature associated with the military order of Knights Templar.

OPENING TIMES

Any reasonable daylight hours

VISIT US

Direction: On the Western Heights above Dover

Train: Dover Priory ¾ mile

KNIGHTS TEMPLAR CHURCH

Bus: Visit traveline.info for the latest bus timetables and routes

Tel: 0370 333 1181

ACQ.1968 🐕 P ⚠
Parking (on the road).

Caution: unguarded drops.

MAP PAGE 327 (5J)
OS MAP 179, 138: TR313407

MAISON DIEU

KENT – ME13 8TS

This attractive flint and timber-framed medieval building was part of a much larger complex, including a Canterbury pilgrims' hostel, a royal lodging and a school. It houses a museum including archaeological finds made here and at a nearby Roman cemetery. Managed by the Maison Dieu Museum Trust.

OPENING TIMES

15 Apr-30 Oct, Sat-Sun & Bank Hols	2pm-5pm
31 Oct-31 Mar	Closed

Group visits at other times by appointment between Apr-Oct

VISIT US

Direction: On main A2 on W corner of Water Lane in village of Ospringe. Public car park 300yds W

Train: Faversham ¾ mile

Bus: Visit traveline.info for the latest bus timetables and routes

Tel: 01795 601714

NON-MEMBERS

Adult **£4.00** | Concession **£2.00**
Child **Free if accompanied by adult**

ACQ.1947 ⬜ 🚹 🚹 📮 ✕ 🖐 ⚠
Caution: steep stairs.

MAP PAGE 327 (4H)
OS MAP 178, 149: TR003609

MILTON CHANTRY

KENT – DA12 2BH

Retaining its 14th-century timber roof, this was in turn a hospital, chantry chapel, pub, barracks and Second World War gas decontamination chamber.

Managed by Gravesham Borough Council.

OPENING TIMES

1 Apr-26 Sep, Sat-Sun & Bank Hols	12pm-5pm*
27 Sep-31 Mar	Closed

*Admission outside these times by appointment only

VISIT US

Direction: In New Tavern Fort Gardens; E of central Gravesend, off A226

Train: Gravesend ¾ mile

Bus: Visit traveline.info for the latest bus timetables and routes

Tel: 01474 337600

ACQ.1972 🎧 📮 ✕ ⚠
Caution: steep stairs.

MAP PAGE 327 (4G)
OS MAP 177/178, 162/163: TQ653743

OLD SOAR MANOR

KENT – TN15 0QX

A small but complete portion of a stone manor house built c. 1290.

Managed by the National Trust on behalf of English Heritage.

OPENING TIMES

1 Apr-30 Sep, Sat-Thu	10am-5pm
1 Oct-31 Mar	Closed

VISIT US

Direction: 1 mile E of Plaxtol

Train: Borough Green and Wrotham 2½ miles

OLD SOAR MANOR

Bus: Visit traveline.info for the latest bus timetables and routes

Tel: 01732 810378

ACQ.1948 ⊗ P ⚠ Parking (limited).

Dogs on leads (grounds only).

Caution: steep stairs.

> **MAP PAGE 327 (4G)**
> **OS MAP 188, 147/148: TQ619541**

RECULVER TOWERS AND ROMAN FORT
KENT – CT6 6SS

Twin 12th-century towers of an atmospheric ruined seaside church, enclosing traces of a Saxon monastery. Within the partly visible walls of one of the first Roman 'Saxon Shore' forts. Download a free audio tour from our website.

Managed by Canterbury City Council.

OPENING TIMES
Exterior only: Any reasonable daylight hours

VISIT US
Direction: At Reculver, 3 miles E of Herne Bay; signed off Thanet Way A299

Train: Herne Bay 4 miles

Bus: Visit traveline.info for the latest bus timetables and routes

Tel: 0370 333 1181

ACQ.1925 ♿ 🐕 💷 ⚠

Disabled access (grounds only – long slope up from car park).

Parking (pay and display), toilets and a café are available at nearby Reculver Visitor Centre (not managed by English Heritage).

Caution: steep slopes.

> **MAP PAGE 327 (4J)**
> **OS MAP 179, 150: TR228693**

ST AUGUSTINE'S ABBEY CONDUIT HOUSE
KENT – CT1 1QH

The Conduit House is part of the monastic waterworks that supplied nearby St Augustine's Abbey.

OPENING TIMES
Exterior only: Any reasonable daylight hours

VISIT US
Direction: In King's Park. Approx. 5-10 min walk from St Augustine's Abbey. Please call or ask at the Abbey for directions

Train: Canterbury East and West, both ¾ mile

Bus: Visit traveline.info for the latest bus timetables and routes

Tel: 0370 333 1181

ACQ.1977 🐕 P ⚠

Parking (on street only).

Caution: deep water.

> **MAP PAGE 327 (4H)**
> **OS MAP 179, 150: TR159580**

ST AUGUSTINE'S CROSS
KENT – CT12 5JB

This Anglo-Saxon style Victorian cross marks what is traditionally believed to be the site of St Augustine's landing in England in AD 597. Nearby was the stream where he allegedly baptised his first English convert.

ST AUGUSTINE'S CROSS

OPENING TIMES
Any reasonable daylight hours

VISIT US
Direction: Cliffs End, Thanet, 2 miles E of Minster off B29048

Train: Minster 2 miles

Bus: Visit traveline.info

Tel: 0370 333 1181

ACQ.1912 ♿ 🐕

> **MAP PAGE 327 (4J)**
> **OS MAP 179, 150: TR340642**

ST JOHN'S COMMANDERY
KENT – CT15 7HG

The 13th-century chapel and hall of a 'Commandery' of Knights Hospitallers, later converted into a farmhouse. Features a medieval crown-post roof and 16th-century ceilings.

OPENING TIMES
By appointment only, please phone Customer Services on 0370 333 1181

VISIT US
Direction: 2 miles NE of Densole, off A260

Train: Kearsney 4 miles; Folkestone Central 6 miles

Bus: Visit traveline.info for the latest bus timetables and routes

ACQ.1978 🐕 P ⚠

Dogs on leads (grounds only).

Caution: steep stairs.

> **MAP PAGE 327 (5J)**
> **OS MAP 179/189, 138: TR232440**

ROCHESTER CASTLE

—— KENT – ME1 1SW ——

Discover the tallest Norman keep in England, the target of famous medieval sieges.

Dominating the bridge where the road from London to Dover crossed the river Medway, Rochester Castle was among the most strategically important fortresses in medieval England. In 1136 William of Corbeil, Archbishop of Canterbury, completed the great stone keep at the command of Henry I. At 37.7 metres (125 feet) high, it was probably the tallest castle keep ever built.

In 1215, garrisoned by rebel barons, the castle endured an epic siege by King John. He used 'the fat of 40 pigs' to fire a mine burrowed beneath the keep, bringing its south-east corner crashing down. Even then the defenders held out behind a stout wall within the building, living on water and horsemeat until finally starved out.

You can still see how the demolished corner tower was rebuilt – it's rounded, not square like the rest – before the keep endured a second siege in 1264, when it beat off an assault by Simon de Montfort's rebel army.

Exploring Rochester's keep shows you why it was so hard to take. After entering the forebuilding at first floor level, you can climb some 200 spiralling steps, winding from the basement cesspit up to the battlements. On the way you'll pass the chapel, displaying a model of the whole castle and a cutaway of the keep. Next comes the vast galleried great hall with its round-headed Norman arches, one of the most impressive spaces in any English castle. Then you climb past the third floor to the keep roof. Enjoy breathtaking views over the nearby cathedral, the historic core of Rochester and the broad sweep of the Medway whose crossing this noble fortress once guarded.

Managed by Medway Council.

OPENING TIMES

1 Apr-30 Sep, daily	10am-6pm
1 Oct-31 Mar, daily	10am-4pm
24-26 Dec & 1 Jan	Closed
Last entry 45 mins before closing	

Due to events that take place in July adjacent to the castle, it may be necessary to close early on some days. Please check the website for details

VISIT US

Direction: By Rochester Bridge (A2): Junction 1 of M2 and Junction 2 of M25. Signposted from A228 Rochester by-pass

Train: Combined train/bus station, 5 minute walk from castle

Bus: Visit traveline.info for the latest bus timetables and routes

Tel: 01634 332901

NON-MEMBERS

Please see website for details

ACQ 1965 🎧 ♿ 🛡 E ⬛ 🚶 ⛹ 👜 ♿
⚠ OVP

Audio tours (small charge).
Dogs on leads (grounds only).
Events (not English Heritage).
Toilets (in castle grounds).
No disabled access to keep.
Caution: steep stairs, falling masonry.

MAP PAGE 327 (4G)
OS MAP 178, 148/163: TQ741686

ST AUGUSTINE'S ABBEY

———— KENT – CT1 1PF ————

Explore this ancient monastery, an outstandingly important landmark in English history.

Founded in AD 598 by St Augustine himself, this once-great abbey proclaims the rebirth of Christianity in southern England. The pagan King Aethelberht of Kent, then the most powerful of the Anglo-Saxon monarchs, married a Christian princess from France. Soon afterwards he accepted baptism by Augustine, a missionary from Rome. He thus became the first Christian Anglo-Saxon ruler.

To mark his conversion, Aethelberht gave Augustine land to build this very first monastery in Anglo-Saxon England. Displaying a wonderful variety of site finds – including personal possessions and intriguing artefacts from graves – the big site museum traces how the Saxon monastery was magnificently rebuilt by the Normans before becoming a Tudor royal palace and Stuart garden.

Using award-winning state-of-the-art technology, adults and children aged ten and over can also take a personal virtual reality tour of the abbey as it looked in about 1500; a fascinating and absorbing experience.

Be sure to explore the extensive and atmospheric abbey ruins in person, too. They're set against a backdrop of Canterbury's medieval buildings, with the cathedral towers soaring in the distance. Guided by the audio tour, you'll discover excavated remains of the oldest Anglo-Saxon churches in England. These were overlaid after 1072 by the huge Norman monastery with its cathedral-sized church, whose crypt and other features you can still clearly see.

The cradle of revived English Christianity, this tranquil but immensely significant place shouldn't be missed by visitors to the Canterbury World Heritage Site.

OPENING TIMES

1 Apr-30 Oct, daily	10am-5pm
31 Oct-31 Mar, Sat-Sun	10am-4pm
24-26 Dec & 1 Jan	Closed

VISIT US

Direction: In Canterbury, ¼ mile east of city centre

Train: Canterbury East and West, both ¾ mile

Bus: Visit traveline.info for the latest bus timetables and routes

Tel: 01227 767345

Local Tourist Information:
Canterbury: 01227 862162

NON-MEMBERS

Adult **£9.00** | Concession **£8.10**
Child **£5.40** | Family 2 Adults **£23.40**
Family 1 Adult **£14.40**

ACQ.1938

Please note: for safety reasons, virtual reality viewers cannot be used by children under ten.

Disabled access (all site can be viewed, but some steps).

Parking (nearby).

MAP PAGE 327 (4H)
OS MAP 179, 150: TR155578

WALMER CASTLE AND GARDENS

KENT – CT14 7LJ

There's plenty to see and do at Walmer Castle, a Tudor artillery fort turned elegant stately home set amid delightful and immensely varied gardens. We've revealed areas of the pleasure grounds inaccessible for over a century, opened up the long-lost chalk quarry Glen Garden, added imaginative play spaces for children in the Woodland Walk and created the attractive Glasshouse Café by the Kitchen Garden.

'The most charming marine chateau that ever was' – as a friend of the Duke of Wellington described it – Walmer Castle began in 1539-40 as one of Henry VIII's Tudor artillery forts defending the Downs, a crucial sheltered anchorage. But within the distinctive 'clover leaf' shell characteristic of Tudor forts, you'll discover the comfortable and fashionable rooms of a country house. For almost three centuries, it's been the official residence of the Lord Warden of the Cinque Ports, an office granted to some of Britain's most celebrated people, including Sir Winston Churchill and Queen Elizabeth the Queen Mother.

Displays highlight the Duke of Wellington, Lord Warden for 23 years until his death here, aged 83, in 1852. You'll see his spartan bedroom, complete with the original armchair in which he died, and a pair of his 'Wellington boots'. Tracing other famous Lords Warden, more rooms are set as in Georgian times, and as during the First World War, when the castle was the hub of high-level conferences. There are multimedia guides designed for children as well as adults.

Recent garden developments recreate the vision of Lord Warden William Pitt the Younger, a former Prime Minister, and his niece and hostess Lady Hester Stanhope. In 1805, they transformed a former chalk quarry on the boundary of the 8-acre gardens into a romantic Glen, now rejuvenated for you to enjoy. The steps descending into it are steep, but there's a viewing platform and accessible vistas from the top. You'll reach the Glen by the winding Woodland Walk, set with surprises and creative play spaces for children – pods made from saplings, a wobbling bridge to cross, a quirky oversized swing and climbing frames.

Nearer the house, you'll find the formal Broadwalk, flanked by vividly planted herbaceous borders and the famous Cloud Hedges; the tranquil Queen Mother's Garden, created to honour her 95th birthday – look out for the bronze corgi on a bench; and the fully working Kitchen Garden, whose flowers, vegetables and fruit you can admire from our light and airy Glasshouse Café. It also supplies produce for the Lord Warden's Tearoom within the castle.

STAY
WITH
US

Walmer Castle's holiday cottages, the *Greenhouse Apartment* and the *Garden Cottage*, both offer great views over the Kitchen Garden and are only a few minutes' walk from the beach.

See p.16 for details on staying at **Walmer** and our other holiday cottages.

OPENING TIMES

1 Apr-30 Jun, daily	10am-5pm
1 Jul-31 Aug, daily*	10am-6pm
1 Sep-30 Oct, daily	10am-5pm
31 Oct-23 Dec, Sat-Sun	10am-4pm
2 Jan-10 Feb, Sat-Sun	10am-4pm
11-19 Feb, daily	10am-4pm
20 Feb-31 Mar, Wed-Sun	10am-4pm

Christmas Opening

24-25 Dec	Closed
26 Dec-1 Jan, daily	10am-4pm

Last entry 1 hour before closing

*Closed from 8-10 July when Lord Warden is in residence

VISIT US

Address: Walmer Castle, Kingsdown Road, Deal, Kent

Direction: On coast S of Walmer, on A258; Junction 13 of M20 or from M2 to Deal

Train: Walmer 1 mile

Bus: Visit traveline.info for the latest bus timetables and routes

Tel: 01304 364288

Local Tourist Information:
Deal: 01304 369576 and
Dover: 01304 205108

NON-MEMBERS

Adult **£14.20** | Concession **£12.80**
Child **£8.50** | Family 2 Adults **£36.90**
Family 1 Adult **£22.70**

Caution: steep steps to and within Glen. Stout footwear recommended.

Disabled access (three ground-floor display rooms, tearooms, shop courtyard and garden only; parking available near approach to castle). Mobility scooters and wheelchairs available on loan. No access to Glen or moat garden.

Please note: dogs (except assistance dogs) not allowed in grounds at any time. No smoking or vaping anywhere on site, including gardens.

Parking: charges apply to non-members, free for Members with valid car sticker.

No coach parking at the site.

MAP PAGE 327 (4J)
OS MAP 179, 138: TR378501

ST LEONARD'S TOWER

KENT – ME19 6PD

An early and well-preserved example of a small freestanding Norman tower keep, surviving almost to its original height. Probably built c. 1080 by Gundulf, Bishop of Rochester.

OPENING TIMES

Exterior only: Any reasonable daylight hours

VISIT US

Direction: Nr West Malling, on unclassified road W of A228

Train: West Malling 1 mile

Bus: Visit **traveline.info** for the latest bus timetables and routes

Tel: 0370 333 1181

[ACQ.1937] 🐾 **P** ⚠ Parking (limited). Caution: falling masonry.

MAP PAGE 327 (4G)
OS MAP 178/188, 148: TQ676571

SUTTON VALENCE CASTLE

KENT – ME17 3LW

The ruins of a small 12th-century Norman keep, with panoramic views over the Weald.

OPENING TIMES

Any reasonable daylight hours

VISIT US

Direction: 5 miles SE of Maidstone, in Sutton Valence village, on A274

Train: Headcorn 4 miles, Hollingbourne 5 miles

Bus: Visit **traveline.info** for the latest bus timetables and routes

Tel: 0370 333 1181

[ACQ.1976] 🐾 ⚠

Caution: steep slopes, steep stairs.

MAP PAGE 327 (4G)
OS MAP 188, 137: TQ815491

TEMPLE MANOR

KENT – ME2 2AH

Part of a Knights Templar manor house, built c. 1240, with a first floor hall displaying traces of wall paintings.

TEMPLE MANOR

Managed by Medway Council.

OPENING TIMES

1 Apr-30 Oct, Sat-Sun	11am-4pm
31 Oct-31 Mar	Closed

For group visits call 01634 332901

VISIT US

Direction: Located in Strood (Rochester), off A228

Train: Strood ¾ mile

Bus: Visit **traveline.info** for the latest bus timetables and routes

[ACQ.1950] 🖼🐾**P**🦽⚠

Disabled access (grounds only).

Dogs on leads (grounds only). Assistance dogs welcome across the site.

Caution: steep stairs.

MAP PAGE 327 (4G)
OS MAP 178, 148/163: TQ733685

UPNOR CASTLE

KENT – ME2 4XG

Set in a riverside village, this Elizabethan artillery fort was built to protect warships in Chatham dockyard. Its furious cannonade failed to stop the Dutch severely damaging the anchored English fleet in 1667. An exhibition highlights the raid.

Managed by Medway Council.

OPENING TIMES

1 Apr-30 Sep, daily	10am-6pm
1-30 Oct, daily	10am-4pm
31 Oct-31 Mar	Closed

Please check website for details

Last entry 45 mins before closing

VISIT US

Direction: At Upnor, on unclassified road off A228

Train: Strood 2 miles

UPNOR CASTLE

Bus: Visit **traveline.info**

Tel: 01634 332902 or when castle is closed 01634 332901

NON-MEMBERS

Please see website for details

[ACQ.1961] 🎧🦽**E**🖼🔔🚶🚶🚫
P📷⚠[OVP]

Audio guide (small charge).

Disabled access (grounds only).

Parking at a slight distance from castle – park before village (not English Heritage).

Caution: steep stairs.

MAP PAGE 327 (4G)
OS MAP 178, 163: TQ759706

WESTERN HEIGHTS, DOVER

KENT – CT17 9DZ

A huge fortification constructed during the Napoleonic Wars and completed in the 1860s, designed to protect Dover from French invasion.

Managed by Western Heights Preservation Society.

OPENING TIMES

Exterior only: Any reasonable daylight hours

Tours of the Drop Redoubt: Guided tours are held on the 3rd Sunday of the month from Apr-Sep, 11am and 2pm. Places must be pre-booked. Visit doverwesternheights.org for details and additional opening times

VISIT US

Direction: Above Dover town on W side of harbour

Train: Dover Priory ¾ mile

WESTERN HEIGHTS, DOVER

Bus: Visit traveline.info for the latest bus timetables and routes

Tel: 01304 211067

ACQ.1968 🎭 P ⚠

Unsuitable for visitors who use wheelchairs or have limited mobility.

Caution: unguarded drops, steep stairs.

> MAP PAGE 327 (5J)
> OS MAP 179, 138: TR312408

OXFORDSHIRE

ABINGDON COUNTY HALL MUSEUM

OXFORDSHIRE – OX14 3HG

Designed by colleagues of Sir Christopher Wren, this delightful 17th-century 'English Baroque' building houses the Abingdon Museum, and has fine rooftop views.

Managed by Abingdon Town Council.

OPENING TIMES

1 Apr-23 Dec, Tue-Sun & Bank Hols	10am-4pm
24 Dec-2 Jan	Closed
3 Jan-31 Mar, Tue-Sun	10am-4pm

Ticketing system in place.
Please check website for details

VISIT US

Direction: In Abingdon, 7 miles south of Oxford; in Market Place

Train: Radley 2½ miles

Bus: Visit traveline.info for the latest bus timetables and routes

Tel: 01235 523703

ABINGDON COUNTY HALL MUSEUM

ENTRY

Free entry to museum. Roof access Apr-Sep weather permitting

Adult	£2
English Heritage Members and Children (over 6 years old only)	£1

ACQ.1952 🧍🧍 🖼 ⊗ ⛽

Limited access to museum floors (no lift).

Caution: steep stairs.

> MAP PAGE 326 (3C)
> OS MAP 164, 170: SU498971

DEDDINGTON CASTLE

OXFORDSHIRE – OX15 0TE

Extensive earthwork remains of an 11th-century castle, associated with Odo, Bishop of Bayeux, half-brother of William the Conqueror.

Managed by Deddington Parish Council.

OPENING TIMES

Any reasonable daylight hours

VISIT US

Direction: S of B4031 on E side of Deddington; 17 miles N of Oxford

Train: King's Sutton 5 miles

Bus: Visit traveline.info for the latest bus timetables and routes

ACQ.1951 🎭 ⚠

Caution: steep slopes.

> MAP PAGE 326 (2C)
> OS MAP 151, 191: SP472316

MINSTER LOVELL HALL AND DOVECOTE

OXFORDSHIRE – OX29 0RR

MINSTER LOVELL HALL AND DOVECOTE

The extensive and picturesque ruins of a 15th-century riverside manor house, including a fine hall, south-west tower and complete nearby dovecote. The home of Richard III's henchman Lord Lovell.

OPENING TIMES

Any reasonable daylight hours

Dovecote – exterior viewing only

VISIT US

Direction: Adjacent to Minster Lovell Church; 3 miles W of Witney, off A40

Train: Charlbury 7 miles

Bus: Visit traveline.info for the latest bus timetables and routes

ACQ.1937	Minster Lovell Hall
ACQ.1957	Dovecote 🎭 🖼 ⚠

Guidebook (from St Kenelm's Church).

Caution: deep water.

Please do not climb on the walls.

> MAP PAGE 326 (2B)
> OS MAP 164, 180: SP325113

NORTH HINKSEY CONDUIT HOUSE

OXFORDSHIRE – OX2 9AS

Roofed conduit for Oxford's first water mains, constructed during the early 17th century.

Managed by Oxford Preservation Trust.

OPENING TIMES

Exterior viewing only:

Apr-Oct, Thu-Sun & Bank Hols	10am-4pm

See website for interior open days

VISIT US

Direction: In North Hinksey off A34; 1½ miles W of Oxford. Located off track leading from Harcourt Hill

Train: Oxford (1½ miles)

Bus: Visit traveline.info for the latest bus timetables and routes

ACQ.1973 🎭 ⚠ Caution: deep water.

No nearby parking, pedestrian access only.

> MAP PAGE 326 (3C)
> OS MAP 164, 180: SP495050

NORTH LEIGH ROMAN VILLA

OXFORDSHIRE – OX29 6QE

The remains of a large, well-built Roman courtyard villa, with a nearly complete mosaic tile floor, patterned in reds and browns.

OPENING TIMES

Grounds open any reasonable daylight hours. See website for details of mosaic house open days

VISIT US

Direction: 2 miles N of North Leigh; 10 miles W of Oxford, off A4095

Train: Hanborough 3½ miles

Bus: Visit traveline.info for the latest bus timetables and routes

ACQ.1952 🐾 🅿 ⚠

Pedestrian access only from main road – 550 metres (600 yards). Track is steep and rough.

Steps to reach mosaic building.

Parking (lay-by, not in access lane).

Caution: unguarded drops.

> MAP PAGE 326 (2B)
> OS MAP 164, 180: SP397154

ROLLRIGHT STONES

OXFORDSHIRE – OX7 5QB

Traditionally a petrified monarch and his courtiers, the Rollright Stones include the King's Men stone circle, the Whispering Knights burial chamber and the King Stone. They span nearly 2,000 years of Neolithic and Bronze Age development.

Managed and owned by the Rollright Trust.

ROLLRIGHT STONES

OPENING TIMES

Entry at any reasonable time all year by permission of The Rollright Trust and English Heritage

VISIT US

Direction: Off unclassified road between A44 and A3400, 3 miles NW of Chipping Norton, near villages of Little Rollright and Long Compton

Train: Moreton-in-Marsh 6½ miles

Bus: Visit traveline.info for the latest bus timetables and routes

Contact: sitemanager@rollright stones.co.uk

ENTRY

Admission charges apply to English Heritage Members and non-members

Adults/Concessions	£1
Children	50p

ACQ.1883 🐾 🅿 ⚠

Parking (in lay-by).

Dogs welcome on leads except inside the stone circle.

Caution: beware of traffic.

> MAP PAGE 326 (2B)
> OS MAP 151, OL45/191:
> SP297309

UFFINGTON CASTLE, WHITE HORSE AND DRAGON HILL

OXFORDSHIRE – SN7 7QJ

Atmospheric sites along the Ridgeway. Uffington 'Castle' is a large Iron Age hillfort, Dragon Hill a natural mound. The famous White Horse is the oldest chalk-cut hill figure in Britain, perhaps over 3,000 years old.

UFFINGTON CASTLE

Managed by the National Trust on behalf of English Heritage.

OPENING TIMES

Any reasonable daylight hours

VISIT US

Direction: S of B4507, 7 miles W of Wantage. Ridgeway National Trail runs directly past the site

Bus: Visit traveline.info for the latest bus timetables and routes

Tel: 01793 762209

ACQ.1936 🐾 🍴 🅿 ⚠

Parking in NT White Horse car park. Pay and display or free to English Heritage Members displaying valid car sticker or with current membership card.

Caution: steep slopes.

> MAP PAGE 326 (3B)
> OS MAP 174, 170: SU301866

WAYLAND'S SMITHY

OXFORDSHIRE – SN7 7QJ

An atmospheric Neolithic long barrow on the Ridgeway, named after the Saxon smith-god Wayland.

Managed by the National Trust on behalf of English Heritage.

OPENING TIMES

Any reasonable daylight hours

VISIT US

Direction: On the Ridgeway (closed to vehicles); ¾ mile NE of B4000, Ashbury – Lambourn Road

Bus: Visit traveline.info for the latest bus timetables and routes

ACQ.1922 🐾 🅿 ⚠

Parking in NT White Horse car park (then 1 mile walk along Ridgeway). Pay and display but free to English Heritage Members displaying valid car sticker.

Caution: unguarded drops.

> MAP PAGE 326 (3B)
> OS MAP 174, 170: SU281854

FARNHAM CASTLE KEEP
SURREY – GU9 0AG

WAVERLEY ABBEY
SURREY – GU9 8EP

CAMBER CASTLE
EAST SUSSEX – TN31 7TD

The impressive motte and shell keep of a castle founded in 1138 by Henry of Blois, Bishop of Winchester. A viewing platform reveals the buried remains of an earlier tower.

Managed by Farnham Castle Ltd.

Remains of the monastic buildings and church of the very first abbey of Cistercian monks to be built in Britain, founded in 1128 and largely rebuilt in the 13th century. Set by a peaceful loop of the river Wey.

Download a free audio tour from our website.

Ruins of an unusually unaltered artillery fort, built by Henry VIII to guard Rye. Limited opening times, but regular guided walks around Rye Harbour Nature Reserve include the castle.

Managed by Rye Harbour Nature Reserve.

OPENING TIMES

1 Apr-24 Dec, Mon-Fri	9am-5pm (or dusk if earlier)
Sat-Sun & Bank Hols	10am-4pm
25 Dec-31 Jan	Closed
1 Feb-31 Mar, Mon-Fri	9am-5pm (or dusk if earlier)
Sat-Sun & Bank Hols	10am-4pm

Last entry 30 mins before closing

Tours of the Bishop's Palace are available on Wednesday afternoons for an additional fee. Please phone 01252 721194 to book

VISIT US

Direction: ½ mile north of Farnham off A287

Train: Farnham ¾ mile

Bus: Visit **traveline.info** for the latest bus timetables and routes

Tel: 01252 721194

ACQ.1933 E 🚶 ♿ ⊗ P ♿ ⚠

Parking for blue badge holders only.

Caution: steep stairs.

MAP PAGE 326 (4D)
OS MAP 186, 145: SU837473

Elizabeth; Snow White and the Huntsman (2014); The Mummy (2017); Cursed (2020); Midsomer Murders; BBC Series, Howards End.

OPENING TIMES

Any reasonable daylight hours

VISIT US

Direction: 2 miles SE of Farnham, off B3001; off Junction 10 of M25

Train: Farnham 2 miles

Bus: Visit **traveline.info** for the latest bus timetables and routes

Tel: 0370 333 1181

ACQ.1961 🚶 ♿ 🐕 P ⚠

Parking (limited).

Access is through two kissing gates and across uneven ground. Cattle may be grazing around footpaths to abbey.

Caution: deep water, falling masonry.

MAP PAGE 326 (5D)
OS MAP 186, 145: SU868453

OPENING TIMES

Aug-Oct open on the first Sat of the month for guided tour starting at 2pm prompt. Meet at the castle, but please be aware there is no vehicular access to the site and the nearest parking is a 1 mile walk away. In addition there are regular guided walks around the Rye Harbour Nature Reserve that include the castle. Please check website or visit sussexwildlifetrust. org.uk/visit/ryeharbour

VISIT US

Direction: 1 mile walk across fields, off the A259; 1 mile S of Rye, off Harbour Road. No vehicle access. Follow the public footpath from Brede Lock

Train: Rye 1¼ miles

Bus: Visit **traveline.info** for the latest bus timetables and routes

Tel: Nature reserve office number 01797 227784 (Mon-Fri, 9am-5pm only)

NON-MEMBERS

Adult **£3.00** | Concession **£1.50**
Child **Free**

ACQ.1967 🚶 🐕 ⚠

Caution: Unguarded drops, falling masonry.

Cattle and sheep may be grazing around footpaths to castle.

MAP PAGE 327 (5H)
OS MAP 189, 125: TQ922185

1066 BATTLE OF HASTINGS, ABBEY AND BATTLEFIELD

EAST SUSSEX – TN33 0AE

There are so many ways to enjoy the scene of England's most renowned and crucial battle. Alongside the battlefield you can also explore abbey ruins and the intriguing traces of a country house, as well as interactive displays in the beautiful abbey gatehouse. An all-round great experience, this vast and varied site provides a unique day out for the whole family.

Its history began on the fateful 14th of October 1066, when after many hours of hard fighting William the Conqueror's Norman invaders finally defeated King Harold Godwinson's English army in this very place. You can discover the dramatic story of the epic conflict in the visitor centre, where a host of interactives, displays of Norman and Anglo-Saxon weaponry, and a compelling film recount the background to the battle, the fighting, and how the Norman victory transformed the nation's history.

Accompanied by an audio tour, which recreates the sounds of combat, you can stand on the abbey terrace to view the slope where the Normans advanced against the hilltop English shield wall. Or you can choose to walk more of the battlefield, using the 'Battlefield 1066' family trails to hunt out dramatic wooden figures including a Norman mounted knight and archer as well as a Saxon axeman and standard bearer.

The turning point of the battle came when Harold Godwinson was killed, perhaps struck in the eye by an arrow. You can stand by the spot where he fell, later marked by the high altar of Battle Abbey, the great monastery William founded as a penance for the terrible bloodshed of the battle and a memorial to the dead. All around, the abbey's ruins stand ready to explore, notably the great dormitory range with its atmospheric pillared and vaulted undercrofts, built just below the place where the English army awaited attack.

As the symbol of Norman triumph, Battle Abbey enjoyed enormous wealth and influence, symbolised by the Great Gatehouse. Built in about 1338, it's among the finest medieval monastic portals in Britain. You can climb to its rooftop for astonishing views over the pretty town of Battle, the abbey ruins, and the landscape of the fighting. Don't miss our displays in the splendidly recreated gatehouse chambers. They vividly illustrate how the abbey operated and ruled its wide estates, and how its monks lived from day to day.

STAY WITH US

South Lodge is a former gatehouse, which sleeps four and comes with its own fully enclosed garden. There is so much to see and experience here, but nothing beats soaking up the atmosphere as the evening sun lights up the mellow stone of the beautiful abbey ruins.

See p.16 for details on staying at Battle and our other holiday cottages.

Site-finds, handling replicas and imaginative interactives share stories of monastic health, worship, finance, manuscript production, writing and much more. You can listen to part of a monastic service, hear a specially recorded carol found in an early 16th-century Battle manuscript, design your own coat of arms to add to the abbey's roll of knights, look down a monks' garderobe loo, try your hand at reassembling a stained glass window and open drawers and boxes to make discoveries of your own.

The displays also trace how, after its suppression by Henry VIII, the abbey became a grand country house. You'll find intriguing survivors of this later life as you wander the extensive grounds, including a thatched ornamental Regency dairy, an underground icehouse, and the Duchess of Cleveland's tranquil, hidden Walled Garden, now replanted with local species of fruit trees and equipped with beehives.

With so much to see, do and experience throughout the site, you'll need a break in our big café, with indoor and outdoor seating among the trees near the gatehouse. There's an imaginative children's playground nearby, with timber play stations inspired by the site's history to climb and swing on – just one of the many activities that children can enjoy as part of their day out.

OPENING TIMES

1 Apr-30 Jun, daily	10am-5pm
1 Jul-31 Aug, daily	10am-6pm
1 Sep-30 Oct, daily	10am-5pm
31 Oct-23 Dec, Sat-Sun	10am-4pm
2 Jan-10 Feb, Sat-Sun	10am-4pm
11-19 Feb, daily	10am-4pm
20 Feb-31 Mar, Wed-Sun	10am-4pm

Christmas Opening	
24-25 Dec	Closed
26 Dec-1 Jan, daily	10am-4pm

VISIT US

Address: Battle Abbey, High Street, Battle, East Sussex TN33 0AE

Direction: In Battle, at south end of High St. Take the A2100 off the A21

Train: Battle ½ mile

Bus: Visit traveline.info for the latest bus timetables and routes

Tel: 0370 333 1181

Local Tourist Information:
Hastings: 0303 003 8265
Rye: 01797 223902

NON-MEMBERS

Peak (28 May-31 Aug, Sat-Sun and Bank Holidays)
Adult £16.50 I Concession £14.90
Child £9.90 I Family 2 Adults £42.90
Family 1 Adult £26.40

Standard (1 Apr-27 May and Sep-Oct, Sat-Sun and Bank Holidays; 28 May-31 Aug, Mon-Fri)
Adult £15.30 I Concession £13.80
Child £9.20 I Family 2 Adults £39.80
Family 1 Adult £24.50

Off-peak (1 Apr-27 May and Sep-Oct, Mon-Fri and Nov-Mar)
Adult £14.20 I Concession £12.80
Child £8.50 I Family 2 Adults £36.90
Family 1 Adult £22.70

Audio tours (suitable for families, the visually impaired and for those in wheelchairs or with learning difficulties. Also available in Dutch, French, German, Japanese and Spanish). Audio tours are complimentary but will not be issued on special events days.

Disabled access (grounds and visitor centre).

Parking: charges apply to non-members, free for Members with valid car sticker.

MAP PAGE 327 (6G)
OS MAP 199, 124: TQ749157

PEVENSEY CASTLE

—— EAST SUSSEX – BN24 5LE ——

Massive Roman fortress, strong medieval castle and emergency Second World War stronghold, Pevensey Castle has witnessed over 1,700 years of history. Engaging displays tell its long story.

Begun in about AD 290, Pevensey was the largest of the Roman 'Saxon Shore' fortresses; its mighty walls, over 500 metres (1,640 feet) long, still stand almost to their full height. Here, in 1066, William the Conqueror landed to begin his invasion of England, building a fortress within the Roman defences. By the 13th century this had developed into a medieval castle, with a powerful gatehouse and towered walls. After centuries of abandonment, the ancient stronghold was pressed back into service in 1940, with machine gun posts cleverly camouflaged into its walls.

In our exhibitions, you'll discover stories of massacre, sieges, and royal prisoners. Find out how British, Canadian and US Second World War soldiers interacted with local people, see a recreated 1940 commander's office, and pick up the phone to hear emergency messages. Children can crack the Pevensey Castle Code, and look into a dungeon and newly opened medieval basement room.

Thanks to the support of our Members, we've recently completed a major project to remove vegetation and protect the castle's historic walls.

OPENING TIMES

1 Apr-30 Oct, daily	10am-5pm
31 Oct-31 Mar, Sat-Sun	10am-4pm
24-26 Dec & 1 Jan	Closed

VISIT US

Direction: Off A259 between villages of Pevensey and Westham

Train: Pevensey & Westham ½ mile

Bus: Visit traveline.info for the latest bus timetables and routes

Tel: 01323 762604

NON-MEMBERS

Adult **£7.80** | Concession **£7.00** | Child **£4.70**
Family 2 Adults **£20.30** | Family 1 Adult **£12.50**

ACQ.1925 🎧 🍴 E ♿ ⬛ Ⓜ 📷 ⚠ OVP

Free on-street parking in Pevensey and Westham villages. Car park (charged) is not managed by English Heritage and not free for Members.

Toilets in Pevensey village.

MAP PAGE 327 (6G)
OS MAP 199, 123/124: TQ645048

BOXGROVE PRIORY WEST SUSSEX – PO18 0EE

In a beautiful setting at the foot of the South Downs, the small Benedictine priory of Boxgrove was founded in about 1117.

Its principal remains are the lodging house for guests and travellers, roofless but standing to full height at the gable ends, and the priory church. This lovely building (not in the guardianship of English Heritage) became Boxgrove's parish church at the Dissolution of the Monasteries.

Today you can explore the church's splendid 12th-century chancel, central tower and unusual transepts, which survive complete, along with an early Tudor chantry chapel with fine Renaissance carvings. There's a model of the monastic buildings in the church.

Nearby, in Boxgrove gravel pit, archaeological excavation (funded by English Heritage) produced much the oldest human bones yet discovered in England: dating from around 500,000 years ago, they belonged to a 1.8-metre (6-foot) tall man.

OPENING TIMES

Any reasonable daylight hours

VISIT US

Direction: N of Boxgrove; 4 miles E of Chichester, on minor road off A27

Train: Chichester 4 miles

Bus: Visit traveline.info for the latest bus timetables and routes

Tel: 0370 333 1181

ACQ.1977 🐕 P ⚠

Caution: falling masonry.

MAP PAGE 326 (6D)
OS MAP 197, 121: SU908076

BRAMBER CASTLE
WEST SUSSEX – BN44 3WE

The remains of a Norman motte-and-bailey castle on the banks of the River Adur, founded by William de Braose c. 1073. The earthworks are dominated by a towering wall of the keep-gatehouse.

OPENING TIMES

Any reasonable daylight hours

VISIT US

Direction: On W side of Bramber village, off A283

Train: Shoreham-by-Sea 4½ miles

Bus: Visit traveline.info for the latest bus timetables and routes

Tel: 0370 333 1181

ACQ.1975 🐕 P ⚠

Parking (limited). Parking: charges apply to non-members, free for Members with valid English Heritage car sticker.

Caution: steep slopes, unguarded drops, falling masonry.

MAP PAGE 326 (6E)
OS MAP 198, 122: TQ185107

CHECK ONLINE

Pre-booking for visits to our staffed sites may be required, check our website for the latest guidance.

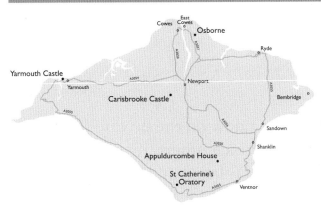

ST CATHERINE'S ORATORY
ISLE OF WIGHT – PO38 2JB

This medieval octagonal lighthouse tower was built in 1328 as penance for plundering church property – casks of wine – from a ship wrecked nearby.

Managed by the National Trust on behalf of English Heritage.

OPENING TIMES
Any reasonable daylight hours

VISIT US
Direction: E of Blackgang roundabout, off A3055. Approx. ¼ mile ascent across fields

Train: Shanklin 9 miles

Bus: Visit traveline.info for the latest bus timetables and routes

Ferry: West Cowes 14 miles, East Cowes 14 miles (both Red Funnel – Tel: 0844 844 9988); Yarmouth 15 miles (Wightlink – Tel: 0333 999 7333)

Tel: 0370 333 1181

ACQ.1952

Caution: steep slopes.

MAP PAGE 326 (7C)
OS MAP 196, OL29: SZ494773

APPULDURCOMBE HOUSE
ISLE OF WIGHT – PO38 3EW

The imposing, partly restored shell of Appuldurcombe, once the grandest mansion on the Isle of Wight. Still an outstanding example of English baroque architecture, it stands amid 11 acres of Capability Brown-designed ornamental grounds. The 1701 east wing has been re-roofed. Sir Richard Worsley, whose marital antics deliciously outraged Georgian England, extended the house in the 1770s.

OPENING TIMES
1 Apr-31 Oct, Sun-Fri	10am-4pm
1 Nov-31 Mar	Closed

VISIT US
Direction: Wroxall ½ mile, off B3327

Train: Shanklin 3½ miles then bus 3

Bus: Visit traveline.info

Ferry: Ryde 11 miles (Wightlink 0333 999 7333; Hovercraft 0345 222 0461); West Cowes 12 miles, East Cowes 12 miles (Red Funnel 0844 844 9988)

Tel: 0370 333 1181

ACQ.1952

Cattle and sheep may be grazing around footpaths to house.

Car park closes at 5pm.

MAP PAGE 326 (7C)
OS MAP 196, OL29: SZ543800

OSBORNE

ISLE OF WIGHT – PO32 6JX

Osborne opens a unique window on the private family life of Queen Victoria and Prince Albert, revealing how the royal couple worked and relaxed and how their children entertained themselves. Victoria's palatial holiday home also offers a beach, acres of grounds and gardens, and the lavishly restored lower terrace. There's lots of entertainment for visitors of all ages.

Shared with the couple's nine children, Osborne originated with the queen's desire for a 'place of one's own – quiet and retired'. Knowing and liking the Isle of Wight from childhood visits, she and Albert were determined to own a property there. In 1845 they bought Osborne, and plans for a new mansion began at once. Eventually a pair of Italianate towers dominated the landscape, looking out on the Solent. Albert lavished tremendous care on designing the surrounding gardens.

The lower terrace has intimate links with the young royal couple, still in their early thirties when they created it. Victoria bought the bronze statue of Andromeda at the Great Exhibition of 1851. She loved to relax in the Shell Alcove, now returned to its original colour scheme. We've also restored the terrace's 'Osborne yellow' walls, while carefully preserving its magnolia and myrtle, offspring of original plantings by the royal pair.

Inside, Osborne's sumptuous state rooms abound in opulent design and decoration. Marble sculptures line the Grand Corridor, and portraits and frescos are reminders of the family's links to the crowned heads of Europe, and of the worldwide extent of the British Empire. Many artefacts at Osborne are on loan from the Royal Collection.

Most lavish of all, the Durbar Room reflects Queen Victoria's pride in her title Empress of India, granted in 1877. So in 1890 she ordered a new banqueting chamber to be built in the 16th-century North Indian style. Symbols of India appear everywhere, with a splendid peacock standing proudly over the chimneypiece. You can also admire an outstanding collection of Indian treasures. Displays help you understand Victoria's relationship with the Empire, and give children the chance to get hands-on with history.

Elsewhere in the house, you can go behind the scenes to visit more intimate royal family apartments. Visit the queen's sitting room and see the balcony where the royal couple listened to nightingales on summer evenings. See Victoria's personal bathtub in the dressing room, and, next door, the bedroom where she died on 22 January 1901. The queen kept Prince Albert's private suite just as it was in his lifetime, and many of the things he used at Osborne still lie where he left them.

DON'T MISS

Osborne's amazing range of items reflecting Victoria and Albert's shared tastes, their affection for their family, and their encouragement of innovative design. Look out for a statue of Albert's pet greyhound, a chair made of stag horns, sculpted marble limbs modelled from those of their children and even a garden seat made from coal. Discover more at english-heritage.org.uk/visit/places/osborne/history-and-stories/collection

Take a further step into the Victorian royal family's private life by exploring Osborne's vast and beautiful grounds. Family visitors shouldn't miss the Swiss Cottage, domain of the royal children. A purpose-built playhouse where they learnt 'normal' life skills, the Swiss Cottage includes a room dressed as on 11 July 1861, when the children prepared afternoon tea for their parents, not long before Prince Albert's tragically premature death.

In the once private royal museum, full of strange objects from all over the world, look out for the clothes worn by two Romanian orphans, rescued from a massacre by the Royal Navy and brought up on the Osborne estate. The Swiss Cottage play area is inspired by the royal children's toy fort.

From the Swiss Cottage Quarter you can make your way to the queen's once strictly private beach, where her children learnt to swim. Its attractions include the restored royal bathing machine, with its plumbed-in toilet.

Take time to recreate a Victorian beach holiday; relax in deckchairs and enjoy traditional seaside refreshments from the beach café. The beach is a ¾ mile walk from the house; a mobility service runs at peak times.

You can also picnic in the grounds, or enjoy a light lunch in the café in the Petty Officers' Quarters.

OPENING TIMES

House and Grounds

1 Apr-30 Jun, daily	10am-5pm
1 Jul-31 Aug, daily	10am-6pm
1 Sep-30 Oct, daily	10am-5pm
31 Oct-6 Nov	Closed

Last entry to grounds 1 hour before closing (last entry to house 30 mins before closing)

Ground Floor House and Grounds
(excluding Swiss Cottage & Museum)

7 Nov-23 Dec, Wed-Sun	10am-4pm
24-25 Dec	Closed
26 Dec-1 Jan, daily	10am-4pm
2 Jan-10 Feb, Sat-Sun	10am-4pm
11-19 Feb, daily	10am-4pm
20 Feb-31 Mar, Wed-Sun	10am-4pm

Last entry to grounds 1 hour before closing (last entry to house 30 mins before closing)

VISIT US

Address: York Avenue, East Cowes, Isle of Wight PO32 6JX

Direction: 1 mile SE of East Cowes. For satnav use postcode PO32 6JT

Train: Ryde Esplanade 7 miles

Bus: Visit traveline.info for the latest bus timetables

The Petty Officers' Quarters café offers light lunches and snacks with handmade cakes and pastries. The Terrace Restaurant, set on the lower terraces, offers light lunches in a relaxed environment, plus all-day cream teas. Don't forget to enquire about afternoon teas, which can be pre-booked. Our Gazelle House refreshment stop offers an enhanced takeaway service of cold snacks and refreshments, with Osborne-made cakes and children's lunch boxes. Please note, non-members will need to buy an admission ticket to the house to visit the Terrace Restaurant.

🎬 *Mrs Brown* (1997); *Victoria and Abdul* (2017); ITV Series *Victoria*.

🍴 Available for corporate and private hire
🏛 Licensed for civil wedding ceremonies

STAY WITH US

No 1 & No 2 Sovereign's Gate both sleep four. The stunning building was built for Queen Victoria and Prince Albert as the ceremonial entrance to Osborne for visiting heads of state. *Pavilion Cottage* sleeps four. Built in the early 1900s, this former Cricket Pavilion brims with period character. After the public leave, explore the tranquil grounds and enjoy the spectacular views across the Solent.

See p.16 for details on staying at Osborne and our other holiday cottages.

Ferry: East Cowes 1½ miles (Red Funnel – Tel: 0844 844 9988); Fishbourne 4 miles; Ryde 7 miles (Wightlink – Tel: 0333 999 7333)

Hovertravel: 0345 222 0461

Tel: 0370 333 1181

Local Tourist Information:
Visit Isle of Wight: 01983 813813
visitisleofwight.co.uk

NON-MEMBERS

Adult **£21.00** | Concession **£18.90**
Child **£12.60** | Family 2 Adults **£54.60**
Family 1 Adult **£33.60**

Pushchairs are not permitted within the house, but are welcome in the gardens.

Disabled access – wheelchair access to the first floor is via a lift. Manual wheelchairs are available to borrow on a first come, first served basis. Mobility scooters are not permitted inside the house, but they can be used in the gardens.

MAP PAGE 326 (6C)
OS MAP 196, OL29: SZ516948

CARISBROOKE CASTLE

ISLE OF WIGHT – PO30 1XY

Guardian of the Isle of Wight for over a thousand years, Carisbrooke Castle is a fascinatingly varied place to visit. Begun soon after the Norman Conquest, it's been in turn a medieval stronghold, an Elizabethan artillery fortress, a king's prison and an Edwardian royal residence. There's a keep to climb for panoramic views and a colourful history to explore. It's also the home of the famous Carisbrooke donkeys.

This great hilltop-crowning fortress originated in Anglo-Saxon times as an earthwork defence against Viking raids. Soon after 1066, the Normans built a castle within it to secure their hold on the Isle of Wight, granted in 1100 to the Norman family of de Redvers. They raised the great Norman shell keep on its towering mound, and after 1262 the formidable Countess Isabella de Fortibus rebuilt the principal accommodation and service buildings.

In 1377, following the addition of its double-towered 14th-century gatehouse, Carisbrooke Castle experienced its only siege, beating off a French raiding force. After the Spanish Armada passed alarmingly close in 1588, the castle was updated as an artillery fortification by surrounding it with 'bastioned' earthworks nearly a mile long, still impressively visible.

Most famous among the castle's varied cast of past residents was Charles I, who was imprisoned here in 1647-48 after his defeat in the Civil War. At first comfortably accommodated in the Constable's Lodging – and provided with his own bowling green, which you can still try out today – he later became a closely guarded captive. He made two unsuccessful attempts to escape, one being foiled only when he became wedged in the window bars. All this time he was plotting to renew the war. Growing impatient with his intrigues, Parliament eventually ordered him taken to London, where he was tried and executed.

Much later, Princess Beatrice, Queen Victoria's youngest and favourite daughter and Governor of the Isle of Wight between 1896-1944, made Carisbrooke Castle her summer home. She also commissioned the altar painting in the castle chapel, in memory of a son killed in action in 1914. The chapel is now the Isle of Wight's county war memorial, honouring over 2,000 local people killed in both World Wars.

The award-winning Edwardian-style Princess Beatrice Garden, designed by Chris Beardshaw, was inspired by the princess, and includes a fountain and plantings in the rich colours of the royal arms. We are grateful to the late Mrs Dorothy Frazer, whose generous bequest and devotion to the island made the creation of this garden possible.

STAY
WITH
US

The *Bowling Green Apartment* sleeps a family of four in contemporary comfort on the second floor of the 19th-century former service block. Enjoy the excitement of staying in a castle after dark.

See p.16 for details on staying at Carisbrooke and our other holiday cottages.

The castle's most beloved modern residents are undoubtedly the renowned Carisbrooke donkeys. These happy animals still demonstrate the tread wheel, which originally raised water 49 metres (160 feet) from the castle well. Today's donkeys have to work much less hard, and you can hear their story in a film hosted by Jupiter the cartoon donkey, voiced by locally raised comedian Phill Jupitus.

Don't miss the Charles I memorabilia and changing exhibitions in the Carisbrooke Castle Museum.

OPENING TIMES

1 Apr-30 Jun, daily	10am-5pm
1 Jul-31 Aug, daily	10am-6pm
1 Sep-30 Oct, daily	10am-5pm
31 Oct-23 Dec, Sat-Sun	10am-4pm
2 Jan-10 Feb, Sat-Sun	10am-4pm
11-19 Feb, daily	10am-4pm
20 Feb-31 Mar, Wed-Sun	10am-4pm
Christmas Opening	
24-25 Dec	Closed
26 Dec-1 Jan, daily	10am-4pm

Last entry 1 hour before closing

VISIT US

Address: Carisbrooke Castle, Castle Hill, Newport, Isle of Wight PO30 1XY

Direction: 1¼ miles SW of Newport. Follow signs to Carisbrooke village, then castle

Train: Ryde Esplanade 9 miles

Bus: Visit traveline.info for the latest bus timetables and routes

Ferry: West Cowes 5 miles, East Cowes 6 miles (both Red Funnel – 0844 844 9988); Fishbourne 6 miles, Ryde 8 miles, Yarmouth 9 miles (Wightlink – Tel: 0333 999 7333)

Tel: 01983 522107

Local Tourist Information: 01983 813813

NON-MEMBERS

Adult **£12.80** | Concession **£11.50** Child **£7.60** | Family 2 Adults **£33.20** Family 1 Adult **£20.40**

Disabled access (grounds and lower levels only).

Tearooms open daily Apr-Oct and weekends during winter (close 1 hour before site closes). 26 Dec-1 Jan, 11am-3pm.

Parking: charges apply to non-members, free for Members with valid English Heritage car sticker.

MAP PAGE 326 (6C) OS MAP 196, OL29: SZ486878

YARMOUTH CASTLE

ISLE OF WIGHT – PO41 0PB

Built following a French raid on the Isle of Wight, Yarmouth Castle was designed to protect strategic Yarmouth harbour and (in conjunction with Hurst Castle – see p.59 – on the mainland) to defend the western end of the Solent against invasion fleets.

The last and most advanced addition to Henry VIII's chain of coastal artillery forts, it was completed after his death in 1547. Unlike Henry's earlier circular forts – such as Deal and Pendennis Castles – Yarmouth Castle is a square blockhouse. It has a heavy gun battery to the front and the first new-style 'arrowhead' bastion built in England protecting its most exposed angle against land attack. In the 1560s its central courtyard was filled in to provide a solid gun platform. Again altered during the 17th century, it was garrisoned until 1885 and re-used during both World Wars.

Inside, you can discover atmospheric recreations of how rooms were used in the 16th century, and an exhibition about the many wrecks in 'Yarmouth Roads', the treacherous stretch of sea which the castle overlooks. There is also a magnificent picnic site, with views over the Solent.

OPENING TIMES

1 Apr-30 Oct, daily	11am-5pm
31 Oct-31 Mar	Closed

VISIT US

Direction: In Yarmouth town centre, adjacent to car ferry terminal. Located just off Quay Street, up the short walkway and through the main gates into the castle

Train: Lymington Pier adjoins the ferry berth for the Wightlink service to Yarmouth

Bus: Visit traveline.info for the latest bus timetables and routes

Ferry: Yarmouth, adjacent (Wightlink – Tel: 0333 999 7333)

Tel: 01983 760444

NON-MEMBERS

Adult £6.60 | Concession £5.90 | Child £4.00
Family 2 Adults £17.20 | Family 1 Adult £10.60

Disabled access (part of ground floor only).

No parking at site: parking 5 minutes walk away (not managed by English Heritage).

MAP PAGE 326 (6B)
OS MAP 196, OL29: SZ354898

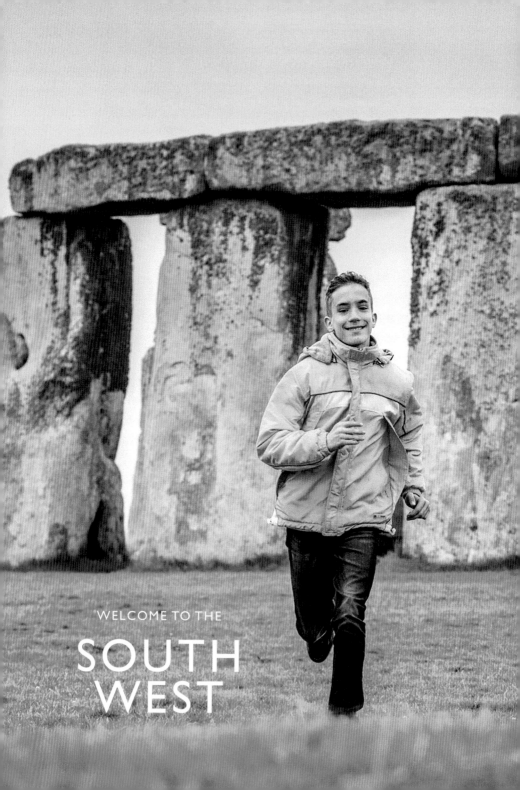

WELCOME TO THE

SOUTH
WEST

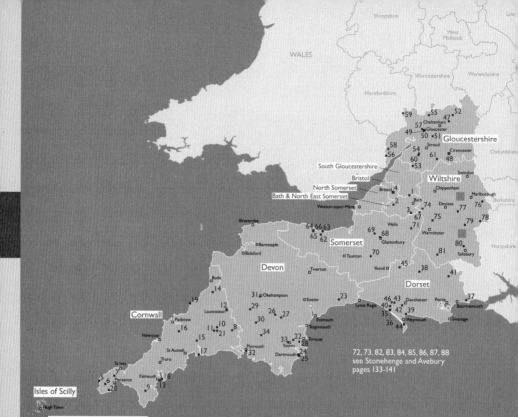

South West

Avebury Pilgrimage in a Day

11 miles | 1 day

(7 miles without the Windmill Hill loop from Avebury)

Walk this circular route and link together all the great sacred sites of Avebury. Tread in the footsteps of our ancestors and be absorbed into the silent Avebury landscape.

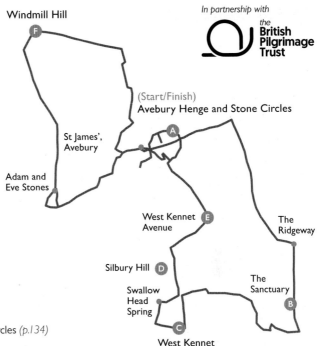

Windmill Hill
F

In partnership with

the **British Pilgrimage Trust**

(Start/Finish)
Avebury Henge and Stone Circles

St James',
Avebury

A

Adam and
Eve Stones

West Kennet
Avenue
E

The
Ridgeway

Silbury Hill
D

Swallow
Head
Spring

The
Sanctuary
B

C

West Kennet
Long Barrow

Discover English Heritage sites along the pilgrimage route

A Avebury Henge and Stone Circles *(p.134)*

B The Sanctuary *(p.135)*

C West Kennet Long Barrow *(p.136)*

D Silbury Hill *(p.135)*

E West Kennet Avenue *(p.136)*

F Windmill Hill *(p.137)*

View more details and a downloadable version of this route at english-heritage.org.uk/pilgrimage

SIR BEVIL GRENVILLE'S MONUMENT

BATH & NE SOMERSET – BA1 9DD

Erected to commemorate the heroism of a Royalist commander and his Cornish pikemen at the Battle of Lansdown, 1643.

OPENING TIMES

Any reasonable daylight hours

VISIT US

Direction: Located 4 miles NW of Bath on the N edge of Lansdown Hill, near the road to Wick

Train: Bath Spa 4½ miles

Bus: Visit traveline.info for the latest bus timetables and routes

ACQ.1953

Parking (in lay-by).

MAP PAGE 325 (3H)
OS MAP 172, 155: ST722703

STANTON DREW CIRCLES AND COVE

BATH & NE SOMERSET – BS39 4EW

The third largest collection of prehistoric standing stones in England. It includes the Great Circle – among the biggest in the country – two smaller circles and a three-stone 'cove'. Recent surveys prove they were part of a much more elaborate ritual site.

STANTON DREW CIRCLES AND COVE

OPENING TIMES

Cove: Any reasonable daylight hours

Two main stone circles: admission fee of £1.00 charged by landowner

25 Dec   Closed

VISIT US

Direction: Cove: in the garden of the Druid's Arms public house. Circles: E of Stanton Drew village

Train: Bristol Temple Meads 7 miles

Bus: Visit traveline.info for the latest bus timetables and routes

ACQ.1883

Cove: parking at Druids Arms. Stones: limited parking at entrance to Stones field.

MAP PAGE 325 (3H)
OS MAP 172/182, 154/155
COVE: ST597631
CIRCLES: ST601633

STONEY LITTLETON LONG BARROW

BATH & NE SOMERSET – BA2 8NR

One of the finest accessible examples of a Neolithic chambered tomb, with its multiple burial chambers open to view.

OPENING TIMES

Any reasonable daylight hours

VISIT US

Direction: 1 mile S of Wellow off A367. Narrow lane west of village leads to small parking area (1 mile)

Train: Bath Spa 6 miles

Bus: Visit traveline.info for the latest bus timetables and routes

ACQ.1884

Parking (limited). ¼ mile walk uphill from parking area.

Caution: steep slopes.

Note: visitors are advised to bring a torch.

MAP PAGE 325 (3H)
OS MAP 172, 142: ST735572

TEMPLE CHURCH

BRISTOL – BS1 6HS

The 'leaning tower' and walls of a large late-medieval church – originally founded by the Knights Templar – which survived Second World War bombing.

OPENING TIMES

Exterior only: Any reasonable daylight hours

VISIT US

Direction: Located in Temple St, off Victoria St

Train: Bristol Temple Meads ¼ mile

Bus: Visit traveline.info for the latest bus timetables and routes

ACQ.1958

Some steps and uneven flagstones around church.

Caution: unguarded drops.

MAP PAGE 325 (3H)
OS MAP 172, 154/155: ST593727

BALLOWALL BARROW

CORNWALL – TR19 7NP

In a spectacular position, this large Bronze Age burial mound was reconstructed by Victorian Cornish antiquarian William Borlase.

Managed by the National Trust on behalf of English Heritage.

OPENING TIMES

Any reasonable daylight hours

VISIT US

Direction: 1 mile W of St Just

Train: Penzance 8 miles

Bus: Visit traveline.info for the latest bus timetables and routes

ACQ.1954

Parking limited.

Caution: unguarded drops, falling rocks.

MAP PAGE 324 (7A)
OS MAP 203, 102: SW355312

CARN EUNY ANCIENT VILLAGE
CORNWALL – TR20 8RB

Among the best-preserved ancient villages in the South West, occupied from Iron Age until late Roman times.

Managed by the Cornwall Heritage Trust.

OPENING TIMES
Any reasonable daylight hours

VISIT US
Direction: 1½ miles W of Sancreed along narrow but signed lanes

Train: Penzance 6 miles

Bus: Visit traveline.info for the latest bus timetables and routes

ACQ.1957 🐕 🏠 📷 P ⚠

Parking (limited) in Brane, 600 metres (660 yards) walk to site.

Joint guidebook for sale at Chysauster.

Caution: unguarded drops.

> MAP PAGE 324 (7A)
> OS MAP 203, 102: SW402288

DUPATH WELL
CORNWALL – PL17 8AD

A charming well-house of c. 1500, standing over an ancient spring believed to cure whooping cough.

Managed by the Cornwall Heritage Trust.

OPENING TIMES
Any reasonable daylight hours

VISIT US
Direction: 1 mile E of Callington off A388

Train: Gunnislake 4½ miles

Bus: Visit traveline.info for the latest bus timetables and routes

ACQ.1937 🐕 P

Parking at farmyard entrance.

> MAP PAGE 324 (6D)
> OS MAP 201, 108: SX375692

CHYSAUSTER ANCIENT VILLAGE
CORNWALL – TR20 8XA

An elevated viewing platform offers you a bird's-eye view of Chysauster, one of the finest examples of a Romano-British village in Britain. Set in beautiful countryside rich in wildlife, the village probably originated as an Iron Age settlement in about 400 BC. Some 50 to 70 people may have lived here in Roman times, before Chysauster was abandoned for unknown reasons during the 3rd century AD. A site model gives you more insights into this ancient settlement and its unique prehistoric landscape.

The village includes substantial remains of nine stone-walled 'courtyard houses', a type found only on the Land's End peninsula and the Isles of Scilly. Lining a 'village street', each had an open central courtyard surrounded by thatched rooms. There's also the entrance to a 'fogou', an underground passage distinctive to west Cornwall sites. Their purpose remains a mystery.

OPENING TIMES

1 Apr-30 Sep, daily	10am-5pm
1-30 Oct, daily	10am-4pm
31 Oct-31 Mar	Closed

Last entry 30 mins before closing

VISIT US
Direction: Located 2½ miles NW of Gulval, off B3311

Train: Penzance 3½ miles

Bus: Visit traveline.info for the latest bus timetables and routes

Tel: 07470 115475

Local Tourist Information:
Penzance: 01736 335530

NON-MEMBERS
Adult **£6.00** | Concession **£5.30**
Child **£3.60** | Family 2 Adults **£15.60**
Family 1 Adult **£9.60**

ACQ.1931 ♿ 🐕 🏛 🏠 🚹 👤 P 🏪
📷 OVP

> MAP PAGE 324 (7B)
> OS MAP 203, 102: SW472350

HALLIGGYE FOGOU

CORNWALL – TR12 6AF

The largest of the mysterious underground passages or 'fogous' associated with Cornish Iron Age settlements. Whether they were refuges, storage chambers or shrines is uncertain.

Managed by the Trelowarren Estate.

OPENING TIMES

Any reasonable daylight hours May-Sep. No access inside fogou Oct-Apr inclusive

VISIT US

Direction: Approximately 1 mile south-east of Garras off B3293, enter the Trelowarren estate by the gatehouses. After 0.8 miles, turn right at crossroads and find parking area on the right, where a panel shows the route to the fogou. See website for further details

Train: Penryn 14 miles

Bus: Visit traveline.info for the latest bus timetables and routes

ACQ.1979 ⚑ 🚶 ⚐ P 🍴 ⚠

Limited parking.

Caution: steep stairs.

Visitors are strongly advised to bring a torch.

MAP PAGE 324 (7B)
OS MAP 203, 103: SW713239

THE HURLERS STONE CIRCLES

CORNWALL – PL14 5LE

Three late Neolithic or early Bronze Age stone circles arranged in a line, a grouping very rare in England.

Once believed to be men turned to stone for playing the Cornish game of hurling on a Sunday.

Managed by the Cornwall Heritage Trust.

OPENING TIMES

Any reasonable daylight hours

VISIT US

Direction: Located ½ mile NW of Minions, off B3254

THE HURLERS STONE CIRCLES

Train: Liskeard 7 miles

Bus: Visit traveline.info for the latest bus timetables and routes

ACQ.1935 ⚑ ⚐ P ⚠

Parking ¼ mile walk.

MAP PAGE 324 (6D)
OS MAP 201, 109: SX258714

KING DONIERT'S STONE

CORNWALL – PL14 6RU

Two richly carved pieces of a 9th-century cross, commemorating Dumgarth, British King of Dumnonia, died c. AD 875.

Managed by the Cornwall Heritage Trust.

OPENING TIMES

Any reasonable daylight hours

VISIT US

Direction: 1 mile NW of St Cleer, off B3254

Train: Liskeard 7 miles

Bus: Visit traveline.info for the latest bus timetables and routes

ACQ.1933 ⚑ P

Parking (in lay-by).

MAP PAGE 324 (6D)
OS MAP 201, 109: SX236688

LAUNCESTON CASTLE

CORNWALL – PL15 7DR

Set on a tall mound, with an unusual keep consisting of a 13th-century round tower inside an earlier shell-keep. The Quaker founder George Fox suffered harsh imprisonment here in 1656. Refreshed interpretation and updated museum from summer 2022.

🎬 *The Trouble With Maggie Cole* (2020).

OPENING TIMES

1 Apr-30 Sep, daily   10am-5pm

LAUNCESTON CASTLE	
1-30 Oct, daily	10am-4pm
31 Oct-31 Mar	Closed

Last entry 30 mins before closing

VISIT US

Direction: In Launceston town centre

Bus: Visit traveline.info for the latest bus timetables and routes

Tel: 01566 772365

Local Tourist Information: Launceston: 01566 772321

NON-MEMBERS

Adult **£6.60** I Concession **£5.90** Child **£4.00** I Family 2 Adults **£17.20** Family 1 Adult **£10.60**

ACQ.1952 ♿ ⚑ E 🔌 🖼 🗃 📷 ⚠ OVP

No disabled access to keep. Low light levels on stairs leading to the view.

Refreshments available.

New guidebook.

MAP PAGE 324 (5D)
OS MAP 201, 112: SX331846

PENHALLAM MANOR

CORNWALL – EX22 6XW

The low, grass-covered, complete ground-plan of a moated 13th-century manor house, in a delightful woodland setting.

OPENING TIMES

Any reasonable daylight hours

Car park	
Apr-Oct	10am-6pm
Nov-Mar	10am-4pm

VISIT US

Direction: Signposted from Week St Mary, off a minor road. From A39 heading north turn right at Treskinnick Cross

Bus: Visit traveline.info for the latest bus timetables and routes

ACQ.1981 ⚑ P ⚠

Limited parking. (15-minute walk from the car park along a forest track.)

Caution: deep water.

MAP PAGE 324 (5D)
OS MAP 190, 111: SX224974

RESTORMEL CASTLE

CORNWALL – PL22 0EE

Restormel's great 13th-century circular keep stands on an earlier Norman mound, on top of a high spur beside the River Fowey. Twice visited by the Black Prince, it finally saw action during the Civil War. Commanding fantastic views, it makes an excellent picnic spot. A trail leads to the Duchy of Cornwall Nursery across the valley.

OPENING TIMES

1 Apr-30 Sep, daily	10am-5pm
1-30 Oct, daily	10am-4pm
31 Oct-31 Mar	Closed

Last entry 30 mins before closing

VISIT US

Direction: Located 1½ miles N of Lostwithiel, off A390

Train: Lostwithiel 1½ miles

Bus: Visit traveline.info for the latest bus timetables and routes

Tel: 01208 872687

Local Tourist Information
Lostwithiel: 01208 872207

NON-MEMBERS

Adult **£6.60** I Concession **£5.90**
Child **£4.00** I Family 2 Adults **£17.20**
Family 1 Adult **£10.60**

[ACQ.1925] [icons] [P] [icons]
[icons] [OVP]

Access via a stock grazing area. Sensible footwear is strongly advised, due to grassy areas around the site.

Refreshments available.

MAP PAGE 324 (6C)
OS MAP 200, 107: SX104614

ST BREOCK DOWNS MONOLITH

CORNWALL – PL30 5PN

Cornwall's largest prehistoric standing stone, originally weighing nearly 17 tonnes, on the summit of St Breock Downs.

Managed by the Cornwall Heritage Trust.

OPENING TIMES

Any reasonable daylight hours

VISIT US

Direction: 3½ miles SW of Wadebridge. 2 miles SW of Burlawn, on road to Rosenannon. Follow finger post, then turn right for approx. 500 metres

Train: Roche 5½ miles

Bus: Visit traveline.info for the latest bus timetables and routes

[ACQ.1965] [icons] [P]

Parking in lay-by.

MAP PAGE 324 (6C)
OS MAP 200, 106: SW968683

ST CATHERINE'S CASTLE

CORNWALL – PL23 1JH

One of two small artillery forts built by Henry VIII to defend Fowey Harbour, consisting of two storeys with gunports at ground level.

OPENING TIMES

Any reasonable daylight hours

VISIT US

Direction: 1½ miles SW of Fowey along a woodland path off Readymoney Road

Train: Par 4 miles

Bus: Visit traveline.info for the latest bus timetables and routes

[ACQ.1909] [icons] [P] [icons]

Parking (Readymoney Cove Car Park, Fowey, ¾ mile walk). Charged.

Caution: steep slopes, unguarded drops, steep stairs.

Please do not climb on the walls.

MAP PAGE 324 (6C)
OS MAP 200/204, 107: SX119509

TREGIFFIAN BURIAL CHAMBER

CORNWALL – TR19 6ER

Remains of a Neolithic chambered tomb, with a stone-lined entrance passage leading into the central chamber.

Managed by the Cornwall Heritage Trust.

OPENING TIMES

Any reasonable daylight hours

VISIT US

Direction: Located 2 miles SE of St Buryan, on B3315

Train: Penzance 5½ miles

Bus: Visit traveline.info for the latest bus timetables and routes

[ACQ.1971] [icons] [P] [icons]

Parking (in lay-by).

Caution: unguarded drops.

MAP PAGE 324 (7A)
OS MAP 203, 102: SW431244

TRETHEVY QUOIT

CORNWALL – PL14 5JY

An impressive Neolithic burial chamber, 2.7 metres (8ft 11in) high. Five standing stones are surmounted by a huge capstone.

Managed by the Cornwall Heritage Trust.

OPENING TIMES

Any reasonable daylight hours

VISIT US

Direction: 1 mile NE of St Cleer, near Darite; off B3254

Train: Liskeard 3½ miles

Bus: Visit traveline.info for the latest bus timetables and routes

[ACQ.1931] [icons] [icons] [P] [icons]

Limited parking.

Please do not climb on the stones.

MAP PAGE 324 (6D)
OS MAP 201, 109: SX259688

PENDENNIS CASTLE

CORNWALL – TR11 4NQ

In a strikingly beautiful setting, Pendennis Castle offers you exciting first-hand experiences of history. You can hear the roar of real guns, look out for enemies on the horizon and meet characters from its dramatic past. There's also a new castle-themed soft play area.

Set on a picturesque rocky headland, Pendennis Castle has plenty of space for families to explore together, and commands breathtaking views over Falmouth, the Fal estuary and the sea. It was begun by Henry VIII in the 1540s, when Cornwall was in the front line of the Tudor conflict between England, France and Spain. Along with its sister castle, St Mawes, on the far side of the estuary, it guarded the vital anchorage of Carrick Roads. You'll witness how it was updated again and again to face new threats over the centuries, right up to the Second World War and after.

In the Tudor keep or 'gun tower', the core and oldest part of the fortress, immerse yourself in the drama as a possible enemy ship is sighted and the gunners rush to their stations. Climb to the top of the round keep for panoramic views.

Threatened again by Spanish landings in Elizabethan times, Henry VIII's fort was expanded to defend the whole headland, producing the extensive fortress you see today.

During the First World War Pendennis became the headquarters of 'Fortress Falmouth'. Hands-on displays recreate parts of the fortress as they were in 1914-18. Exhibits include the letters of Battery Quartermaster Sergeant 'Tommy' Thomas, who died of wounds in France, aged 27. They're now back in the very room where some were written.

Highlighting the castle's original Tudor, Napoleonic, Victorian and 20th-century guns, an intriguing

display traces how its artillery developed to meet the changing threat of ever more deadly enemy weapons. Between April and October, it's hard to miss the thunderous live firing of a noonday gun, using one of the castle's guns.

A Castle Explorers family trail guides you round the fortress. Follow the tunnel down to the Half Moon Battery and you'll be transported back to the Second World War. In the underground magazine, you might even get recruited into a gun-firing team. In the meticulously recreated Battery Observation Post bunker, you can scan the horizon for enemy ships and eavesdrop on telephone conversations between the commander and the gun crews.

Take a break from watching out for enemies on the horizon in the café, offering delicious meals and snacks inspired by the castle's heritage.

Picturesque Pendennis can also serve as a spectacular venue – from a dramatic coastal wedding to a memorable corporate event. The pre-bookable education suite fits up to 35 children.

Combine your trip to Pendennis with a visit to her sister fortress at St Mawes (p.112).

⊤ Available for corporate and private hire

🔺 Licensed for civil wedding ceremonies

Enjoy the grounds and be in the heart of the action on event days when you stay in the *Custodian's House* or *Callie's Cottage* on the castle lawns. Both offer ideal bases from which to explore this picturesque part of southern Cornwall.

See p.16 for details on staying at **Pendennis** and our other holiday cottages.

STAY WITH US

OPENING TIMES

1 Apr-30 Jun, daily	10am-5pm
1 Jul-31 Aug, daily	10am-6pm
1 Sep-30 Oct, daily	10am-5pm
31 Oct-23 Dec, Sat-Sun	10am-4pm
2 Jan-10 Feb, Sat-Sun	10am-4pm
11-19 Feb, daily	10am-4pm
20 Feb-31 Mar, Wed-Sun	10am-4pm

Christmas Opening

24-25 Dec	Closed
26 Dec-1 Jan, daily	10am-4pm

Last entry 30 mins before closing

The castle may close from 4pm on Saturdays if a wedding is booked. Please check with the site in advance

The castle keep may close for 1 hour if an event is booked

Free guided tours of the Half Moon Battery and Tudor gun tower. Check availability on arrival

VISIT US

Address: Pendennis Castle, Falmouth, Cornwall TR11 4NQ

Direction: Follow the A39 through Falmouth and then follow the signs for 'scenic route'. For satnav to main car park use TR11 4NQ or for drop-off zone/limited disabled parking use TR11 4LP

Train: Falmouth Docks ½ mile

Bus: Visit traveline.info for the latest bus timetables and routes

Tel: 01326 316594

Local Tourist Information: Falmouth: 01326 741194

NON-MEMBERS

Peak (28 May-31 Aug, Sun-Thu)
Adult **£14.80** | Concession **£13.30**
Child **£8.80** | Family 2 Adults **£38.40**
Family 1 Adult **£23.60**

Standard (1 Apr-27 May and Sep-Oct, Sun-Thu; 28 May-31 Aug, Fri-Sat)
Adult **£13.80** | Concession **£12.40**
Child **£8.30** | Family 2 Adults **£35.90**
Family 1 Adult **£22.10**

Off-peak (1 Apr-27 May and Sep-Oct, Fri-Sat and Nov-Mar)
Adult **£12.80** | Concession **£11.50**
Child **£7.60** | Family 2 Adults **£33.20**
Family 1 Adult **£20.40**

Wheelchair access to the grounds, but steep slopes or drops in places. There is also full wheelchair access to the shop, tearoom, weapons of war display and barracks.

Tearoom closes ½ hour before the castle.

MAP PAGE 324 (7C)
OS MAP 204, 103/105: SW824318

TINTAGEL CASTLE

CORNWALL – PL34 0HE

Linked by long tradition with the legend of King Arthur, romantically sited Tintagel was a focus of princely power during a shadowy era of Cornish history. A spectacular footbridge now connects its rocky headland and island, letting you explore this fabled place as our ancestors once did.

Tintagel means 'the fortress with the narrow entrance' – a slender neck of land which, according to legend, could be defended by just three men. During the 5th to 7th centuries, the island fortress was the stronghold of post-Roman Cornish rulers. Ongoing archaeological excavations prove it was the home of a high-status community with strong links to the Mediterranean.

Memories of Tintagel's past glories inspired many legends, most famously linking it with King Arthur. In the 12th century, Geoffrey of Monmouth wrote that Duke Gorlois of Cornwall shut his wife Ygraine away here to protect her from the lusts of Uther Pendragon, King of Britain. But Merlin magically transformed Uther into the likeness of Ygraine's husband: he slept with her here, and fathered Arthur.

Staking his claim to a part in Arthurian legend, Richard, Earl of Cornwall – Henry III's immensely wealthy younger brother – built a castle here in the 1230s. Its atmospheric ruins stand partly on the mainland and partly on the island: in medieval times the two halves were connected by a bridge.

For the first time in over 500 years, a daringly designed footbridge re-establishes this long-lost connection. Some 68 metres (223 feet) long, it's crafted of oak and steel, and floored with 40,000 local Delabole slate tiles. At its exact centre is a gasp-inducing 4cm gap, symbolising the transition from present to past and history to legend. The Tintagel bridge was made possible by the support of Julia and Hans Rausing.

Over on the rocky island, you'll discover the ruins of the castle hall and evocative traces of 5th- to 7th-century houses. A medieval garden with 'story stones' remembers Tintagel's links to the tale of the doomed lovers Tristan and Iseult. All around are spectacular coastal views.

Complete your exploration in the exhibition, where you'll see fascinating artefacts discovered here and a 3D model revealing how Tintagel developed through time. Imaginative book sculptures trace how this romantic site inspired writers from medieval Malory to Victorian Tennyson.

Children will love the beach below the castle (only accessible at low tide after a climb over rocks) with Merlin's Cave to explore. Everyone will enjoy our Beach Café, with its varied menu focused on locally sourced Cornish treats.

Please note: Entrance to the castle is managed through timed tickets, and due to limited availability, booking in advance online is strongly recommended. Go to **english-heritage.org.uk/ tintagel** for the latest information and to book.

OPENING TIMES

1 Apr-30 Sep, daily	10am-6pm
1-30 Oct, daily	10am-5pm
31 Oct-30 Nov, Wed-Sun	10am-4pm
1-23 Dec, Fri-Sun	10am-4pm
2 Jan-10 Feb, Sat-Sun	10am-4pm
11-19 Feb, daily	10am-4pm
20 Feb-31 Mar, Wed-Sun	10am-4pm

Christmas Opening

24-25 Dec	Closed
26 Dec-1 Jan, daily	10am-4pm

Last entry 1 hour before closing

VISIT US

Address: Tintagel Castle, Castle Road, Tintagel, Cornwall PL34 0HE

Direction: On Tintagel Head, 600 metres (660 yards) along steep, uneven track from Tintagel; no vehicles except Land Rover service (not managed by English Heritage and extra charge payable)

Bus: Visit traveline.info

Tel: 01840 770328

NON-MEMBERS

Peak (28 May-31 Aug, Sun-Thu)
Adult £18.90 | Concession £17.00
Child £11.40 | Family 2 Adults £49.20
Family 1 Adult £30.30

Standard (1 Apr-27 May and Sep-Oct, Sun-Thu; 28 May-31 Aug, Fri-Sat)
Adult £17.60 | Concession £15.80
Child £10.60 | Family 2 Adults £45.80
Family 1 Adult £28.20

Off-peak (1 Apr-27 May and Sep-Oct, Fri-Sat and Nov-Mar)
Adult £16.30 | Concession £14.70
Child £9.80 | Family 2 Adults £42.40
Family 1 Adult £26.10

Limited availability – pre-booking strongly recommended.
See website for latest information

We have introduced step-free access to the island via our new footbridge. However, there are no step-free routes around the island itself, so disabled access is limited from this point. Access is possible to the exhibition, Beach Café and shop. Please see website for full details.

Parking (600 metres (660 yards) in the village) – not managed by English Heritage.

MAP PAGE 324 (5C)
OS MAP 200, 111: SX049891

🎬 *The Kid Who Would Be King* (2019).

STAY WITH US

Fort House sleeps four. This spacious single-storey cottage stands in a private garden, whose terrace provides uninterrupted views of the coastline. Ideal for families with young children, due to the fenced and sheltered garden.

See p.16 for details on staying at St Mawes and our other holiday cottages.

ST MAWES CASTLE

———— CORNWALL – TR2 5DE ————

Beautifully positioned overlooking the Fal estuary, St Mawes Castle is the best-preserved and most elaborately decorated of Henry VIII's Tudor artillery forts. Enhanced presentation highlights its stories for family explorers.

Along with Pendennis Castle on the other side of the estuary, St Mawes guarded the important anchorage of Carrick Roads. Mounting heavy ship-sinking guns, it was one of the chain of forts built to counter an invasion threat from Catholic Europe. Displays reveal how the ambitious Cornish merchant Thomas Treffry of Fowey masterminded its building, bedecking it with carvings praising the Tudor dynasty and becoming its first captain.

A model introduces the castle's charming clover-leaf design, hands-on games help families discover its ornate sculptures, and audio tracks bring Tudor characters to life.

The castle's re-presented collection of historic guns tells the story of how St Mawes guarded the Cornish coast for over 450 years, right up to 1956.

There are wonderful views of the sea and passing ships from the battlements. Add to your adventures by travelling to the castle by ferry.

OPENING TIMES

1 Apr-30 Oct, daily	10am-5pm
31 Oct-23 Dec, Sat-Sun	10am-4pm
27 Dec-10 Feb, Sat-Sun	10am-4pm
11-19 Feb, daily	10am-4pm
20 Feb-31 Mar, Wed-Sun	10am-4pm
Christmas Opening 24-26 Dec	Closed

Last entry 30 mins before closing

The castle may be closed on a Saturday if an event is booked. Please check with the property in advance

VISIT US

Direction: In St Mawes on A3078

Train: Penmere (Falmouth), 4 miles via Prince of Wales Pier and ferry

Bus: Visit traveline.info for the latest bus timetables and routes

Ferry: St Mawes passenger ferry from Falmouth or King Harry Car Ferry from Feock

Tel: 01803 866618

Local Tourist Information: St Mawes: 01326 270440

NON-MEMBERS

Adult £7.80 | Concession £7.00 | Child £4.70 Family 2 Adults £20.30 | Family 1 Adult £12.50

ACQ.1961

Parking: charges apply to non-members, free for Members with valid English Heritage car sticker.

MAP PAGE 324 (7C) OS MAP 204, 105: SW841328

BERRY POMEROY CASTLE

DEVON – TQ9 6LJ

The perfect romantic ruin, tucked away in woodland. Within the 15th-century walls of the Pomeroy family castle looms the dramatic ruined shell of the great Elizabethan and Jacobean mansion of the Seymours, never completed.

OPENING TIMES

1 Apr-30 Sep, daily	10am-5pm
1-30 Oct, daily	10am-4pm
31 Oct-31 Mar, Sat-Sun	10am-4pm
24-26 Dec & 1 Jan	Closed
Last entry 30 mins before closing	

VISIT US

Direction: 2½ miles E of Totnes off A385

Train: Totnes 3½ miles

Bus: Visit traveline.info for the latest bus timetables and routes

Tel: 01803 866618

NON-MEMBERS

Adult **£7.80** I Concession **£7.00**
Child **£4.70** I Family 2 Adults **£20.30**
Family 1 Adult **£12.50**

ACQ.1977 [icons] P
[icons] OVP

Wheelchair and rugged mobility scooter access (grounds and ground floor only).

Limited parking (no coach access) at end of long drive (approx. ¾ mile).

Tearooms (not managed by English Heritage) Tel: 01803 849473 for opening times.

MAP PAGE 325 (6F)
OS MAP 202, OL20/110:
SX839623

BLACKBURY CAMP

DEVON – EX24 6JE

An Iron Age hillfort with impressive ramparts and defended single entrance. Now a picturesque spot for a picnic, surrounded by woodland.

OPENING TIMES

Any reasonable daylight hours

VISIT US

Direction: Off B3174/A3052

Train: Honiton 6½ miles

Bus: Visit traveline.info for the latest bus timetables and routes

ACQ.1930 [icons] P [icon]

Caution: steep slopes.

MAP PAGE 325 (5G)
OS MAP 192/193, 115: SY187924

DARTMOUTH, BAYARD'S COVE FORT

DEVON – TQ6 9AX

Small Tudor artillery fort guarding Dartmouth's inner harbour, picturesquely sited on the quayside.

See also Dartmouth Castle, p.114.

OPENING TIMES

Any reasonable daylight hours

VISIT US

Direction: Located in Dartmouth, on the riverside

Train: Kingswear Station on the Torbay & Paignton Railway and then catch the Dartmouth Lower Ferry or Passenger Ferry

Bus: Visit traveline.info for the latest bus timetables and routes

ACQ.1954 [icons]

Caution: steep stairs, sheer drop into water.

Please do not climb on the walls.

MAP PAGE 325 (6F)
OS MAP 202, OL20: SX879509

GRIMSPOUND

DEVON – PL20 6TB

The best-known prehistoric Dartmoor settlement. Remains of 24 Bronze Age houses survive within a massive boundary wall.

Managed by the Dartmoor National Park Authority.

OPENING TIMES

Any reasonable daylight hours

VISIT US

Direction: 6 miles SW of Moretonhampstead, off B3212

Bus: Visit traveline.info for the latest bus timetables and routes

ACQ.1977 [icons] P

Parking in lay-by.

MAP PAGE 324 (5E)
OS MAP 191, OL28: SX701809

MEMBERS' rewards

Don't forget to check out our **Members' Rewards** scheme. It gives you access to a variety of exclusive offers, discount deals, fantastic competitions and unforgettable experiences.

See p.322 for details.

DARTMOUTH CASTLE

—— DEVON – TQ6 0JN ——

In a lovely waterfront setting, Dartmouth Castle defended the busy port of Dartmouth against many enemies for over 550 years. Imaginative installations bring its history to life.

Begun in the 1380s by John Hawley, privateering mayor of Dartmouth, about a century later the castle became probably the very first fortification in Britain purpose-built to mount 'ship-sinking' heavy cannon. It was also equipped with a massive 250-metre-long iron chain spanning the Dart estuary, which could be drawn up to stop incoming enemy ships, making them an easy target for gunfire. An animated film explores how this feat of medieval engineering worked.

Installations bring the castle's story right up to its last call to action in the Second World War, and a dramatic audio and light display in the 19th-century gun battery shows a crew preparing to fire a heavy gun. Families can explore hands-on the weapons used to defend the fortress, trying on helmets and handling cannonballs. You're also introduced to characters from Dartmouth's history, and young history hunters can follow 'John Hawley's Explorer Trail', an activity trail throughout the castle.

Take the scenic boat trip to the castle (weather dependent) from the bustling town quay. The best views of the castle are from the water, so be sure to have your camera ready.

OPENING TIMES

1 Apr-30 Oct, daily	10am-5pm
31 Oct-31 Mar, Sat-Sun	10am-4pm
24-26 Dec & 1 Jan	Closed

Last entry 30 mins before closing

VISIT US

Direction: 1 mile SE of Dartmouth off B3205, narrow approach road. No coach access

Train: Kingswear Station on the Torbay & Paignton Railway and then catch the Dartmouth Lower Ferry or Passenger Ferry

Bus: Visit traveline.info for the latest bus timetables and routes

Ferry: The Dartmouth Castle Ferry operates from Dartmouth between Easter and end of October

Tel: 01803 834445

Local Tourist Information:
Dartmouth: 01803 834224

NON-MEMBERS

Adult **£9.00** I Concession **£8.10** I Child **£5.40**
Family 2 Adults **£23.40** I Family 1 Adult **£14.40**

ACQ.1909 🐕 ♨ ⬜ 🧍 👪 **P** 🎒 🚻 💷 ⚠ OVP

Parking (not owned by English Heritage, charged).

Tearooms and toilets (not managed by English Heritage).

MAP PAGE 325 (6F)
OS MAP 202, OL20: SX887503

HOUND TOR DESERTED MEDIEVAL VILLAGE

DEVON – TQ13 9XG

The remains of four 13th-century Dartmoor longhouses built of granite boulders, with their barns and garden plots. People lived at one end of the longhouse, their livestock at the other, divided by a passage. Set in an area originally farmed in the Bronze Age, this isolated moorland hamlet was probably abandoned by the early 15th century.
A free downloadable audio tour is available from our website.

Managed by the Dartmoor National Park Authority.

OPENING TIMES
Any reasonable daylight hours

VISIT US
Direction: 2½ miles west of Haytor Vale on B3387, right turn to Hound Tor and Manaton, continue for 1½ miles

Bus: Visit traveline.info for the latest bus timetables and routes

ACQ.1972

Parking at Swallerton Gate (½ mile walk south-east across moor to monument).

MAP PAGE 324 (5E)
OS MAP 191, OL28: SX746788

KIRKHAM HOUSE, PAIGNTON

DEVON – TQ3 3AX

Late medieval house, restored in the 1960s. Furnished with modern furniture, illustrating traditional craftsmanship.
Managed in association with the Paignton Heritage Society.

OPENING TIMES
15, 18 Apr, 2 May, 3, 10, 17, 24, 31 Jul, 7, 14, 21, 28-29 Aug	2pm-5pm
10-11 Sep	11am-4pm

VISIT US
Direction: Located in Kirkham St, off Cecil Rd, Paignton

Train: Paignton ½ mile

Bus: Visit traveline.info for the latest bus timetables and routes

ACQ.1948

Caution: steep stairs.

MAP PAGE 325 (6F)
OS MAP 202, OL20/110: SX885610

LYDFORD CASTLE, TOWN BANKS AND SAXON TOWN

DEVON – EX20 4BH

A Norman earthwork castle and a later Norman stone keep, built as a prison and notorious for harsh punishments. Beautifully sited on the fringe of Dartmoor, it stands within the defences of a Saxon fortified 'borough'.

Download a free audio tour from our website.

LYDFORD CASTLE, TOWN BANKS AND SAXON TOWN

OPENING TIMES
Any reasonable daylight hours

VISIT US
Direction: In Lydford off A386; 8½ miles S of Okehampton

Bus: Visit traveline.info for the latest bus timetables and routes

ACQ.1934	Castle
ACQ.1965	North of Town Banks
ACQ.1968	South of Town Banks
ACQ.1972	Norman Fort

Parking (not owned by English Heritage).
Caution: steep slopes, steep stairs.

MAP PAGE 324 (5E)
OS MAP 191/201, OL28: SX509848

MERRIVALE PREHISTORIC SETTLEMENT

DEVON – PL20 6ST

Bronze Age settlement remains, along with ritual sites including Bronze Age cairns and cists, late Neolithic stone rows and a stone circle. Constructed c. 3000-1000 BC.

Managed by the Dartmoor National Park Authority.

OPENING TIMES
Any reasonable daylight hours

VISIT US
Direction: South of B3357 W of Princetown

Train: Gunnislake 10 miles

Bus: Visit traveline.info for the latest bus timetables and routes

ACQ.1973

Parking at Four Winds car park. Five minute walk west across moor.

MAP PAGE 324 (6E)
OS MAP 191, OL28: SX554748

OKEHAMPTON CASTLE

DEVON – EX20 1JA

The remains of the largest castle in Devon. Begun soon after the Norman Conquest, it was converted into a sumptuous residence in the 14th century by Hugh Courtenay, Earl of Devon. Riverside picnic area and woodland walks.

OPENING TIMES

1 Apr-30 Oct, daily	10am-5pm
31 Oct-31 Mar	Closed

Last entry 30 mins before closing

VISIT US

Direction: Located ½ mile SW of Okehampton town centre (signposted). Turn into Castle Road by Post Office. Close to A30

Train: Okehampton 0.8 miles, regular service from Exeter

Bus: Visit traveline.info for the latest bus timetables and routes

Tel: 01837 52844

Local Tourist Information: Okehampton: 01837 52295

NON-MEMBERS

Adult **£6.60** | Concession **£5.90**
Child **£4.00** | Family 2 Adults **£17.20**
Family 1 Adult **£10.60**

ACQ.1967 🎧 📷 🐕 ♿ 💻 🚶 👤 P
🎪 📷 🔔 ⚠ OVP

Woodland Walk Guide available from kiosk.

MAP PAGE 324 (5E)
OS MAP 191, OL28/113:
SX583942

ROYAL CITADEL, PLYMOUTH

DEVON – PL1 2PD

Plymouth's most important historic building and one of Britain's finest 17th-century fortresses. Commissioned by Charles II in 1665 to counter a threatened Dutch invasion, it's still in military use today.

OPENING TIMES

Access by 2-hour guided tour only Apr-Oct. Security measures are in force as the site is a working military establishment. Photography is prohibited. Tickets must be booked online at least 24 hours in advance. Check website for further details

VISIT US

Direction: At E end of Plymouth Hoe

Train: Plymouth 1 mile

Bus: Visit traveline.info for the latest bus timetables and routes

ENTRY

Charge for tours

ACQ.1966 ♿ 🚫 ⚠

Parking on Plymouth Hoe. No large bags. Bags may be searched. No toilets on site.

Disabled access (some steep slopes).

Caution: unguarded drops, steep stairs.

MAP PAGE 324 (6D)
OS MAP 201, OL20/108:
SX480538

TOTNES CASTLE

DEVON – TQ9 5NU

Classic Norman motte-and-bailey castle, founded soon after the Conquest to overawe the Saxon town. A later shell-keep crowns its steep mound, offering sweeping views across the rooftops to the River Dart.

TOTNES CASTLE

OPENING TIMES

1 Apr-30 Oct, daily	10am-5pm
31 Oct-31 Mar, Sat-Sun	10am-4pm
24-26 Dec & 1 Jan	Closed

Last entry 30 mins before closing

VISIT US

Direction: In centre of Totnes, entrance on Castle Street. By car, follow signs for Historic Town Centre, turn onto Castle Street from Station Road (opposite train station). On foot from town centre, turn north off High Street (towards the train station)

Train: Totnes ¼ mile and South Devon Railway (Totnes Riverside) ½ mile

Bus: Visit traveline.info for the latest bus timetables and routes

Tel: 01803 864406

Local Tourist Information: Totnes: 01803 269190

NON-MEMBERS

Adult **£6.60** | Concession **£5.90**
Child **£4.00** | Family 2 Adults **£17.20**
Family 1 Adult **£10.60**

ACQ.1947 🐕 📷 🐎 P 🎪 📷 ⚠ OVP

Parking charged (not managed by English Heritage) 64 metre (210 feet) walk from castle, cars only, narrow approach roads).

Keep accessible only via steep steps.

New guidebook planned for summer 2022.

MAP PAGE 324 (6E)
OS MAP 202, OL20/110:
SX800605

UPPER PLYM VALLEY

DEVON – PL7 5EJ

Some 300 Bronze Age and medieval sites, covering 6 square miles of Dartmoor landscape.

OPENING TIMES

Any reasonable daylight hours

VISIT US

Direction: 4 miles E of Yelverton

ACQ.1978 🐕 🐎 P

Parking – ½ mile walk to monuments. Limited parking at Trowlesworthy car park – OS map strongly advised.

MAP PAGE 324 (6E)
OS MAP 202, OL20/OL28:
SX580660

ABBOTSBURY ABBEY REMAINS
DORSET – DT3 4JR

Part of a monastic building, perhaps the abbot's lodging, of the Benedictine Abbey of Abbotsbury. St Catherine's Chapel is within half a mile.

OPENING TIMES
Any reasonable daylight hours

VISIT US
Direction: Located in Abbotsbury, off B3157, near the churchyard

Train: Upwey 7½ miles

Bus: Visit traveline.info for the latest bus timetables and routes

Tel: 0370 333 1181

ACQ.1948

Parking charged (not English Heritage).

MAP PAGE 325 (5H)
OS MAP 194, OL15: SY578852

ABBOTSBURY, ST CATHERINE'S CHAPEL
DORSET – DT3 4JH

High on a hilltop overlooking Abbotsbury Abbey, this sturdily buttressed 14th-century chapel was built by the monks as a place of pilgrimage and retreat.

ABBOTSBURY, ST CATHERINE'S CHAPEL

OPENING TIMES
Any reasonable daylight hours

VISIT US
Direction: ½ mile S of Abbotsbury; by steep path from village, off B3157

Train: Upwey 7 miles

Bus: Visit traveline.info

Tel: 0370 333 1181

ACQ.1922

Parking charged (not English Heritage).

Caution: steep slopes.

MAP PAGE 325 (5H)
OS MAP 194, OL15: SY573848

CHRISTCHURCH CASTLE AND NORMAN HOUSE
DORSET – BH23 1AS

Remains of Christchurch Castle, including parts of the keep and the 12th-century riverside 'Constable's House' – a very early example of domestic architecture with a rare Norman chimney. The important priory church is nearby.

OPENING TIMES
Any reasonable daylight hours

VISIT US
Direction: Located in Christchurch, near the Priory

Train: Christchurch ¾ mile

Bus: Visit traveline.info

Tel: 0370 333 1181

ACQ.1946

On-street parking.

Caution: deep water, steep slopes, steep stairs.

MAP PAGE 325 (5J)
OS MAP 195, OL22: SZ160927

FIDDLEFORD MANOR
DORSET – DT10 2BX

The principal parts of a small stone manor house, probably begun c. 1370 for William Latimer, Sheriff of Somerset and Dorset. The hall and solar chamber display outstanding timber roofs.

Please note: The adjoining building is a private residence and is not open to visitors.

OPENING TIMES
1 Apr-30 Sep, daily	10am-6pm
1 Oct-31 Mar, daily	10am-4pm
24-26 Dec & 1 Jan	Closed

VISIT US
Direction: 1 mile E of Sturminster Newton off A357

Bus: Visit traveline.info for the latest bus timetables and routes

ACQ.1961

Disabled access (ground floor only – with 1 step).

Free car park. Not suitable for large coaches.

Caution: deep water, steep stairs.

MAP PAGE 325 (4H)
OS MAP 194, 129: ST801136

JORDAN HILL ROMAN TEMPLE
DORSET – DT3 6PL

The foundations of a 4th-century AD Romano-British temple.

OPENING TIMES
Any reasonable daylight hours

VISIT US
Direction: Located 2 miles NE of Weymouth, off A353

Train: Upwey or Weymouth, 2 miles

Bus: Visit traveline.info for the latest bus timetables and routes

Tel: 0370 333 1181

ACQ.1933

On-street parking.

MAP PAGE 325 (5H)
OS MAP 194, OL15: SY699821

KINGSTON RUSSELL STONE CIRCLE

DORSET – DT3 4JX

A late Neolithic or early Bronze Age circle of 18 fallen stones, on a hilltop overlooking Abbotsbury and the sea.

OPENING TIMES

Any reasonable daylight hours

VISIT US

Direction: Turn left off Bishop's Road, approximately 1½ miles NE of Abbotsbury, immediately after the 90° right-hand bend

Train: Weymouth (1½ miles) or Dorchester South/West (8 miles)

Bus: Visit traveline.info for the latest bus timetables and routes

ACQ.1887

Limited parking on road verge at entrance to farm. Access to stone circle on foot only via public footpaths, approx. ½ mile. No off-road vehicle access.

Cattle and sheep may be grazing around footpaths to site.

> MAP PAGE 325 (5H)
> OS MAP 194, OL15: SY578878

KNOWLTON CHURCH AND EARTHWORKS

DORSET – BH21 5AE

A ruined medieval church stands at the centre of a large prehistoric henge, part of an important cluster of Neolithic and early Bronze Age monuments.

KNOWLTON CHURCH AND EARTHWORKS

OPENING TIMES

Any reasonable daylight hours

VISIT US

Direction: SW of Cranborne on Lumber Lane off B3078

Bus: Visit traveline.info for the latest bus timetables and routes

ACQ.1959

Parking limited.

Caution: steep slopes.

> MAP PAGE 325 (5J)
> OS MAP 195, 118: SU024103

MAIDEN CASTLE

DORSET – DT2 9PP

Among the largest Iron Age hillforts in Europe, Maiden Castle's huge multiple ramparts enclose an area equivalent to 50 football pitches. Excavations have revealed the site's 6,000-year history, from Neolithic ritual to late Roman times. Download the free audio experience, 'Echoscape', from our website.

OPENING TIMES

Any reasonable daylight hours

VISIT US

Direction: 2 miles S of Dorchester, off A354, N of bypass

Train: Dorchester South/West (2 miles)

MAIDEN CASTLE

Bus: Visit traveline.info for the latest bus timetables and routes

Tel: 0370 333 1181

ACQ.1908

Caution: unguarded drops.

> MAP PAGE 325 (5H)
> OS MAP 194, OL15: SY669884

THE NINE STONES

DORSET – DT2 9LX

Small late Neolithic circle of nine standing stones, now in a wooded glade. Winterbourne Poor Lot Barrows (p.120) are nearby.

Please note: Site not accessible at present. See website for re-opening date.

OPENING TIMES

Any reasonable daylight hours

VISIT US

ACQ.1895

Please note: permissive footpath to site parallel to A35 currently closed.

Caution: beware of traffic.

> MAP PAGE 325 (5H)
> OS MAP 194, OL15/117: SY611904

THE PERFECT GIFT

Give the gift of membership and you'll be giving friends and family the opportunity to enjoy the fantastic benefits of becoming a member of English Heritage.

Visit: english-heritage.org.uk/join/the-gift-of-membership

PORTLAND CASTLE

———— DORSET – DT5 1AZ ————

Overlooking and defending Portland harbour, this coastal artillery fortress was built by Henry VIII to counter threats from France and Spain. It retains its squat, rounded, seaward form, designed to deflect incoming cannon shot.

Much fought over during the Civil War, Portland Castle was taken and retaken several times by both Parliamentarians and Royalists. It later protected shipping against pirates, and vainly tried to control the local smuggling industry, before 'standing-to' again when Napoleonic invasion loomed.

Following a spell as a private home, it became a station for seaplanes flying anti-submarine patrols during the First World War. During the Second World War it served as an ordnance store and accommodation for British and American soldiers. In 1944 British and American forces carried out top-secret preliminary training for the D-Day landings in nearby bays.

Experience the fort's long and varied story through presentations, interactive exhibits and an audio tour. Be sure to visit the Tudor kitchen, armoury and gun decks. The Governor's Garden, designed by Christopher Bradley-Hole as part of the Contemporary Heritage Garden series, is a perfectly sheltered spot to enjoy the dramatic sea and harbour views.

Enjoy refreshments in the Captain's House Tearoom, including a range of home-made sandwiches, cakes and snacks made with locally sourced ingredients.

OPENING TIMES

1 Apr-30 Oct, daily	10am-5pm
31 Oct-31 Mar	Closed

Last entry 30 mins before closing

Parts of the castle may be closed if an event is booked. Please call the site in advance or check website

VISIT US

Direction: Overlooking Portland Harbour in Castletown, Isle of Portland

Train: Weymouth 4½ miles

Bus: Visit traveline.info

Tel: 01305 820539

Local Tourist Information:
Portland: 01305 821361

NON-MEMBERS

Adult £7.80 | Concession £7.00 | Child £4.70
Family 2 Adults £20.30 | Family 1 Adult £12.50

Disabled access – Captain's House, parts of ground floor of castle (no lift available to other parts) and Governor's Garden.

Parking: charges apply to non-members, free for Members with valid English Heritage car sticker.

Captain's House Tearoom closes 1 hour before the castle.

New guidebook.

MAP PAGE 325 (6H)
OS MAP 194, OL15: SY685744

SHERBORNE OLD CASTLE DORSET – DT9 3SA

WINTERBOURNE POOR LOT BARROWS
DORSET – DT2 9EB

A 'cemetery' of 44 Bronze Age burial mounds of varying types and sizes, by the A35 main road.

OPENING TIMES
Any reasonable daylight hours

VISIT US
Direction: 2 miles W of Winterbourne Abbas, S of junction of A35 with a minor road to Compton Valence. Access via Longlands Lane – 1 mile east of site south of A35

Train: Dorchester West or South, both 7 miles

Bus: Visit traveline.info for the latest bus timetables and routes

ACQ.1961

Park on roadside approx. 1 mile south along Longlands Lane, follow public right of way, Jubilee Trail for 1 mile (approx.) west over farmland.

MAP PAGE 325 (5H)
OS MAP 194, OL15/117:
SY590907

Originally a fortified 12th-century bishop's palace, Sherborne Old Castle became the home of Sir Walter Ralegh. Later a powerful Royalist base, it saw fierce fighting during the Civil War. Look out for wildlife in the grounds. Refreshed interpretation panels.

OPENING TIMES
Please note that Sherborne Old Castle will be undergoing conservation/maintenance works. There may be restrictions to opening times and temporary access arrangements. Please check website for details

VISIT US
Direction: Situated at the end of Castleton Road, off B3145

Train: Sherborne ¾ mile

Bus: Visit traveline.info for the latest bus timetables and routes

Local Tourist Information: Sherborne: 01935 815341

NON-MEMBERS
Adult **£6.60** I Concession **£5.90**
Child **£4.00** I Family 2 Adults **£17.20**
Family 1 Adult **£10.60**

ACQ.1956 OVP

Refreshments available.

Parking: charges apply to non-members, free for Members with valid English Heritage car sticker.

Secure cycle parking available.
National network route 26.

MAP PAGE 325 (4H)
OS MAP 183, 129: ST648168

CHECK ONLINE
Pre-booking for visits to our staffed sites may be required, check our website for the latest guidance.

BELAS KNAP LONG BARROW
GLOUCESTERSHIRE – GL54 5AL

A particularly fine restored example of a Neolithic long barrow: remains of 31 people were found in the chambers.

Managed by Gloucestershire County Council.

OPENING TIMES
Any reasonable daylight hours

VISIT US
Direction: Near Charlton Abbots; ½ mile on Cotswold Way

Train: Cheltenham 9 miles

Bus: Visit traveline.info for the latest bus timetables and routes

ACQ.1928 🐕 💺 P ⚠

Parking with ½ mile steep walk to monument.

Caution: unguarded drops.

> MAP PAGE 325 (1J)
> OS MAP 163, OL45: SP021254

CIRENCESTER AMPHITHEATRE
GLOUCESTERSHIRE – GL7 1XW

Earthwork remains of one of the largest Roman amphitheatres in Britain, serving the Roman city of Corinium (now Cirencester).

Managed by Cirencester Town Council.

OPENING TIMES
Any reasonable daylight hours

VISIT US
Direction: Located W of Cirencester, next to the bypass. Access from the town, or along Chesterton Lane from the W end of the bypass, onto Cotswold Ave

Train: Kemble 4 miles

Bus: Visit traveline.info for the latest bus timetables and routes

ACQ.1973 💺 P ⚠

Caution: steep slopes.

> MAP PAGE 325 (2J)
> OS MAP 163, OL45/169: SP020014

GLOUCESTER, BLACKFRIARS
GLOUCESTERSHIRE – GL1 2HS

Among the most complete surviving friaries of Dominican 'black friars' in England, finished in about 1270. After the Dissolution, it was converted into a Tudor mansion and cloth factory, but its medieval features are now visible again. There's a magnificent 13th-century scissor-braced timber roof over the former friars' library.

Managed by Gloucester City Council.

GLOUCESTER, BLACKFRIARS

OPENING TIMES
1 Apr-30 Sep, Sun-Tue	10am-3pm
25 Dec & 1 Jan	Closed
Oct-Mar by appointment only	

VISIT US
Direction: In Blackfriars Lane, off Ladybellegate St, off Southgate St, Gloucester

Train: Gloucester ½ mile

Bus: Visit traveline.info for the latest bus timetables and routes

Tel: 01452 503050

ACQ.1955 💺 🐕 ▲ ⚤ 💺 P ⚠

Civil wedding ceremonies (through Gloucester City Council). Parking adjacent. (Charge applies. Not managed by English Heritage). Caution: steep stairs. New guidebook.

> MAP PAGE 325 (1H)
> OS MAP 162, 179: SO829184

GLOUCESTER, GREYFRIARS
GLOUCESTERSHIRE – GL1 1TS

Substantial remains of a medieval friary church of Franciscan 'grey friars', rebuilt in the early 16th century.

OPENING TIMES
Any reasonable daylight hours

VISIT US
Direction: On Greyfriars Walk

Train: Gloucester ½ mile

Bus: Visit traveline.info for the latest bus timetables and routes

ACQ.1969 💺 🐕 ⚠

Caution: falling masonry.

> MAP PAGE 325 (1H)
> OS MAP 162, 179: SO832184

HAILES ABBEY

GLOUCESTERSHIRE – GL54 5PB

Set in lovely Cotswold countryside, Hailes Abbey was one of medieval England's most renowned pilgrim shrines. The strikingly presented museum displays the abbey's treasures and tells the intriguing story of the 'Holy Blood of Hailes'.

The Cistercian abbey was founded in 1246 by Richard Earl of Cornwall, Henry III's younger brother and among the richest men in Europe. It became a major pilgrimage destination after 1270, when Richard's son Edmund presented it with a sensational relic – allegedly no less than a phial of Christ's own blood – Pilgrims flocked to its shrine and financed the rebuilding of the abbey on a magnificent scale. The ruins, picturesquely 'soft-capped' with turf for preservation, include cloister buildings and the footprint of the church, which was inspired by Westminster Abbey.

In the 1530s its relic was denounced as a fake, and the abbey was suppressed by Henry VIII and comprehensively looted. The outstanding museum helps you imagine it in all its glory. You can see lavish sculpture, heraldic floor tiles and even one of the oldest surviving medieval spectacle frames. More artefacts are displayed in a miniature glass 'cloister'.

Nearby, the delightful little parish church houses stained glass and tiles from the abbey, and outstanding medieval wall paintings.

Owned by the National Trust, managed and maintained by English Heritage.

OPENING TIMES

1 Apr-30 Oct, Wed-Sun & Bank Hols	10am-5pm
31 Oct-31 Mar, Sat-Sun	10am-4pm
24-26 Dec & 1 Jan	Closed

Last entry 30 mins before closing

VISIT US

Direction: 2 miles NE of Winchcombe off B4632. On the Cotswold Way National Trail

Train: Cheltenham 10 miles. From March to October, Hayles Abbey Halt (600m from site) can be reached from Cheltenham, Winchcombe or Broadway by diesel railcar on the Gloucestershire and Warwickshire Steam Railway. See **gwsr.com** for timetables and prices

Bus: Visit traveline.info for the latest bus timetables and routes

Tel: 01242 602398

NON-MEMBERS

Adult **£7.80** | Concession **£7.00** | Child **£4.70** Family 2 Adults **£20.30** | Family 1 Adult **£12.50**

National Trust members free, but charged for audio tour (£1) and special events

Disabled access (ramp to museum, disabled toilet).
Refreshments available.

MAP PAGE 325 (1J)
OS MAP 150/163, OL45: SP050300

GREAT WITCOMBE ROMAN VILLA

GLOUCESTERSHIRE – GL3 4TW

Remains of a large and luxurious Roman villa built c. AD 250, with a bath-house and possibly the shrine of a water spirit.

OPENING TIMES

Exterior:

1 Apr-30 Sep, daily	10am-6pm
1 Oct-31 Mar, daily	10am-4pm

There is no access to the buildings, which house the mosaics

VISIT US

Direction: Located 5 miles SE of Gloucester off Cirencester Road; 400 metres (440 yards) from Cotswold Way National Trail

Train: Gloucester 6 miles

Bus: Visit traveline.info

ACQ.1919 ⊀ P ⚠

Parking: charges apply to non-members, free for Members with valid car sticker. No access for coaches. No parking anywhere on the access tracks. 300-metre walk to site.

Caution: steep slopes, unguarded drops, falling masonry.

MAP PAGE 325 (2J)
OS MAP 163, 179: SO899142

KINGSWOOD ABBEY GATEHOUSE

GLOUCESTERSHIRE – GL12 8RS

This 16th-century gatehouse, sole survivor of a Cistercian abbey, is one of the latest monastic buildings in England. Displays a richly sculpted window.

OPENING TIMES

Exterior: Reasonable daylight hours

See website for details of events and access to interior

VISIT US

Direction: In Kingswood, off B4060; 1 mile SW of Wotton-under-Edge

Train: Yate 8 miles

Bus: Visit traveline.info

ACQ.1950 ⊗ P

On-street parking.

MAP PAGE 325 (2H)
OS MAP 162/172, 167: ST747920

NYMPSFIELD LONG BARROW

GLOUCESTERSHIRE – GL11 5AU

Large Neolithic burial mound with spectacular views over the Severn Valley. Its burial chambers are uncovered for viewing.

Managed by Gloucestershire County Council.

OPENING TIMES

Any reasonable daylight hours

VISIT US

Direction: Located 1 mile NW of Nympsfield on B4066

Train: Stroud 5 miles

Bus: Visit traveline.info for the latest bus timetables and routes

ACQ.1975 ⊀ P

MAP PAGE 325 (2H)
OS MAP 162, 167/168: SO794013

ODDA'S CHAPEL

GLOUCESTERSHIRE – GL19 4BX

Among the most complete Saxon churches in England, built in 1056 by Earl Odda and rediscovered in 1865. Deerhurst's Saxon parish church is nearby.

OPENING TIMES

1 Apr-30 Sep, daily	10am-6pm
1 Oct-31 Mar, daily	10am-4pm
24-26 Dec & 1 Jan	Closed

VISIT US

Direction: Located in Deerhurst off B4213, at Abbots Court; SW of parish church

Train: Cheltenham 8 miles

Bus: Visit traveline.info for the latest bus timetables and routes

ACQ.1962 ⊗ P

Parking (charges apply, not English Heritage).

MAP PAGE 325 (1J)
OS MAP 150, 179: SO869298

OFFA'S DYKE

GLOUCESTERSHIRE – NP16 7JR

Three-mile wooded section of the great 8th-century boundary dyke built by Offa, King of Mercia. Includes the Devil's Pulpit, with fine views of Tintern Abbey.

OPENING TIMES

Any reasonable daylight hours

VISIT US

Direction: Located 3 miles NE of Chepstow, off B4228. Via Tidenham Forestry Commission car park. 1 mile walk (waymarked) down to the Devil's Pulpit on Offa's Dyke

Train: Chepstow 7 miles

Bus: Visit traveline.info for the latest bus timetables and routes

ACQ.1973 ⊀ P ⚠

Parking (not English Heritage).

Caution: steep slopes, unguarded drops, steep stairs.

Strong footwear is recommended.

MAP PAGE 325 (2H)
OS MAP 162, OL14/167
SO546011-ST549975

OVER BRIDGE

GLOUCESTERSHIRE – GL2 8BZ

A single-arch stone bridge spanning the River Severn, built in 1825-30 by the great engineer Thomas Telford.

OPENING TIMES

Any reasonable daylight hours

VISIT US

Direction: 1 mile NW of Gloucester, at junction of A40 (Ross) and A417 (Ledbury)

Train: Gloucester 2 miles

Bus: Visit traveline.info for the latest bus timetables and routes

ACQ.1978 ⊀ ⚠

Caution: deep water, steep slopes.

MAP PAGE 325 (1H)
OS MAP 162, 179: SO816196

ST BRIAVELS CASTLE

GLOUCESTERSHIRE – GL15 6RG

Well-preserved castle, former hunting lodge of King John, with fine gatehouse built by Edward I in 1292 and late Victorian restoration. Now a youth hostel.

OPENING TIMES

Exterior (moat area):
Any reasonable daylight hours

Inner Bailey (grounds only):
1 Apr-30 Oct, daily   1pm-4pm

Limited access to interior as working youth hostel (call in advance to check)

VISIT US

Direction: In St Briavels; 7 miles NE of Chepstow off B4228

Train: Lydney 6 miles; Chepstow 8 miles

Bus: Visit traveline.info for the latest bus timetables and routes

Tel: 01594 530272 (Youth Hostel)

ACQ.1982 🚻 👥 🐕 P 🍴 ⚠

Caution: falling masonry.

Please do not climb on the walls.

MAP PAGE 325 (2H)
OS MAP 162, OL14: SO559046

ST MARY'S CHURCH, KEMPLEY

GLOUCESTERSHIRE – GL18 2AT

ST MARY'S CHURCH, KEMPLEY

Delightful Norman church, displaying one of the most complete sets of medieval wall paintings in England, dating from the 12th to 15th centuries (and recently conserved by our Members' wall paintings appeal).

Managed in association with the Friends of Kempley Church.

OPENING TIMES

1 Apr-31 Oct, daily	10am-6pm
Nov & Feb, Sat-Sun	10am-4pm
1-31 Mar, daily	10am-6pm

Dec-Jan by appointment only

VISIT US

Direction: 1 mile N of Kempley off B4024; 6 miles NE of Ross-on-Wye

Train: Ledbury 8 miles

Bus: Visit traveline.info for the latest bus timetables and routes

Email: freetoenter.sites@english-heritage.org.uk for group bookings

ACQ.1979 ♿ 🐕 P

Audio tour available from website.

Parking (in lay-by). Disabled access (1 step).

MAP PAGE 325 (1H)
OS MAP 149, 189: SO670313

ULEY LONG BARROW (HETTY PEGLER'S TUMP)

GLOUCESTERSHIRE – GL11 5AR

Restored Neolithic chambered mound, 37 metres (121 feet) long, atmospherically sited overlooking the Severn Valley. The internal chambers are accessible through a very low entrance.

Managed by Gloucestershire County Council.

ULEY LONG BARROW

OPENING TIMES

Any reasonable daylight hours

VISIT US

Direction: Located 3½ miles NE of Dursley, on B4066. Take care crossing road

Train: Stroud 6 miles

Bus: Visit traveline.info for the latest bus timetables and routes

ACQ.1883 🐕 P ⚠

Parking (in lay-by).

Warning: cross road with care.

Caution: steep slopes.

Note: visitors are advised to bring a torch.

MAP PAGE 325 (2H)
OS MAP 162, 167/168: SO790000

WINDMILL TUMP LONG BARROW, RODMARTON

GLOUCESTERSHIRE – GL7 6PU

A Neolithic chambered tomb with an enigmatic 'false entrance'.

Managed by Gloucestershire County Council.

OPENING TIMES

Any reasonable daylight hours

VISIT US

Direction: 1 mile SW of Rodmarton on Oathill Lane

Train: Kemble 5 miles

Bus: Visit traveline.info for the latest bus timetables and routes

ACQ.1979 🐕 P

Parking in lay-by.

MAP PAGE 325 (2J)
OS MAP 163, 168: ST933973

CLEEVE ABBEY

—— SOMERSET – TA23 0PS ——

Gain a vivid insight into monastic life at Cleeve Abbey and admire its strikingly displayed tiled pavement.

Atmospheric Cleeve Abbey boasts the most impressively complete and unaltered set of monastic cloister buildings in England. Standing roofed and two storeys high, they include the gatehouse, the 15th-century refectory with its glorious angel roof, and an unusual 'painted chamber'. The great dormitory is one of the finest in the country. Beneath it are the vaulted warming room, and the sacristy with early 13th-century tilework and decoration.

Cleeve's crowning glory is the magnificent tiled floor of its earliest refectory. Decked from end to end with high-quality heraldic tiles dating from around 1270, it's the only large-scale survival of a decorated medieval monastic refectory floor in Britain. Its royal and baronial heraldry celebrates the abbey's wealthy patrons. Buried in the late 15th century and rediscovered in 1876, it had suffered from exposure to the elements. Now it's displayed within a purpose-built timber shelter, complete with seating and viewing platforms.

An exhibition and touchscreen virtual tour tell the story of abbey life. A story bag, 'Brother Cedric and the Missing Sheep', is a fun way for families to explore the abbey.

OPENING TIMES

1 Apr-30 Oct, Wed-Sun & Bank Hols	10am-5pm
31 Oct-31 Mar	Closed
Last entry 30 mins before closing	

VISIT US

Direction: Located in Washford, ¼ mile S of A39

Train: Washford ½ mile (West Somerset Steam Railway)

Bus: Visit traveline.info for the latest bus timetables and routes

Tel: 01984 640377

Local Tourist Information: Watchet: 01984 632101

NON-MEMBERS

Adult £7.80 I Concession £7.00 I Child £4.70
Family 2 Adults £20.30 I Family 1 Adult £12.50

ACQ.1951

Disabled access (grounds and ground floor only, plus toilet).

Dogs on leads (in grounds only).

Refreshments available.

MAP PAGE 325 (4F)
OS MAP 181, OL9: ST047407

DAW'S CASTLE

SOMERSET – TA23 0JP

Clifftop fortress begun by King Alfred to defend the people of Watchet against Viking attacks.

OPENING TIMES

Any reasonable daylight hours

VISIT US

Direction: ½ mile W of Watchet off B3191

Train: Watchet (West Somerset railway) ¾ mile

Bus: Visit traveline.info for the latest bus timetables and routes

ACQ.1983 🐾 🐄 ⚠

Parking in Watchet (paid, not English Heritage) and walk ½ mile via SW Coastal Path.

Caution: steep slopes.

MAP PAGE 325 (4F)
OS MAP 181, OL9: SS989432

DUNSTER, BUTTER CROSS

SOMERSET – TA24 6RT

The repositioned stump of a medieval stone cross, once a meeting place for butter sellers.

Managed by the National Trust on behalf of English Heritage.

OPENING TIMES

Any reasonable daylight hours

VISIT US

Direction: Beside minor road to Alcombe, 350 metres (400 yards) NW of Dunster parish church

Train: Dunster (West Somerset Railway) 1 mile

Bus: Visit traveline.info for the latest bus timetables and routes

ACQ.1951 🐾 P ⚠

Parking in village (charged).

Caution: beware of traffic.

MAP PAGE 325 (4F)
OS MAP 181, OL9: ST823604

DUNSTER, GALLOX BRIDGE

SOMERSET – TA24 6SR

This ancient stone bridge – originally 'gallows bridge' – once carried packhorses bringing fleeces to Dunster market.

Managed by the National Trust on behalf of English Heritage.

OPENING TIMES

Any reasonable daylight hours

VISIT US

Direction: Located off A396 at the S end of Dunster village

Train: Dunster ¾ mile (West Somerset Railway)

Bus: Visit traveline.info for the latest bus timetables and routes

ACQ.1951 ♿ 🐾 P ⚠

Parking in village (charged).

Caution: deep water.

MAP PAGE 325 (4F)
OS MAP 181, OL9: SS989432

DUNSTER, YARN MARKET

SOMERSET – TA24 6SG

This fine 17th-century timber-framed octagonal market hall is a monument to Dunster's once-flourishing cloth trade.

Managed by the National Trust on behalf of English Heritage.

OPENING TIMES

Any reasonable daylight hours

VISIT US

Direction: In Dunster High St

Train: Dunster (West Somerset Railway) ½ mile

Bus: Visit traveline.info for the latest bus timetables and routes

ACQ.1951 ♿ 🐾 P ⚠

Parking in village (charged).

Caution: beware of traffic, falling masonry.

MAP PAGE 325 (4F)
OS MAP 181, OL9: SS992438

While in the region, why not visit **Stonehenge**, one of the wonders of the world and the best-known prehistoric monument in Europe. There's a world-class visitor centre, plus a spacious shop and café.

See **p.138** for details.

FARLEIGH HUNGERFORD CASTLE

SOMERSET – BA2 7RS

Sir Thomas Hungerford, Speaker of the Commons, began this fortified mansion in the 1370s. It was extended in the 15th century by his son Walter, Lord Hungerford, distinguished soldier and statesman. Remains include two tall corner towers and a complete chapel, displaying family monuments and wall paintings. You can still see many Hungerford coffins in its crypt, some with 'death masks'.

The remarkable Hungerford family included two members executed during the Wars of the Roses and another – who imprisoned his wife here for four years – beheaded by Henry VIII. A Tudor Lady Hungerford burnt her murdered husband's body in the kitchen furnace.

Discover Farleigh's story through an audio tour and extensive displays in the Priests' House. There's a virtual tour for disabled visitors, family and educational facilities, and a schools base.

🎬 *The White Princess* (2017).

OPENING TIMES

1 Apr-30 Oct, daily	10am-5pm
31 Oct-31 Mar, Sat-Sun	10am-4pm
24-26 Dec & 1 Jan	Closed
Last entry 30 mins before closing	

VISIT US

Direction: In Farleigh Hungerford, 9 miles SE of Bath; 3½ miles W of Trowbridge on A366

Train: Avoncliffe 2 miles; Trowbridge 3½ miles

Bus: Visit traveline.info for the latest bus timetables and routes

Tel: 01225 754026

Local Tourist Information: Trowbridge: 01225 710535

NON-MEMBERS

Adult **£6.60** | Concession **£5.90**
Child **£4.00** | Family 2 Adults **£17.20**
Family 1 Adult **£10.60**

ACQ.1915 🎧 ♿ 🍴 ■ E ♿ 🖥 🧍
🧍 P 🎪 📷 ⚠ OVP

Dogs on leads (grounds only).
Refreshments available.

MAP PAGE 325 (3H)
OS MAP 173, 143/156: ST801576

GLASTONBURY TRIBUNAL

SOMERSET – BA6 9DP

A fine 15th-century merchant's house and shop, probably built for Glastonbury Abbey, with an early Tudor facade, bay window and panelled interiors.

Managed by Glastonbury Antiquarian Society.

OPENING TIMES

1 Apr-31 Mar, Sat & Sun	12pm-4pm
25 Dec	Closed

VISIT US

Direction: In Glastonbury High St

Bus: Visit traveline.info for the latest bus timetables and routes

NON-MEMBERS

Museum
Please see website for details

ACQ.1932 🏛 ♿ P ⚠

Disabled access (ground floor – 2 steps).
Parking (charged, not English Heritage).
Caution: steep stairs.

MAP PAGE 325 (4H)
OS MAP 182/183, 141: ST499389

SHARE THE FUN

Check our website for up-to-the-minute information on our year-long programme of events.

english-heritage.org.uk/events

MEARE FISH HOUSE

SOMERSET – BA6 9SP

A unique survivor both in function and design, this housed the keeper of medieval Glastonbury Abbey's (then) adjacent fishery lake.

OPENING TIMES

Any reasonable daylight hours.
Key available from Manor House farm

VISIT US

Direction: In Meare village, on B3151

Bus: Visit traveline.info for the latest bus timetables and routes

ACQ.1911

Parking (in village on Muddy Lane).

MAP PAGE 325 (4G)
OS MAP 182, 141: ST458417

NUNNEY CASTLE

SOMERSET – BA11 4LW

A striking moated tower-house castle, built in the 1370s by Sir John de la Mere. Held by Royalists during the Civil War, it fell to Parliamentarian cannon, the damaged portion finally collapsing on Christmas Day 1910.

OPENING TIMES

Any reasonable daylight hours

VISIT US

Direction: Located in Nunney, 3½ miles SW of Frome, off A361 (no coach access)

Train: Frome 3½ miles

Bus: Visit traveline.info for the latest bus timetables and routes

ACQ.1926

Parking (not English Heritage).
Caution: deep water, steep slopes.
Please do not climb on the walls.

MAP PAGE 325 (4H)
OS MAP 183, 142: ST737457

MUCHELNEY ABBEY   SOMERSET – TA10 0DQ

There's a lot to enjoy at atmospheric Muchelney Abbey, set amid the Somerset Levels. Beside the foundations of this wealthy medieval Benedictine abbey (and its Anglo-Saxon predecessor) stands the abbots' lodgings, a complete early Tudor house. This includes a magnificent chamber with ornate fireplace and stained glass, rooms with wall paintings imitating cloth hangings, timber-roofed kitchens and parts of the richly decorated cloister walk. Don't miss the thatched two-storey monks' lavatory, unique in Britain.

New displays trace the abbey's history and highlight finds from the site. There's a touchscreen tour for visitors with mobility issues, and a new family trail.

The nearby parish church (with 17th-century painted ceiling) and medieval Priest's House are not managed by English Heritage.

OPENING TIMES

1 Apr-30 Oct, Wed-Sun & Bank Hols	10am-5pm
31 Oct-31 Mar	Closed

Last entry 30 mins before closing

VISIT US

Direction: In Muchelney, 2 miles S of Langport via Huish Episcopi

Bus: Visit traveline.info for the latest bus timetables and routes

Cycle: Sustrans: National Route 339

Tel: 01458 250664

Local Tourist Information:
Langport: 01458 253527

NON-MEMBERS

Adult **£7.80** I Concession **£7.00**
Child **£4.70** I Family 2 Adults **£20.30**
Family 1 Adult **£12.50**

ACQ.1927

Disabled access (grounds and most of ground floor, adapted toilet).

Refreshments available.

New guidebook.

MAP PAGE 325 (4G)
OS MAP 193, 129: ST429249

BRADFORD-ON-AVON TITHE BARN

WILTSHIRE – BA15 1LF

A spectacular monastic stone barn, 51 metres (168 feet) long and 10 metres (33 feet) wide. Its magnificent timber-cruck roof supports a hundred tons of stone roof tiles.

Built in the early 14th century as part of a 'grange' or outlying farm belonging to Shaftesbury Abbey, the richest nunnery in England, it was in use until 1974.

Managed by Bradford-on-Avon Preservation Trust.

OPENING TIMES

1 Apr-31 Mar, daily	10.30am-4pm
24-26 Dec & 1 Jan	Closed

Barn may be closed during local events. Check English Heritage website for details

VISIT US

Direction: Located ½ mile S of town centre off B3109

Train: Bradford-on-Avon ½ mile

Bus: Visit traveline.info for the latest bus timetables and routes

ACQ.1939

Parking (adjacent, not managed by English Heritage – charge applies).

MAP PAGE 325 (3H)
OS MAP 173, 156: ST823604

BRATTON CAMP AND WHITE HORSE

WILTSHIRE – BA13 4TA

Bratton Camp is an Iron Age hillfort, which enclosed an earlier Neolithic long barrow and a Bronze Age burial mound as well as a 'town' of huts, stores and workshops. Below it stands the Westbury White Horse. Cut in 1778, this replaced an earlier horse, perhaps made in the late 1600s to commemorate King Alfred's decisive victory over the Vikings at 'Ethandun', probably fought nearby in AD 878.

OPENING TIMES

Any reasonable daylight hours

VISIT US

Direction: 2 miles E of Westbury off B3098, 1 mile SW of Bratton

Train: Westbury 3 miles

Bus: Visit traveline.info for the latest bus timetables and routes

ACQ.1930

Parking (not English Heritage).

Caution: steep slopes.

MAP PAGE 325 (3J)
OS MAP 184, 143: ST900516

CHISBURY CHAPEL

WILTSHIRE – SN8 3JA

An appealing thatched and flint-walled chapel, with the remains of fine windows and plasterwork and a 'consecration cross' within. It was built by the lord of Chisbury Manor in the 13th century, both as a symbol of his status and to save his tenants the inconvenient journey to Great Bedwyn parish church. In use until 1547, it later served as a barn. Set by the earthwork defences of Iron Age Chisbury Camp.

OPENING TIMES

Any reasonable daylight hours

VISIT US

Direction: 300m walk off unclassified road, ¼ mile E of Chisbury, off A4; 6 miles E of Marlborough

Train: Bedwyn 1 mile

Bus: Visit traveline.info for the latest bus timetables and routes

ACQ.1982

Parking (in lay-by).

MAP PAGE 325 (3K)
OS MAP 174, 157: SU280660

HATFIELD EARTHWORKS (MARDEN HENGE)

WILTSHIRE – SN10 3RL

The earthworks of one of the largest Neolithic henges in Britain. The outer enclosure, raised in about 2500 BC, is formed on three sides by a bank and ditch, and on the other by a loop in the river Avon. Within is a second Neolithic henge, and the scanty remains of a monumental mound, once allegedly over 64 metres (210 feet) in diameter and a smaller version of Silbury Hill (p.135).

Excavations at the henge in 1969 and 2010 revealed evidence of Neolithic activity here. Ongoing research by the University of Reading is revealing more about this important site, and has recently suggested that the great sarsen stones used at Stonehenge were hauled through Marden on their way from the Marlborough Downs to Stonehenge, 10 miles away.

OPENING TIMES

Any reasonable daylight hours.
Note: Only a small section of henge accessible, marked with a fingerpost

VISIT US

Direction: 5½ miles SE of Devizes, off A342; NE of village of Marden. Look for the fingerpost

Train: Pewsey 5 miles

Bus: Visit traveline.info for the latest bus timetables and routes

[ACQ.1972] 🐕 🐎 ⚠

Caution: steep slopes, beware of traffic.

MAP PAGE 325 (3J)
OS MAP 173, 130: SU092583

LUDGERSHALL CASTLE AND CROSS

WILTSHIRE – SP11 9QT

Ruins and extensive earthworks of a mainly 12th- to 14th-century royal castle, including a 'strong tower' probably built by King John and a hall and royal apartments added by Henry III. More a palatial hunting lodge than a fortress, Ludgershall was favoured by Plantagenet kings from Henry II to Edward III as a resting place on their travels to the west, and a base for hunting in Savernake Forest.

The remains of a market cross stand at the centre of the village, once an important medieval market town which elected two MPs.

OPENING TIMES

Any reasonable daylight hours

VISIT US

Direction: Located on the N side of Ludgershall, off A342

Train: Andover 7 miles

Bus: Visit traveline.info for the latest bus timetables and routes

[ACQ.1915] Castle

[ACQ.1952] Cross

🐕 P 🏞 ⚠

Parking (limited).

Caution: steep slopes.

Please do not climb on the walls.

MAP PAGE 325 (3K)
OS MAP 184/185, 131: SU264512

NETHERAVON DOVECOTE

WILTSHIRE – SP4 9RH

A charming early 18th-century brick dovecote, with a pyramid roof and dormer windows. It still contains most of its 700 or more nesting boxes for doves or pigeons.

Dovecotes were 'living larders', providing fresh meat in winter as well as eggs and fertiliser, but their occupants ravaged surrounding crops, and until 1761 only important landowners could build them.

OPENING TIMES

Exterior viewing from nearby Millenium Park, as there is no access across the field in which the dovecote is situated

VISIT US

Direction: In Netheravon, 4½ miles N of Amesbury on A345

Train: Pewsey 9 miles, Grateley 11 miles

Bus: Visit traveline.info for the latest bus timetables and routes

[ACQ.1939] 🐕

MAP PAGE 325 (3J)
OS MAP 184, 130: SU147484

DON'T FORGET

Remember to take your membership card.

OLD WARDOUR CASTLE

———— WILTSHIRE – SP3 6RR ————

New interpretation and an interactive family game help you explore the tumultuous story of Old Wardour Castle and its owners.

Beautifully sited beside a lake, the castle was built by John, Lord Lovel in the late 14th century as a lightly fortified but luxurious residence. A hexagonal tower house ranged round a central courtyard, its design is unique in England. It also pioneered the inclusion of self-contained suites for noble guests.

Modernised by the staunchly Roman Catholic Arundell family, the castle saw much fighting during the Civil War. In 1643 the 61-year-old Lady Arundell, with a garrison of just 25 soldiers, had to surrender it to 1,300 Parliamentarians after a five-day siege. But the Parliamentarians were almost immediately besieged in turn by Royalists led by her son, Henry, Lord Arundell. After an eventful three-month siege, they finally capitulated in March 1644.

'Can you keep your castle?', a new family game, uses activities and challenges to follow the changing fortunes of the castle's owners.

The abandoned castle became a romantic ruin within the landscaped grounds of New Wardour Castle (not managed by English Heritage, no public access). Almost the last addition was the Georgian fantasy-Gothic Grotto, an artificial cave.

The castle is set in a Registered Landscape.

🎬 *Robin Hood; Prince of Thieves* (1991).

🔲 Licensed for civil wedding ceremonies

OPENING TIMES

1 Apr-30 Oct, daily	10am-5pm
31 Oct-31 Mar, Sat-Sun	10am-4pm
24-26 Dec & 1 Jan	Closed

Last entry 30 mins before closing

Parts of the castle may be closed if an event is booked. Please call site or check website for details

VISIT US

Direction: Located off A30 3½ miles SW of Tisbury. Also accessible from A350 (narrow rural roads). Coaches approach with care

Train: Tisbury 3½ miles

Bus: Visit traveline.info for the latest bus timetables and routes

Tel: 01747 870487

Local Tourist Information:
Shaftesbury: 01747 853514

NON-MEMBERS

Adult £6.60 | Concession £5.90 | Child £4.00
Family 2 Adults £17.20 | Family 1 Adult £10.60

ACQ.1936 🎧 📷 ♿ 🔱 🛡 🐾 📷 🔲 🚶 🔲 P
📷 📷 ♿ ⚠ OVP

Disabled access (grounds and ground floor only), disabled toilet.

Refreshments available.

MAP PAGE 325 (4J)
OS MAP 184, 118: ST939263

OLD SARUM

—— WILTSHIRE – SP1 3SD ——

Explore the lost city of Old Sarum, crowning a ridge with sweeping views towards Salisbury. Iron Age people raised its mighty prehistoric earthworks in about 500 BC, and within them Saxons and, most importantly, the Normans later settled.

In 1086 William the Conqueror summoned all the great landowners of England here to swear an oath of loyalty. A Norman castle on the inner mound was soon joined by a royal palace. By the mid-12th century a bustling town occupied much of the great earthwork, complete with a noble new Norman cathedral. An original copy of Magna Carta was sent to the cathedral in 1215, and can still be seen in its successor, Salisbury Cathedral.

However, soldiers and priests quarrelled, and life on the almost waterless hilltop became intolerable, so the settlement migrated downhill to what became Salisbury, where a new cathedral was founded in 1220. Thereafter Old Sarum went into steep decline, with its cathedral demolished and its castle abandoned. Though largely uninhabited, it continued to 'elect' two MPs until 1832, becoming the most notorious of the corrupt 'Rotten Boroughs' swept away by the Reform Act.

Today, the remains of the prehistoric fortress and of the Norman palace, castle and cathedral evoke echoes of thousands of years of history.

OPENING TIMES

1 Apr-30 Oct, daily	10am-5pm
31 Oct-31 Mar, daily	10am-4pm
24-25 Dec	Closed

Last entry 30 mins before closing

VISIT US

Direction: 2 miles N of Salisbury, off A345

Train: Salisbury 2 miles

Bus: Visit traveline.info for the latest bus timetables and routes; also Stonehenge Tour service. See thestonehengetour.info

Tel: 01722 335398

Local Tourist Information:
Salisbury: 01722 342860

NON-MEMBERS

Adult **£6.60** | Concession **£5.90** | Child **£4.00**
Family 2 Adults **£17.20** | Family 1 Adult **£10.60**

ACQ.1892

Disabled access (outer bailey and grounds only, disabled toilet).

Toilets located in the car park.

Parking: charges apply to non-members, free for Members with valid English Heritage car sticker.

Refreshments available.

MAP PAGE 325 (4J)
OS MAP 184, 130: SU138327

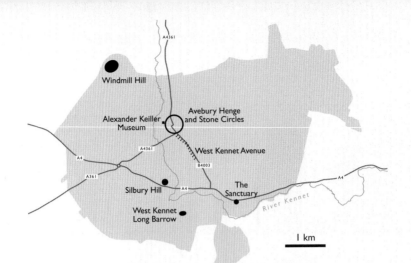

THE STONEHENGE, AVEBURY AND ASSOCIATED SITES WORLD HERITAGE SITE

Stonehenge and Avebury and their associated sites were inscribed onto the UNESCO World Heritage List in 1986. They stand alongside over 1,000 other outstanding sites across the world – such as the Great Wall of China and India's Taj Mahal – selected for their 'outstanding universal value' to all people.

Stonehenge and Avebury were chosen for their extraordinary prehistoric monuments. These help us to understand the Neolithic and Bronze Age world, and demonstrate around 2,000 years of continuous use and monument building between 3700 and 1600 BC.

A management plan for both the Avebury and Stonehenge parts of the World Heritage Site brings a whole range of organisations and individuals together, working in partnership to manage the site and protect its outstanding universal value.

Take time to visit both parts of the World Heritage Site and you will be well rewarded. At Stonehenge, displays in the spectacular visitor centre explore the evocative prehistoric landscape surrounding

this iconic monument. You can also view the rich collections in the Wiltshire Museum in Devizes and The Salisbury Museum, and learn more about the people who built the prehistoric monuments of the World Heritage Site. Experience a very different but equally rich visit to the Avebury area, with its many impressive prehistoric monuments and the Alexander Keiller Museum, displaying finds from the immediate region.

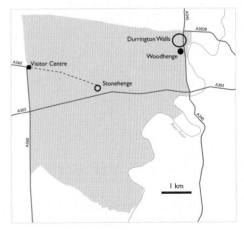

AVEBURY HENGE AND STONE CIRCLES

WILTSHIRE – SN8 1RF

AVEBURY, ALEXANDER KEILLER MUSEUM

WILTSHIRE – SN8 1RF

Opened in 1938, the museum was created by archaeologist and marmalade heir Alexander Keiller, who bought, saved, investigated and restored parts of Avebury stone circle and its nearby avenue. Many archaeological finds are presented in the original museum; the nearby Barn Gallery has interactive displays and a children's area.

OPENING TIMES

Please see website for details

VISIT US

Direction: In Avebury, 7 miles W of Marlborough

Train: Pewsey 10 miles; Swindon 11 miles

Bus: Visit traveline.info for the latest bus timetables and routes

NON-MEMBERS

Adult **£5.50** | Child **£2.80**
Family 2 Adults **£13.80**
Family 1 Adult **£8.30**

Parking: S of Avebury off A4361. Free to English Heritage Members with a valid car sticker.

Parking (limited).

Shop and café not managed by English Heritage.

MAP PAGE 325 (3J)
OS MAP 173, 157: SU099700

Avebury henge and stone circles are among the greatest marvels of prehistoric Britain. Built and altered between 2600-2400 BC, the henge survives as a huge circular bank and ditch. Within it was a circle of originally about one hundred great sarsen stones, the largest circle in Britain. This enclosed two smaller stone circles, each enclosing a central stone setting.

Avebury is part of a much bigger complex of Neolithic and Bronze Age ceremonial sites, including West Kennet Avenue and The Sanctuary. Earlier West Kennet Long Barrow and Windmill Hill and later Silbury Hill are nearby. You can reach many of these sites by pleasant walks from Avebury village. This extraordinary assemblage of monuments seemingly formed a huge 'sacred landscape', whose purpose can still only be guessed at.

Avebury and its surroundings, with Stonehenge, are a World Heritage Site.

OPENING TIMES

Any reasonable daylight hours

VISIT US

See Alexander Keiller Museum

Parking (see Alexander Keiller Museum).

MAP PAGE 325 (3J)
OS MAP 173, 157: SU102700

DIG DEEPER INTO THE STORY OF STONEHENGE

Our two nearby partner museums give you even more insight into Stonehenge. See dazzling Bronze Age gold at **Wiltshire Museum** in Devizes, and learn about Stonehenge's place in the wider prehistoric world at the **The Salisbury Museum**. See p.303-304 for details.

USUAL FACILITIES MAY NOT BE AVAILABLE AROUND THE SUMMER SOLSTICE 20-22 JUNE

THE SANCTUARY

Begun around 2500 BC, the Sanctuary was originally a setting of timber posts arranged in six concentric circles, together with two concentric circles of standing stones. Today concrete slabs and posts indicate these long-vanished components.

Various objects such as animal bones, pottery, flint tools and

even human remains were buried at the site, but its function remains a mystery. Like the similar monuments at Woodhenge and Durrington Walls, the Sanctuary complex was probably a free-standing ceremonial site rather than a building. Later, the West Kennet Avenue of standing stones was constructed to connect it with

Avebury henge, reinforcing the status of this enigmatic but clearly very important site. Part of the Avebury section of the World Heritage Site.

OPENING TIMES
Any reasonable daylight hours

VISIT US
Direction: ½ mile S of West Kennett, beside S side of A4

Train: Pewsey 9 miles, Bedwyn 12 miles

Bus: Visit traveline.info for the latest bus timetables and routes

ACQ.1944

Very limited parking in lay-by on S side of A4.

Caution: beware of traffic.

MAP PAGE 325 (3J)
OS MAP 173, 157: SU118680

SILBURY HILL

Dramatically dominating the landscape around Avebury, mysterious Silbury Hill is the largest prehistoric artificial mound in Europe. Approximately 37 metres (120 feet) high and 500 metres (1,640 feet) in diameter, it compares in size with the roughly contemporary Egyptian pyramids.

The mound was built in a series of stages over perhaps 100 years around 2400 BC, starting with a small gravel mound. Antiquarians and archaeologists have dug three separate tunnels into its centre, but found no central burial. Though Silbury Hill's position near the source of the River Kennet was clearly important, its purpose and significance remain unknown. Part of the Avebury section of the World Heritage Site.

No access to the hill itself. This is to prevent erosion of archaeological deposits and rare chalk grassland (the hill is a Site of Special Scientific Interest).

OPENING TIMES
Viewing area during any reasonable daylight hours. Strictly no access to the hill itself

VISIT US
Direction: 1 mile W of West Kennett on A4

Train: Pewsey 9 miles, Swindon 13 miles

Bus: Visit traveline.info for the latest bus timetables and routes

ACQ.1883

Disabled access (viewing area).

Parking: charges apply to non-members, free for Members with valid car sticker.

MAP PAGE 325 (3J)
OS MAP 173, 157: SU100685

USUAL FACILITIES MAY NOT BE AVAILABLE AROUND THE SUMMER SOLSTICE 20-22 JUNE

WEST KENNET AVENUE

NEAR AVEBURY, WILTSHIRE – SN8 1RD

WEST KENNET LONG BARROW

NEAR AVEBURY, WILTSHIRE – SN8 1QH

An avenue, originally of around 100 pairs of prehistoric standing stones, forming a winding 1½ mile link or pathway between the henge and stone circles of Avebury and the Sanctuary. The section nearest Avebury has been restored. Many of the pairs, set around 20-30 metres (approx. 80 feet) from the next pair and around 15 metres (50 feet) apart, seem to follow a set form, with a squat diamond-shaped stone matched with a slender straight-sided stone. Part of the Avebury section of the World Heritage Site.

OPENING TIMES

Any reasonable daylight hours

VISIT US

Direction: Runs alongside B4003

Train: Pewsey 9 miles, Swindon 12 miles

Bus: Visit **traveline.info** for the latest bus timetables and routes

ACQ.1944 🎁 P

Parking: please park at Avebury, Alexander Keiller Museum.

MAP PAGE 325 (3J)
OS MAP 173, 157: SU105695

One of the largest, most impressive and most accessible Neolithic long barrow chambered tombs in Britain. It crowns a ridge above the River Kennet, with views across to Silbury Hill. Its grassed-over chalk mound, over 100 metres (328 feet) long and 3 metres (10 feet) high, is an oasis of wild flowers in summer. You can explore the five atmospheric burial chambers within, constructed of massive boulders and opening off a central passage fronted by a façade of huge sarsens.

Built around 3650 BC, it is among the oldest visible monuments in the Avebury landscape. The remains of at least 36 people were deposited here, over a short period of time and according to a system; children predominate in some chambers, adults in others. Part of the Avebury section of the World Heritage Site.

OPENING TIMES

Any reasonable daylight hours

VISIT US

Direction: ¾ mile SW of West Kennett, along footpath off A4

Train: Pewsey 9 miles, Swindon 13 miles

Bus: Visit **traveline.info** for the latest bus timetables and routes

ACQ.1883 ⊗ P ⚠

Very limited parking in lay-by, S of A4 10-15 minutes uphill walk, on gravel and then grass track.

Caution: unguarded drops.

MAP PAGE 325 (3J)
OS MAP 173, 157: SU105677

WINDMILL HILL

NEAR AVEBURY, WILTSHIRE
– SN4 9NW

WOODHENGE AND DURRINGTON WALLS WILTSHIRE – SP4 7AR

The classic Neolithic 'causewayed enclosure', constructed around 3675 BC and thus pre-dating the Avebury henge. Its three concentric but intermittent ditches cover an area of approximately 22 acres. Large quantities of animal bones, cereal crops, stone tools, artefacts and pottery were found here, suggesting the communal gathering of people to feast, trade and carry out ritual ceremonies. This site can be reached by a 40-50 minute walk from Avebury village, along footpaths. Part of the Avebury section of the World Heritage Site.

Woodhenge is a late Neolithic monument, where concrete markers now indicate the location of six concentric oval rings of timber posts. The timber structure is surrounded by a circular bank and ditch and is aligned north-east towards the summer solstice sunrise. A small central flint cairn marks the location of a child burial.

Nearby is Durrington Walls, a massive circular earthwork henge 500 metres (1,640 feet) in diameter, also built in the late Neolithic period, in about 2500 BC. Excavations here have revealed two concentric timber monuments, similar to Woodhenge, and the remains of many small buildings, possibly the houses where the builders

or users of Stonehenge lived. At the Stonehenge visitor centre you can see replicas based on these buildings. Recent geophysical surveys suggest that the henge bank was built on the site of a circle of large timber posts, and that the whole complex was surrounded by a huge circuit of big pits or shafts, making Durrington a still more significant monument.

Part of the Stonehenge section of the World Heritage Site.

OPENING TIMES

Any reasonable daylight hours

VISIT US

Direction: 1½ miles N of Amesbury, signposted off A345, just S of Durrington

Train: Salisbury 9 miles

Bus: Visit traveline.info for the latest bus timetables and routes

| ACQ 1971 | Durrington Walls |
| ACQ 1932 | Woodhenge |

 Limited car parking.

MAP PAGE 325 (4J)
OS MAP 184, 130: SU151434

OPENING TIMES

Any reasonable daylight hours

VISIT US

Direction: 1¼ miles NW of Avebury

Train: Swindon 11 miles

Bus: Visit traveline.info for the latest bus timetables and routes

ACQ 1944

Sheep may be grazing on site.

MAP PAGE 325 (3J)
OS MAP 173, 157: SU087714

Avebury Monuments: Ownership, Guardianship and Management

Avebury Henge and Stone Circles, the Alexander Keiller Museum, West Kennet Avenue and Windmill Hill are in the freehold ownership of the National Trust. The Sanctuary is in Department for Digital, Culture, Media and Sport (DCMS) ownership. Silbury Hill and West Kennet Long Barrow are in private ownership.

All the sites are in English Heritage guardianship, in the case of Alexander Keiller Museum on behalf of DCMS. The museum collection is on loan from DCMS.

All the sites are managed by the National Trust on behalf of English Heritage, and the two organisations share the cost of managing and maintaining the properties.

USUAL FACILITIES MAY NOT BE AVAILABLE AROUND THE SUMMER SOLSTICE 20-22 JUNE

STONEHENGE

WILTSHIRE – SP4 7DE

Visiting Stonehenge is an unmissable experience. Follow in the footsteps of Neolithic and Bronze Age ancestors as you explore the iconic stone circle and its surrounding prehistoric monuments at this World Heritage Site. Discover more about the story of the circle and its people in our visitor centre exhibitions.

BUILDING STONEHENGE

The monument was begun in about 3000 BC, in the Neolithic period. First, a circular ditch was dug around a ring of pits, probably holding standing stones and into which many cremations were placed.

Some five hundred years later, the central stone settings were raised. It has recently been discovered that the larger 'sarsens', some weighing twenty tons or more, were brought from West Woods near Marlborough, 15 miles (24 kilometres) due north of Stonehenge. These were set up in an outer circle of 30 uprights, probably with a continuous circle of joining lintels. Within this were five trilithons (two upright stones capped by a horizontal lintel) arranged in a horseshoe shape.

Among the sarsens, the smaller bluestones, transported over 150 miles (240 kilometres) from the Preseli Hills in Pembrokeshire, were set in a double arc. Later, about 2300 BC, they were rearranged into an outer circle and an inner oval. At the centre was the sandstone Altar Stone. The enormous Heel Stone marks the position of the rising sun at midsummer.

The remains you see today are the final phase of this ancient monument, after 4,000 years of decay and destruction.

At any time of day or night, get a stunning real-time virtual experience of standing within the stone circle by visiting **stonehengeskyscape.co.uk**

Stonehenge is an astonishing testament to the engineering skills and communal effort of prehistoric people. Transporting the stones over long distances and raising them into position involved huge amounts of labour. Simple tools were used to smooth the stones and craft the joints linking the uprights with the horizontal lintels – a unique feature of Stonehenge.

There has long been debate about the meaning and function of Stonehenge. Archaeologists still advance new theories about why people built it. The orientation of the stones to the rising and setting of the sun at the solstices shows that these times were important for the people who built and used Stonehenge.

Stonehenge wasn't built in isolation. When it was begun, this area was already the focus of an early Neolithic monument complex, including long barrows and cursus monuments. Durrington Walls (p.137), site of a large Neolithic settlement, Woodhenge (p.137) and numerous other timber monuments were constructed as Stonehenge was being built. After major construction ended, many early Bronze Age round barrows were raised nearby.

YOUR STONEHENGE: 150 YEARS OF PERSONAL PHOTOS

This special exhibition, created entirely from photos sent in by visitors, offers a fascinating glimpse of the role the stones have played in people's lives. Closes 4 September 2022.

CIRCLES OF STONE: STONEHENGE AND PREHISTORIC JAPAN

Visit the first ever UK exhibition about prehistoric stone circles in Jomon Japan. Opens late September 2022.

NEW
FOR
2022

VISITING THE STONES AND THEIR LANDSCAPE

The awe-inspiring stone circle will always be the focus of any visit. Reunited with its ancient processional approach, it is surrounded by a landscape rich in prehistoric monuments.

A shuttle bus runs every few minutes to the stones and back, or you can choose to walk the 1.3 miles along unmade paths through the surrounding landscape, which is owned and cared for by the National Trust. You can see nearby monuments from this route, including the Stonehenge Cursus and the Cursus Barrows.

You can venture further into the landscape to see other monuments and perspectives on the stone circle. Pick up an orientation leaflet to see walking routes, and look out for panels explaining the features you pass by. Sturdy footwear, suitable clothes and sun protection are recommended.

The audio tour at Stonehenge is available to download onto your own device at english-heritage.org.uk/visit/places/stonehenge/plan-your-visit/stonehenge-audio-guides/

See Stonehenge close up with an unforgettable Stone Circle Experience outside usual opening times. There's limited availability, so you'll need to book in advance. Find out how at english-heritage.org.uk/stonehenge-experience

VISITOR CENTRE: EXHIBITIONS AND FACILITIES

At the visitor centre you'll find permanent and temporary exhibitions as well as spacious facilities to help you make the most of your day out at Stonehenge.

OPENING TIMES

1 Apr–27 May, daily	9.30am–5pm
28 May–4 Sep, daily	9.30am–7pm
5 Sep–31 Mar, daily	9.30am–5pm
Christmas Opening	
25 Dec	Closed

Opening times on 20-21 Jun are subject to change due to summer solstice. See website for details english-heritage.org.uk/stonehenge

Opening times on 21 Dec are subject to change due to winter solstice. See website for details

Last entry 2 hours before closing

In bad weather visitors may not be able to use the walkway round the stone circle

Stone circle experience outside normal opening hours by advance booking only. Please book during weekday office hours on telephone 0370 333 1181 or online at english-heritage.org.uk/stonehenge-experience

VISIT US

Address: Stonehenge Visitor Centre, nr Amesbury, Wiltshire SP4 7DE

Direction: satnav – use Stonehenge Visitor Centre and follow brown tourist signs. Off A360

Train: Salisbury 9½ miles

Bus: Wilts & Dorset Stonehenge Tour service.
See thestonehengetour.info

Tel: 0370 333 1181 (Customer Services)

Local Tourist Information: Amesbury Library: 01980 623491 and Salisbury: 01722 342860

In the exhibition gallery, an immersive 360-degree introductory film gives you the experience of being inside the stone circle, and a widescreen presentation reveals how the Stonehenge landscape changed through prehistory. Showcases display an intriguing range of archaeological treasures excavated from Stonehenge and nearby sites. You'll discover tools used by the monument's builders, artefacts found at Durrington Walls and jewellery from surrounding burial mounds. Many of the artefacts have kindly been loaned by The Salisbury Museum and Wiltshire Museum.

To discover more about the people who lived at Stonehenge, visit the wonderful archaeology collections of our partners, The Salisbury Museum (see p.303) and Wiltshire Museum in Devizes (see p.304). English Heritage Members get 25% discount on entry.

Our café is a lovely spot for all ages to enjoy refreshments, and the next-door shop stocks a great range of products, many exclusive to Stonehenge.

Outside the visitor centre, discover examples of a sarsen and a bluestone, and see how the giant sarsens may have been moved. You can also wander among our reconstructed Neolithic houses to experience the lifestyles of the people who built Stonehenge.

Pre-booking visits is recommended. Please see the website for the latest information.

For details of how we're keeping you safe, please visit our website.

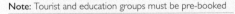

🎬 *Transformers: The Last Knight* (2017).

NON-MEMBERS

Peak (28 May-31 Aug, Sat-Sun and Bank Holidays)
Adult £26.00 | Child £15.60
Family 2 Adults £67.60 | Family 1 Adult £41.60

Standard (1 Apr-27 May and Sep-Mar, Sat-Sun and Bank Holidays*; 28 May-31 Aug, Mon-Fri)
Adult £24.00 | Concession £21.60 | Child £14.40
Family 2 Adults £62.40 | Family 1 Adult £38.40

Off-peak (1 Apr-27 May and Sep-Mar, Mon-Fri)
Adult £22.00 | Concession £19.80 | Child £13.20
Family 2 Adults £57.20 | Family 1 Adult £35.20

*Bank Holidays in spring and summer priced as Sat-Sun. Winter Bank Holidays priced as Mon-Fri.

Usually pre-booking is not required, although it is always recommended. Please check the website for the latest booking and visitor guidance

National Trust England members admitted free

Note: Tourist and education groups must be pre-booked

ACQ. 1918 🔊♿🔋🔌E✋🖥🐾🚶🚻🚫P🍴🍷
♿ OVP

Stonehenge visitor centre and shuttle buses are wheelchair accessible but the grass path around the stones can get muddy.

Download an audio tour (12 languages) to your mobile device for free from the Apple App Store or Google Play Store. Free WiFi is available at the visitor centre.

Guidebooks (available to purchase in English, French, German, Italian, Japanese, Mandarin, Russian and Spanish).

Assistance dogs only. The National Trust has recently created dog-free zones in all fields that are grazed by sheep in the Stonehenge landscape where there is permissive access. Further details and map of where dogs are allowed can be found on the NT website. Please check website before bringing pets to Stonehenge.

Parking is free for Members with a valid English Heritage car sticker and advanced ticket holders.

MAP PAGE 325 (4J)   OS MAP 184, 130: SU122422

THE HERITAGE OF SCILLY

——— ISLES OF SCILLY ———

The stunningly beautiful Isles of Scilly hold vast arrays of archaeological riches both above and below sea level.

This compact archipelago of about 100 islands lies around 28 miles to the south-west of Land's End. None of them is any bigger than three miles across and only five are inhabited. Despite their landmass of only 6.18 square miles, these islands contain a remarkable number of historic sites. These range from traditional farmhouses and dwellings to ritual burial monuments, cist grave cemeteries and Romano-Celtic shrines. Early settlements provide evidence of a distinctively Scillonian prehistoric culture that thrived in the island group from around 4,500 years ago. At that time the sea level was lower, and much of Scilly formed a single landmass.

More recently, defensive monuments constructed during the Civil War and the Second World War stand as testament to the strategic importance of the islands.

The Gulf Stream keeps the climate warm, enabling exotic plants and wildlife to thrive in this designated Area of Outstanding Natural Beauty.

Travel details are available from Island Rover (who operate the round the island tour bus) on 01720 422131. Alternatively St Mary's Community Bus operates a similar route, but to a more frequent timetable. Contact Visit Isles of Scilly on 01720 424031 for details.

BANT'S CARN BURIAL CHAMBER AND HALANGY DOWN ANCIENT VILLAGE
ST MARY'S, ISLES OF SCILLY

The remains of a Romano-British village in a wonderfully scenic location. On the hill above stands a Neolithic or Bronze Age burial mound with entrance passage and inner chamber.

OPENING TIMES
Any reasonable daylight hours

VISIT US
Direction: 1 mile N of Hugh Town

ACQ.1950 Caution: unguarded drops. Please do not climb on the monuments.

MAP PAGE 324 (5B)
OS MAP 203, 101: SV910123

CROMWELL'S CASTLE
TRESCO, ISLES OF SCILLY

Standing on a rocky promontory guarding the lovely anchorage between Bryher and Tresco, this round tower is one of the few surviving Cromwellian fortifications in Britain, built after the conquest of the Royalist Scillies in 1651.

OPENING TIMES
Any reasonable daylight hours

VISIT US
Direction: On the shoreline, approach with care, ¾ mile NW of New Grimsby

ACQ.1950 Caution: deep water, steep stairs.

MAP PAGE 324 (4A)
OS MAP 203, 101: SV882159

GARRISON WALLS
ST MARY'S, ISLES OF SCILLY

You can enjoy a two-hour walk alongside the ramparts of these defensive walls and earthworks, dating from the 16th to 18th centuries. Other remains include

GARRISON WALLS

the Elizabethan Star Castle and the Powder House exhibition.

OPENING TIMES
Any reasonable daylight hours. Powder House open daily 10am-4pm

VISIT US
Direction: Around the headland W of Hugh Town

ACQ.1973 Caution: steep slopes, sheer drops.

MAP PAGE 324 (5B)
OS MAP 203, 101: SV898104

HARRY'S WALLS
ST MARY'S, ISLES OF SCILLY

An unfinished artillery fort, built above St Mary's Pool harbour in 1552-53.

OPENING TIMES
Any reasonable daylight hours

VISIT US
Direction: ¼ mile NE of Hugh Town

ACQ.1950 P Caution: unguarded drops.

MAP PAGE 324 (5B)
OS MAP 203, 101: SV909109

INNISIDGEN LOWER AND UPPER BURIAL CHAMBERS
ST MARY'S, ISLES OF SCILLY

Two Neolithic or Bronze Age communal burial cairns of Scillonian type, with fine views. The upper cairn is the best preserved on the islands.

OPENING TIMES
Any reasonable daylight hours

VISIT US
Direction: 1¾ miles NE of Hugh Town

ACQ.1950

MAP PAGE 324 (5B)
OS MAP 203, 101: SV922127

KING CHARLES'S CASTLE
TRESCO, ISLES OF SCILLY

The ruins of a mid-16th-century coastal artillery fort, later garrisoned – hence the name – by Civil War Royalists. Reached from New Grimsby by footpath.

OPENING TIMES
Any reasonable daylight hours

VISIT US
Direction: Located ¾ mile NW of New Grimsby. Coastal location, approach with care

ACQ.1950 Caution: sheer drops. Please do not climb on the walls.

MAP PAGE 324 (4A)
OS MAP 203, 101: SV882161

OLD BLOCKHOUSE
TRESCO, ISLES OF SCILLY

Substantial remains of a small 16th-century gun tower protecting Old Grimsby harbour, vigorously defended during the Civil War.

OPENING TIMES
Any reasonable daylight hours

VISIT US
Direction: On Blockhouse Point, at the S end of Old Grimsby harbour

ACQ.1950 Caution: steep stairs.

MAP PAGE 324 (4B)
OS MAP 203, 101: SV897155

PORTH HELLICK DOWN BURIAL CHAMBER
ST MARY'S, ISLES OF SCILLY

A large and imposing Scillonian Bronze Age entrance grave, with kerb, inner passage and burial chamber all clearly visible.

OPENING TIMES
Any reasonable daylight hours

VISIT US
Direction: 1¾ miles E of Hugh Town

ACQ.1950 Caution: steep slopes.

MAP PAGE 324 (5B)
OS MAP 203, 101: SV928108

Framlingham Castle, Suffolk

EAST OF ENGLAND

East of England

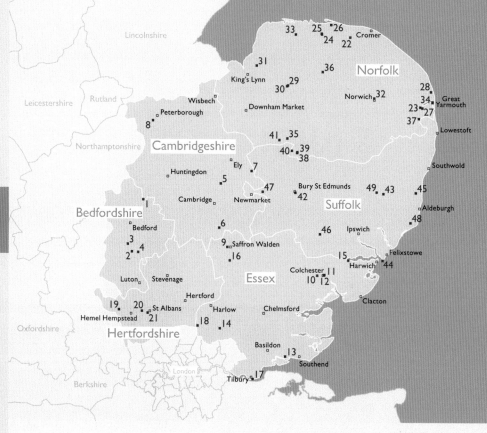

St Edmund Way

22 miles | 2 days

From Thetford Priory, cross the border between Norfolk and Suffolk, walking the old Icknield Way through the King's Forest, via the Anglo-Saxon village of West Stow and four ancient Suffolk churches, to Bury St Edmunds. Visit the remains of the city's colossal ruined abbey, the burial place of the King of East Anglia, St Edmund, standing side-by-side with the cathedral, where the choir sings evensong almost every day.

In partnership with

the British Pilgrimage Trust

Discover English Heritage sites along the pilgrimage route

A Thetford Priory *(p.169)*

B Church of the Holy Sepulchre *(p.169)*

C Bury St Edmunds Abbey *(p.170)*

View more details and a downloadable version of this route at **english-heritage.org.uk/pilgrimage**

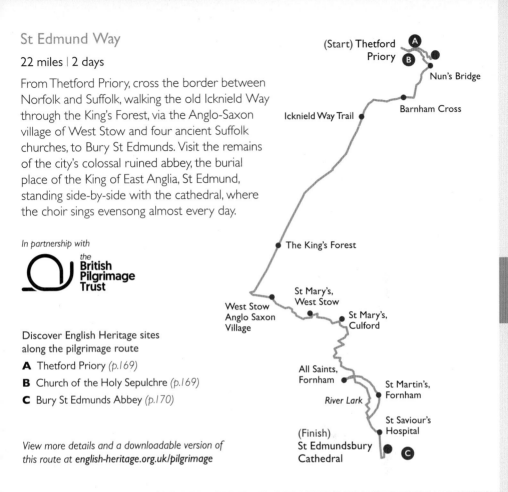

(Start) Thetford Priory Ⓐ Ⓑ

Nun's Bridge

Barnham Cross

Icknield Way Trail

The King's Forest

West Stow Anglo Saxon Village

St Mary's, West Stow

St Mary's, Culford

All Saints, Fornham

St Martin's, Fornham

River Lark

St Saviour's Hospital

(Finish) St Edmundsbury Cathedral Ⓒ

WREST PARK

BEDFORDSHIRE – MK45 4HR

Our ongoing programme of restoration means that there's always something new for you to discover in Wrest Park's vast and infinitely varied gardens. From stately formal gardens and lakes to secluded woodland paths, hidden surprises and a children's playground, there's a treat for everyone here.

Enlivened by charming follies and garden buildings, unexpected vistas and a wealth of statues, Wrest's 90-acre gardens reflect England's love affair with landscape. At the heart of the extensive waterside and woodland walks stands the iconic Archer Pavilion. A baroque showstopper built between 1709 and 1711, it was designed by fashionable architect Thomas Archer. Once the ultimate garden dining room, it still retains its outstanding interior decoration beneath a dome topped by a gleaming golden orb finial. Its breathtaking setting at the end of the Long Water makes it the most dramatic of the delightful set pieces for which Wrest's gardens are renowned.

Seek out Jemima, Marchioness Grey's enchanting Bath House, disguised in the Picturesque style as a thatched Classical ruin. Designed by Edward Stevens in 1769-71, it features a cold water plunge pool and attached changing room with a pebble floor set with a pattern of deer vertebrae. We've recently restored its original surroundings, and the Cascade filling the Bath Pond flows again. It's an ideal picnicking spot.

There's a lot more to see in these wonderful gardens. You can wander Capability Brown's pathways to the Chinese Bridge and Chinese Temple, its copper roof bedecked with sparkling golden bells. Nearby you'll find a memorial to Brown, one of many leading garden designers employed by the de Grey family to develop Wrest's grounds over three centuries.

And there's more. Strolling the intricate woodland paths of the Duke of Kent's 18th-century Great Garden, you'll discover a peaceful dogs' cemetery for de Grey family pets. Not far away are the secluded Ladies' Lake and a set of ancient Graeco-Roman altars in a woodland clearing. Other walks lead you to the splendid 1830s Orangery. Nearer the great mansion, you can view the sculpture gallery in the Dairy, step into the Rose Garden and the vibrantly planted Italian Garden, or visit the formal French Parterre.

All this remarkable garden history is being progressively brought to life in a 20-year-long restoration project. You'll find the gardeners happy to answer questions.

In addition to the gardens, you can visit parts of the ground floor of the French chateau-style mansion, designed and built by Thomas, Earl de Grey in 1834-39. Its unfurnished but opulently decorated state rooms include the Grand

STAY
WITH
US

You can now enjoy exclusive access to Wrest Park's gardens when staying at the *Gardener's House*. Set in the former walled kitchen garden, this holiday cottage provides spacious accommodation over three floors, and can sleep up to 8 people.

See p.16 for details on staying at **Wrest Park** and our other holiday cottages.

Staircase, the Library, the Drawing Room and the Dining Room. Countess Henrietta's Sitting Room, furnished as it appeared in the 1860s, looks through to a lofty conservatory. An exhibition reveals the history of the de Grey family, and you can admire family portraits.

You can also combine a day out at Wrest Park with a guided journey through 2,000 years of history in the archaeological store, housing treasures from English Heritage sites around the country. This fabulous array of over 153,000 artefacts ranges from prehistoric antlers to Victorian dress fittings. There are also 6,000 items from London houses and 1,000 historic wallpapers. Look out for guided tours throughout the year.

Within the Walled Garden, the spacious café offers a seasonal menu using locally sourced produce, and has indoor and outdoor seating overlooking a children's play area.

Please note: No flash photography or stiletto heels in the house.

🎬 *Strictly Come Dancing* (2015); *The Royals* (2015); *Death of Stalin* (2017); *The Crown* (2019); *Harlots* (2019); *The Great* (2020); *Belgravia* (2020); *The Serpent* (2020).

🎦 Available for corporate and private hire

🎭 Licensed for civil wedding ceremonies

OPENING TIMES

1 Apr-30 Jun, daily	10am-5pm
1 Jul-31 Aug, daily	10am-6pm
1 Sep-30 Oct, daily	10am-5pm
31 Oct-23 Dec, Sat-Sun	10am-4pm
2 Jan-10 Feb, Sat-Sun	10am-4pm
11-19 Feb, daily	10am-4pm
20 Feb-31 Mar, Wed-Sun	10am-4pm
Christmas Opening	
24-25 Dec	Closed
26 Dec-1 Jan, daily	10am-4pm
Last entry 1 hour before closing	

If the state rooms are closed to visitors due to an event, the exhibition and Countess's Sitting Room will remain open. Last entry to the gardens may sometimes be earlier than the usual one hour before closing. Garden access for those already arrived will continue uninterrupted. Please call to check

VISIT US

Address: Wrest Park, Silsoe, Luton, Bedfordshire MK45 4HR

Direction: ¾ mile E of Silsoe off A6, 10 miles S of Bedford

Train: Flitwick 4 miles

Bus: Visit traveline.info

Tel: 0370 333 1181

NON-MEMBERS

Adult **£14.20** | Concession **£12.80** | Child **£8.50** Family 2 Adults **£36.90** | Family 1 Adult **£22.70**

Limited number of mobility scooters available. Pre-booking essential.

MAP PAGE 328 (5E)   OS MAP 153, 193: TL091355

BUSHMEAD PRIORY
BEDFORDSHIRE – MK44 2LD

A rare survival of the complete refectory of a small priory of Augustinian 'black canons' – communities of priests living together like monks. Founded in 1195, Bushmead apparently housed only a prior and four canons.

The impressive refectory, where the canons ate together, is its only remaining building. It displays a fine original timber roof and notable early 14th-century wall paintings, including the Creation of Eve.

OPENING TIMES
1 May-30 Sep, pre-booked tours only on the first Sat of the month. Please call Customer Services on 0370 333 1181 to book

VISIT US
Direction: Located off B660, 2 miles S of Bolnhurst

Train: St Neots 6 miles

Bus: Visit traveline.info for the latest bus timetables and routes

NON-MEMBERS
Adult **£9.00** | Concession **£8.10**
Child **£5.40** | Family 2 Adults **£23.40**
Family 1 Adult **£14.40**

ACQ.1974 ✈ P

MAP PAGE 328 (4E)
OS MAP 153, 225: TL115607

DE GREY MAUSOLEUM, FLITTON
BEDFORDSHIRE – MK45 5EJ

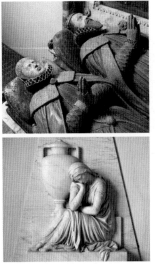

Among the largest sepulchral chapels attached to any English church, this mausoleum houses a remarkable sequence of 17 monuments to the de Grey family of Wrest Park. They span nearly 250 years (1614-1859). Download the audio tour from our website before visiting.

OPENING TIMES
Please check the website or phone Customer Services on 0370 333 1181

VISIT US
Direction: Access via nave of St John the Baptist church in Flitton, on an unclassified road, 1½ miles W of A6 at Silsoe

Train: Flitwick 2 miles

Bus: Visit traveline.info for the latest bus timetables and routes

ACQ.1979 ✈

MAP PAGE 328 (5E)
OS MAP 153, 193: TL059359

HOUGHTON HOUSE
BEDFORDSHIRE – MK45 2EY

The shell of a large 17th-century mansion commanding impressive views, reputedly inspiration for the 'Palace Beautiful' in John Bunyan's *Pilgrim's Progress*. It was begun around 1615 for Mary Sidney Herbert, Dowager Countess of Pembroke, an accomplished poet, patron of the arts and pioneer scientist, as a focus for lavish entertaining. The architecture is an unusual mixture of the Jacobean and the new Classical styles: the ground floors of two Italianate loggias survive, possibly the work of Inigo Jones.

Audio tour available to download from our website.

OPENING TIMES
Daily   10am-6pm or dusk if earlier

VISIT US
Direction: 1 mile NE of Ampthill off B530, 8 miles S of Bedford

Train: Flitwick or Stewartby, both 3 miles

Bus: Visit traveline.info for the latest bus timetables and routes

ACQ.1938 ✈ P ⚠

Caution: falling masonry.

MAP PAGE 328 (5D)
OS MAP 153, 193: TL039395

DENNY ABBEY AND THE FARMLAND MUSEUM
CAMBRIDGESHIRE – CB25 9PQ

A fascinating building with an immensely varied history, Denny Abbey was in turn a Benedictine monastery, a home for elderly Knights Templar and a nunnery. When Henry VIII dissolved the nunnery in 1539, it became a farm, with the nuns' great refectory as its barn. It remained a working farm until the 1960s. All these changes produced an intriguing jigsaw puzzle of features, which graphic panels help you solve.

Alongside is the family-friendly Farmland Museum, telling the story of rural life in the Cambridgeshire Fens. It includes a fenman's hut, craftsmen's workshops and a 1940s village shop display.

Managed by the Farmland Museum. dennyfarmlandmuseum.org.uk

DENNY ABBEY AND THE FARMLAND MUSEUM

OPENING TIMES

1 Apr-30 Oct, Thu-Sun & Bank Hols	10am-4pm
31 Oct-31 Mar	Closed

Last entry 30 mins before closing

VISIT US

Direction: Located 6 miles N of Cambridge on A10

Train: Waterbeach 3 miles

Bus: Visit traveline.info

Tel: 01223 860988

NON-MEMBERS

Museum and Abbey
Adult **£6.00** | Concession **£5.00**
Child **£3.50** | Family 2 Adults **£17.00**

There will be a premium payable by all visitors, including Members, on special event days – please visit dennyfarmlandmuseum.org.uk for details

ACQ.1952

Disabled access (museum and abbey ground floor only).

Dogs on leads (restricted areas only).

Tearoom (now open during full opening times).

Caution: falling masonry.

MAP PAGE 329 (4F)
OS MAP 154, 226: TL492685

DUXFORD CHAPEL
CAMBRIDGESHIRE – CB22 4NL

A modest but complete and attractive 14th-century chantry chapel, perhaps originally a hospital.

DUXFORD CHAPEL

OPENING TIMES

Any reasonable daylight hours

VISIT US

Direction: Off A505 on Station Road, Whittlesford, between Whittlesford Station car park and the Red Lion Hotel

Train: Whittlesford, adjacent

Bus: Visit traveline.info for the latest bus timetables and routes

ACQ.1947

MAP PAGE 329 (4F)
OS MAP 154, 209: TL485473

ISLEHAM PRIORY CHURCH
CAMBRIDGESHIRE – CB7 5RX

The best example in England of a small Norman Benedictine priory church. It survives surprisingly unaltered, despite later conversion into a barn.

OPENING TIMES

Exterior: Any reasonable daylight hours. **Interior:** Key available summer 9am-6pm and winter 9am-4pm from Mrs R Burton, 72 West Street, Isleham CB7 5RA

VISIT US

Direction: Located in centre of Isleham, 16 miles NE of Cambridge on B1104

Train: Newmarket 8½ miles, Ely 9 miles

Bus: Visit traveline.info for the latest bus timetables and routes

ACQ.1944

Caution: falling masonry.

MAP PAGE 329 (3F)
OS MAP 143, 226: TL642743

LONGTHORPE TOWER

SAVED BY MEMBERS

———— CAMBRIDGESHIRE – PE3 6LU ————

Modest little Longthorpe Tower houses a great treasure – the most important set of medieval domestic wall paintings in northern Europe. Imperilled by time and decay, they're being expertly conserved as part of the Save Our Story Members' Appeal.

Built both for defence and for show in about 1300, the tower was an addition to the manor house of Robert Thorpe, an ambitious lawyer and local landowner knighted for his service to King Edward II. Between about 1320 and 1340 he commissioned the spectacular wall paintings to adorn his inner sanctum, the first floor private chamber. Covering almost every surface of its walls and ceiling, they're designed to entertain, enlighten and impress, as well as proclaiming Robert's educated taste and loyalty to the crown. They offer an extraordinary insight into the medieval view of the world.

Kings, saints, angels and musicians mingle with naturalistic birds and animals and fabulous mythical beasts – including the bonnacon, notorious for its flaming excrement. On one wall, the Seven Ages of Man traces life from babyhood to old age, and on another a rare Wheel of the Five Senses symbolises taste, touch, smell, hearing and sight as a monkey, spider's web, vulture, boar and cockerel. Royal figures form a backdrop to the place where Robert would have sat, and over all the vaulted ceiling represents the canopy of Heaven.

Rediscovered under layers of whitewash in 1945, these precious paintings are severely endangered by cracking plaster, natural environmental decay and well-meant but damaging earlier repairs. In partnership with the Courtauld Institute, we've monitored them using the latest investigative techniques, and are working on their long-term conservation.

Managed by Nene Park Trust. nenepark.org.uk

OPENING TIMES

| 2 Apr-30 Oct, Sat-Sun | 10am-4.30pm |
| 31 Oct-31 Mar | Closed |

Last entry 30 mins before closing

Group and education visits outside these times by arrangement

Please ensure you check the website or call before visiting for latest access, booking and opening information – nenepark.org.uk/longthorpe-tower

VISIT US

Direction: Located 2 miles W of Peterborough on A47

Train: Peterborough 1½ miles

Bus: Visit traveline.info for the latest bus timetables and routes

Tel: 01733 234193

NON-MEMBERS

Adult **£5.50** I Concession **£5.00**
Child **£3.30** I Family 2 Adults **£14.30**
Family 1 Adult **£8.80**

ACQ.1947 🎧 Ⓔ ▢ ⊗ ▢ ⚠

Parking in car park at St Botolph's Church, Thorpe Road, approximately 100 metres from site.

No wheelchair access.

Caution: steep stairs.

MAP PAGE 328 (3E)
OS MAP 142, 227/235: TL162984

AUDLEY END HOUSE AND GARDENS

ESSEX – CB11 4JF

Whether you're exploring servants' domains and 'Mrs Crocombe's' kitchen, state rooms, fully working stables, the organic kitchen garden or the beautiful grounds, you'll find a warm welcome at Audley End. Costumed storytellers now reveal even more of its history.

BRINGING AUDLEY END TO LIFE

This noble Jacobean mansion in its landscaped setting is simply the best place in England to discover how a great mansion worked, both for servants and their masters. Throughout the summer, costumed interpreters in the Service Wing and working stables help you vividly experience Victorian servants' lives.

Audley End takes its name from Sir Thomas Audley, Henry VIII's Lord Chancellor. His grandson Thomas Howard, Earl of Suffolk, rebuilt the house on a palatial scale, making it one of the largest mansions in Jacobean England. Today, Audley's interior largely represents the taste of the third Lord Braybrooke, who redecorated many of its rooms in the Jacobean style during the 1820s.

THE STATE ROOMS

Make yourself at home in the state rooms – feel free to play the piano in the Library, admire the Georgian state bed or step into Lady Braybrooke's private apartments.

🎬 *The Crown* (2016); *Trust* (2018).

THE SERVICE WING

The Victorian Service Wing provides you with a unique insight into life 'below stairs' during the 1880s. The kitchens were once the domain of Mrs Avis Crocombe, Victorian cook and 21st-century YouTube celebrity. Kitchens, dairy, larder and laundries are fully equipped with original and reproduction Victorian fittings, and animated with lifelike sights and sounds. Costumed interpreters demonstrate traditional cooking and washing techniques on selected days. (Every weekend, May-September, excluding some event weekends, plus other days throughout the year.) You can also enjoy volunteer-led guided tours of the Service Wing and (on selected days) the Butler's Pantry.

THE NURSERY SUITE AND COAL GALLERY

The 1830s Nursery Suite uncovers the hidden world of the privileged Braybrooke children. You can try on period costumes, play with hands-on replicas of 1830s toys, and discover the personalities of the eight Braybrooke children. The sights and sounds within the Coal Gallery show you how servants provided warmth and hot water for the aristocratic family and their guests.

NEW
FOR
2022

On selected dates, find out more about Audley End from our costumed storytellers. Meet the Curious Collector in the house, showcasing the mysterious and imaginative artefacts the Braybrooke family collected over the years. Play along with our costumed Playing Card, telling stories of the parties when guests dressed as playing cards. Encounter the Garden Storyteller, revealing the secrets and significance of the plants and wildlife in the Walled Garden.

THE STABLES

Meet our resident horses in the lovely stables, which are set as in the 1880s. Discover the vital part horses played in the life of the mansion and estate, and enjoy regular riding displays, hands-on demonstrations of horse-care and other horsey activities throughout the day. Lively interactive displays 'virtually' introduce you to Audley's Victorian outdoor staff, and you can even try dressing up as a period stable worker.

THE GARDENS

Remodelled by Capability Brown, Audley End's award-winning gardens offer many delights. Admire the Elysian Garden and Tea House Bridge; walk up to the Temple of Concord; visit the memorial to Second World War Polish resistance soldiers and enjoy the restored 19th-century formal garden. For practical gardeners, the organic Walled Kitchen Garden is a must. Nearby are the children's play area and Cart Yard Café.

Please note: Photography in the house is only permitted in the Nursery and Coal Gallery. No stiletto heels allowed in the house.

You can now pre-order a summer picnic or afternoon tea from our tearoom to enjoy in the grounds of Audley End. Please telephone site 48 hours in advance to book your picnic, presented in an English Heritage jute bag. (Not available at weekends or during school holidays.)

STAY WITH US

Book a relaxing break in our *Cambridge Lodge*. Enjoy stunning views of the River Cam and the manicured lawns, and stroll through the grounds in private once the gates have closed to the public.

See p.16 for details on staying at **Audley** and our other holiday cottages.

OPENING TIMES

House

1 Apr–30 Oct, daily	10.30am–4.30pm
31 Oct–23 Dec, Sat–Sun	10.30am–2.30pm
26 Dec–1 Jan, daily	10.30am–2.30pm
2 Jan–10 Feb, Sat–Sun	10.30am–2.30pm
11–19 Feb, daily	10.30am–2.30pm
20 Feb–31 Mar, Wed–Sun	10.30am–2.30pm

Grounds, Stables & Servants Wing

1 Apr–30 Jun, daily	10am–5pm
1 Jul–31 Aug, daily	10am–6pm
1 Sep–30 Oct, daily	10am–5pm
31 Oct–23 Dec, Sat–Sun	10am–4pm
26 Dec–1 Jan, daily	10am–4pm

2 Jan–10 Feb, Sat–Sun	10am–4pm
11–19 Feb, daily	10am–4pm
20 Feb–31 Mar, Wed–Sun	10am–4pm

Christmas Opening

24–25 Dec	Closed

Last entry to the grounds is 1 hour before closing (last entry to house varies, please see website)

VISIT US

Address: Audley End House & Gardens, off London Road, Saffron Walden, Essex CB11 4JF

Direction: 1 mile W of Saffron Walden on B1383 (M11 exit 8 or 10)

Train: Audley End 1¼ miles. Note: Footpath is beside busy main road

Bus: Visit traveline.info for the latest bus timetables and routes

Tel: 0370 333 1181

Local Tourist Information:
Saffron Walden: 01799 524002
Cambridge: 01223 791500

NON-MEMBERS

Adult **£21.00** | Concession **£18.90**
Child **£12.60** | Family 2 Adults **£54.60**
Family 1 Adult **£33.60**

Disabled access (grounds, Great Hall, Stable Yard and Service Wing only. Please call for more information).

MAP PAGE 329 (5F)
OS MAP 154, 195: TL525382

COLCHESTER, BLUEBOTTLE GROVE

ESSEX – CO3 4DZ

First-century Iron Age earthworks, defending pre-Roman 'Camulodunum', capital of the British Catuvellauni tribe. Conquered by the Romans in AD 43, it later became Colchester.

Lexden Earthworks (below) are nearby.

Managed by Colchester Borough Council.

OPENING TIMES

Any reasonable daylight hours

VISIT US

Direction: 2 miles W of Colchester off A604. From Lexden Straight Road, turn left into Heath Road, left into Church Lane, right into Beech Hill and follow signs to site

Train: Colchester or Colchester Town, both 2½ miles

Bus: Visit traveline.info for the latest bus timetables and routes

Tel: 01206 282929

ACQ.1925 🐕 ⚠

Caution: steep slopes.

MAP PAGE 329 (5H)
OS MAP 168, 184: TL965246

COLCHESTER, LEXDEN EARTHWORKS

ESSEX – CO3 9DD

Iron Age earthworks defending pre-Roman Colchester. Lexden Tumulus was the burial place of a wealthy British chieftain – perhaps a king. It contained both British and imported Roman treasures.

Bluebottle Grove (above) is nearby.

Managed by Colchester Borough Council.

OPENING TIMES

Any reasonable daylight hours

VISIT US

Direction: On Lexden Straight Road, 2 miles W of Colchester off A604

COLCHESTER, LEXDEN EARTHWORKS

Train: Colchester or Colchester Town, both 2½ miles

Bus: Visit traveline.info for the latest bus timetables and routes

Tel: 01206 282929

ACQ.1925 🐕

MAP PAGE 329 (5H)
OS MAP 168, 184: TL965246

COLCHESTER, ST BOTOLPH'S PRIORY

ESSEX – CO2 7EE

Remains of one of England's first Augustinian priories, founded c. 1100. An impressive example of early Norman architecture, the church has massive pillars and round arches and an elaborate west front.

Managed by Colchester Borough Council.

OPENING TIMES

1-30 Apr, daily	7.30am-7pm
1 May-31 Aug, daily	7.30am-8pm
1-14 Sep, daily	7.30am-7pm
15-30 Sep, daily	7.30am-6.30pm
1-14 Oct, daily	7.30am-6pm
15-31 Oct, daily	7.30am-5pm
1 Nov-29 Feb, daily	7.30am-4pm
1-14 Mar, daily	7.30am-5pm
15-31 Mar, daily	7.30am-6pm

VISIT US

Direction: Nr Colchester Town station

Train: Colchester Town, adjacent

COLCHESTER, ST BOTOLPH'S PRIORY

Bus: Visit traveline.info for the latest bus timetables and routes

Tel: 01206 282929

ACQ.1912 🐕 ♿ ⚠

Caution: falling masonry.

MAP PAGE 329 (5H)
OS MAP 168, 184: TL999249

COLCHESTER, ST JOHN'S ABBEY GATE

ESSEX – CO2 7EZ

This elaborately decorated gatehouse is the sole survivor of the wealthy Benedictine abbey of St John. Built c. 1400 to strengthen the abbey's defences, it was stormed by Parliamentarian troops during the Civil War.

Managed by Colchester Borough Council.

OPENING TIMES

Exterior only: Any reasonable daylight hours

VISIT US

Direction: On St John's Green on southern side of central Colchester

Train: Colchester Town ¼ mile

Bus: Visit traveline.info for the latest bus timetables and routes

Tel: 01206 282929

ACQ.1983 🐕 ⚠

Dogs on leads (exterior only).

Caution: falling masonry.

MAP PAGE 329 (5H)
OS MAP 168, 184: TL998248

HILL HALL ESSEX – CM16 7QQ

OPENING TIMES

1 Apr-30 Sep	Pre-booked guided tours only

To book please call 0370 333 1181 (Customer Services)

VISIT US

Direction: 3 miles SE of Epping. Entrance ½ mile N of Theydon Mount Church

Train: Epping or Theydon Bois 2½ miles

Bus: Visit traveline.info for the latest bus timetables and routes

Built in 1568-77 for the scholar, diplomat and politician Sir Thomas Smith, this splendid Elizabethan mansion is among the earliest Renaissance houses in England.

Its multi-columned Classical-style exterior imitates examples Smith had admired on his ambassadorial travels in France and Flanders. Its interior is adorned with very rare survivals of high-quality figurative wall paintings, among the finest in English Heritage's collection. Now mainly visible

to view in two rooms, they probably once extended throughout the house. One series depicts the Old Testament story of Hezekiah; the other the Classical legend of Cupid and Psyche. Expertly painted, they may be by Flemish artists, or English imitators: Sir Thomas himself may have overseen their design.

Hill Hall has now been divided into private houses, but parts remain open to the public by prior arrangement.

NON-MEMBERS

Adult **£9.00** | Concession **£8.10**
Child **£5.40** | Family 2 Adults **£23.40**
Family 1 Adult **£14.40**

ACQ.1976 🐕 🏠 🚻 👪 🅿 🖼

MAP PAGE 329 (6F)
OS MAP 167/177, 174: TQ489995

PRIOR'S HALL BARN, WIDDINGTON ESSEX – CB11 3SB

Among the finest medieval barns in eastern England, probably built for New College, Oxford. Tree-ring dating showed that its timbers were felled in 1417-42. It was originally constructed of around 900 separate timber components, the product of some 400 oaks.

Clad with black weatherboarding in traditional Essex style, it contains a breathtaking aisled interior with a crown post roof, little altered over the centuries. The two huge porches allowed harvest carts to be wheeled in and unloaded under cover.

OPENING TIMES

2 Apr-25 Sep, Sat-Sun	10am-6pm
26 Sep-31 Mar	Closed

VISIT US

Direction: In Widdington, on unclassified road 2 miles SE of Newport, off B1383

Train: Newport 2 miles

Bus: Visit traveline.info for the latest bus timetables and routes

ACQ.1976 ♿ 🚫 🅿 ⚠

Caution: trip hazards.

MAP PAGE 329 (5F)
OS MAP 167, 195: TL537318

HADLEIGH CASTLE
ESSEX – SS7 2AP

The romantic ruins of a royal castle, on a ridge overlooking the Essex marshes and the Thames Estuary. The first castle was begun in about 1215 by Hubert de Burgh, King John's powerful Justiciar, but it was extensively rebuilt by Edward III during the 1360s, to which date most of the surviving remains belong. Conveniently accessible from London by royal barge, the castle was probably a personal retreat, where Edward could stay in privacy and comfort.

After Edward's death in 1377, Hadleigh's tenancy passed to a series of absentee royal relations, including three of Henry VIII's queens. Eventually it was substantially demolished for building materials. Yet Edward III's two big eastern drum towers still remain, with the commanding south-east tower – allegedly used by Georgian revenue men looking out for smugglers – still standing three storeys high.

OPENING TIMES
Any reasonable daylight hours

VISIT US
Direction: ¾ mile S of A13 at Hadleigh

Train: Leigh-on-Sea 1½ miles by direct footpath

Bus: Visit traveline.info for the latest bus timetables and routes

ACQ.1948 [icons]

Caution: steep slopes, falling masonry.

MAP PAGE 329 (6G)
OS MAP 178, 175: TQ810860

MISTLEY TOWERS
ESSEX – CO11 1HB

Two imposing Classical towers, which stood at each end of a highly unconventional Georgian church. One of only two churches designed by Robert Adam, it was built in about 1776. When the centre of the church was demolished in 1870, the columns from its porticos were added to the towers.

Managed by Mistley Thorn Residents' Association.

OPENING TIMES
Exterior: Any reasonable daylight hours

Interior: Key available from The Mistley Thorn Hotel, High Street, Mistley CO11 1HE, 100m to the right of the site, daily   10am-4pm

VISIT US
Direction: Located on B1352, 1½ miles E of A137 at Lawford, 9 miles E of Colchester

Train: Mistley ¼ mile

Bus: Visit traveline.info for the latest bus timetables and routes

ACQ.1958 [icons]

Disabled access (exterior only).

Dogs on leads (exterior only).

Caution: falling masonry.

MAP PAGE 329 (5H)
OS MAP 168/169, 184/197: TM116320

WALTHAM ABBEY GATEHOUSE AND BRIDGE
ESSEX – EN9 1XQ

Fine 14th-century gatehouse and other remains of the abbey refounded by Harold Godwinson, the last Saxon King of England. Famous for its miraculous 'Holy Cross', it became one of the greatest monasteries in medieval England. According to tradition, King Harold's body was secretly buried here after his death at the Battle of Hastings, and you can see the alleged site of his grave in the abbey grounds.

Managed by Lee Valley Regional Park Authority.

OPENING TIMES
Any reasonable daylight hours

VISIT US
Direction: In Waltham Abbey off A112

Train: Waltham Cross 1¼ miles

Bus: Visit traveline.info for the latest bus timetables and routes

Tel: 0845 677 0600

ACQ.1976 [icons]

Parking (charges apply, not English Heritage).

Caution: falling masonry.

MAP PAGE 329 (6F)
OS MAP 166, 174
GATEHOUSE: TL381007
HAROLD'S BRIDGE: TL382009

TILBURY FORT

—— ESSEX – RM18 7NR ——

Tilbury Fort on the Thames Estuary defended London's seaward approach from Tudor times to the Second World War.

Henry VIII built the first permanent fort here, and Queen Elizabeth I famously delivered her Armada Speech at nearby Tilbury in 1588. King Charles II ordered his chief engineer, Sir Bernard de Gomme, to build the great artillery fort you can see today, with work beginning in 1670. It's the best example of a 17th-century bastioned fortress in England, with its complete circuit of moats and outworks still substantially surviving. Highland prisoners were held here after the Jacobite Rising of 1745, and much later the fort's guns helped shoot down a raiding Zeppelin in 1916.

As you enter the fort you'll pass through the magnificent Watergate, and you can also see the historic Landport gate. Visit the exhibition in the east gunpowder magazine to discover the fort's role in the defence of London and trace advances in military engineering. The atmospheric Victorian magazine tunnels in the north-east bastion give an insight into the life of a 19th-century gunner. Be sure to step onto the fort ramparts for impressive views of the Thames and the historic riverside town of Gravesend.

> 🎬 *Sharpe's Regiment* (1996); *The Brothers Grimsby* (2016); *Tulip Fever* (2017); *Wonder Woman* (2017); *Taboo* (2017); *SS-GB* (2017); *Peterloo* (2018).

OPENING TIMES

1 Apr-30 Oct, Wed-Sun & Bank Hols	10am-5pm
31 Oct-31 Mar, Sat-Sun	10am-4pm
24-26 Dec & 1 Jan	Closed

Last entry 30 mins before closing

VISIT US

Direction: Off A13 and A1089, close to the Port of Tilbury. Beyond The Worlds End pub

Train: Tilbury Town 1½ miles

Bus: Visit traveline.info for the latest bus timetables and routes

Ferry: Gravesend – Tilbury Ferry, then ¼ mile walk

Tel: 01375 858489

NON-MEMBERS

Adult **£7.80** | Concession **£7.00** | Child **£4.70**
Family 2 Adults **£20.30** | Family 1 Adult **£12.50**

Disabled access (exterior and Fort Parade Ground).

Dogs on leads (restricted areas).

MAP PAGE 329 (7G)
OS MAP 177/178, 162/163: TQ651753

BERKHAMSTED CASTLE

HERTFORDSHIRE – HP4 1LJ

Substantial remains of a strong motte-and-bailey castle dating from the 11th to 15th centuries. Richard, Earl of Cornwall added a 13th-century palace complex.

Managed by the Berkhamsted Castle Trust.

berkhamstedcastle.org.uk

OPENING TIMES

Summer, daily	10am-6pm
Winter, daily	10am-4pm
25 Dec & 1 Jan	Closed

VISIT US

Direction: Near Berkhamsted station

Train: Berkhamsted, adjacent

Bus: Visit traveline.info for the latest bus timetables and routes

ACQ.1929 🐕 ⚠

Caution: deep water, steep slopes, steep stairs, falling masonry.

MAP PAGE 328 (6D)
OS MAP 165, 181: SP995082

OLD GORHAMBURY HOUSE

HERTFORDSHIRE – AL3 6AH

OLD GORHAMBURY HOUSE

Remains of an immense mansion built 1563-68 by Sir Nicholas Bacon, Queen Elizabeth's Lord Keeper, and visited by the queen at least four times. Its elaborate Classical two-storey porch and other elements survive.

OPENING TIMES

Any reasonable daylight hours but not earlier than 8am or later than 6pm (last access to drive at 5.30pm and gate is locked at 6pm)

Access is via the permissive path Gorhambury Drive. This is closed to the public on 1 Jun, most Weds and Sats from Sep to Jan, and occasionally at other times, so it is not possible to visit the site on these days. Please check gorhamburyestate.co.uk for current closure details before you visit

The walk or cycle up Gorhambury Drive to the site is about 2 miles from the nearest parking. Closer access by car, followed by a ½ mile walk, is limited to Thu only, May-Sep 2pm-5pm

VISIT US

Direction: Just off A4147 on western outskirts of St Albans by the Roman Theatre of Verulamium (AL3 6AE). Walk or cycle 2 miles up permissive path Gorhambury Drive. Access by car is limited (see opening times)

Train: St Albans Abbey 3 miles, St Albans 3½ miles

Bus: Visit traveline.info for the latest bus timetables and routes

ACQ.1959 🐾 ⚠

Caution: unguarded drops, falling masonry.

MAP PAGE 328 (6E)
OS MAP 166, 182: TL110076

ROMAN WALL, ST ALBANS

HERTFORDSHIRE – AL3 4AJ

Part of the 2-mile-long wall built AD 265-70 to defend the Roman city of Verulamium, including the foundations of towers and the London Gate.

OPENING TIMES

Any reasonable daylight hours

ROMAN WALL, ST ALBANS

VISIT US

Direction: Located in Verulamium Park on the S side of St Albans, ½ mile from the centre, off the A4147

Train: St Albans Abbey ½ mile, St Albans City 1¼ miles

Bus: Visit traveline.info for the latest bus timetables and routes

ACQ.1931 ♿ 🐾 🐕 ⚠ Steep slopes.

MAP PAGE 328 (6E)
OS MAP 166, 182: TL137066

BACONSTHORPE CASTLE

NORFOLK – NR25 6LL

Atmospherically sited moated ruins of a fortified manor house, chronicling the fortunes of the ambitious Heydon family. Begun during the Wars of the Roses, it was later given its turreted Elizabethan outer gatehouse, before the family went bankrupt.

Download a free audio tour from the English Heritage website before you visit.

OPENING TIMES

Any reasonable daylight hours

VISIT US

Direction: ¾ mile N of village of Baconsthorpe off unclassified road, 3 miles E of Holt

Train: Sheringham 4½ miles

Bus: Visit traveline.info

ACQ.1966 🐾 P ⚠

Parking: charges apply to non-members, free for Members with valid car sticker.

Caution: deep water, falling masonry.

MAP PAGE 329 (1H)
OS MAP 133, 252: TG121382

BERNEY ARMS WINDMILL

NORFOLK – NR30 1SB

One of the tallest marsh mills in the Norfolk Broads, Berney Arms windmill stands over 70 feet (21 metres) high, visible for miles around. Probably built c. 1870 to grind a component of cement, it remained in use until 1948, ending its days powering a still-visible scoop wheel to drain surrounding marshes.

Supported by the RSPB.

OPENING TIMES

Currently closed for essential maintenance work. Please check website for current information

VISIT US

Direction: 3½ miles NE of Reedham on the N bank of River Yare. Accessible by hired boat, or by footpath from Halvergate (3½ miles)

Train: Berney Arms ¼ mile

Tel: 01493 857900

ACQ.1950 🐕 ⚠

Dogs on leads (exterior only). Assistance dogs allowed inside.

Caution: steep stairs.

MAP PAGE 329 (2J)
OS MAP 134, OL40: TG465049

BINHAM MARKET CROSS

NORFOLK – NR21 0DW

Tall shaft of a 15th-century cross, on the site of an annual fair held from the 1100s until the 1950s.

OPENING TIMES

Any reasonable daylight hours

VISIT US

Direction: Located on the Binham village green

Train: Wighton on the Wells & Walsingham Light Railway 3½ miles

Bus: Visit traveline.info for the latest bus timetables and routes

ACQ.1949 ♿ 🐕

MAP PAGE 329 (1H)
OS MAP 132, 251: TF984396

BINHAM PRIORY

NORFOLK – NR21 0DQ

Among the most impressive monastic ruins in Norfolk. The virtually complete nave adjoining the ruins is now the parish church, with a striking 13th-century west front, tiers of Norman arches and painted screens.

Site finds display and children's activity area within the church.

Managed by Binham Parochial Church Council.

OPENING TIMES

Binham Priory (monastic ruins): Any reasonable daylight hours

BINHAM PRIORY

Priory Church:
Summer, daily	9am-6pm
Winter, daily	9am-4pm

VISIT US

Direction: ¼ mile NW of village of Binham on road off B1388

Train: Wighton on the Wells & Walsingham Light Railway 3½ miles

Bus: Visit traveline.info for the latest bus timetables and routes

Tel: 01328 830362

ACQ.1933 📷 ♿ 🐕 E 🚶 🚻 ♿
P ⚠

Exhibition and toilets are in adjacent parish church.

Caution: unguarded drops, falling masonry.

MAP PAGE 329 (1H)
OS MAP 132, 251: TF982399

BLAKENEY GUILDHALL

NORFOLK – NR25 7NA

Remains of a 15th-century merchant's house with brick-vaulted undercroft, recalling Blakeney's medieval prosperity. Later the guildhall of local fish merchants.

Managed by Blakeney Parish Council.

OPENING TIMES

Adjacent to Blakeney Quay, the exterior can be viewed at any time. For access to the interior, check our website

VISIT US

Direction: In Blakeney off A149

Train: Sheringham 9 miles

Bus: Visit traveline.info for the latest bus timetables and routes

Tel: 01263 741106

ACQ.1956 🐕 ⚠

Dogs on leads (exterior only). Assistance dogs allowed inside.

Caution: steep stairs.

MAP PAGE 329 (1H)
OS MAP 133, 251: TG028441

BURGH CASTLE ROMAN FORT

NORFOLK – NR31 9QB

The imposing towered walls of a Roman 'Saxon Shore' fort, with panoramic views over Breydon Water.

Owned and managed by Norfolk Archaeological Trust.

OPENING TIMES

Any reasonable daylight hours

VISIT US

Direction: At far W end of Breydon Water on unclassified road, 3 miles W of Great Yarmouth

Train: Great Yarmouth 5 miles

Bus: Visit traveline.info for the latest bus timetables and routes

ACQ.1929 ♿ 🐕 **P** ⚠

Car park locked at 6pm.

There is a circular all-access route around the fort – see norfarchtrust.org.uk for further details.

Caution: steep slopes, steep stairs, falling masonry.

MAP PAGE 329 (2J)
OS MAP 134, OL40: TG475047

CAISTER ROMAN FORT NORFOLK – NR30 5JS

Excavated remains of a Roman 'Saxon Shore' fort, built around AD 200 and occupied until the late 4th century.

Managed by Great Yarmouth Borough Council.

OPENING TIMES

Any reasonable daylight hours

VISIT US

Direction: From Great Yarmouth, follow the A149 northbound and then the A149 Caister Bypass. Follow brown tourist signs for Caister Roman Fort. From other directions follow signs for Great Yarmouth and then brown tourist signs from the Caister Bypass roundabout. Parking and the entrance to the Fort are situated off a lay-by on Norwich Road ¼ mile from the roundabout

Train: Great Yarmouth 3 miles

Bus: Visit traveline.info for the latest bus timetables and routes

Tel: 01493 846534

ACQ.1954 🐕

On-street parking close by.

Step-free access to part of the monument.

MAP PAGE 329 (2J)
OS MAP 134, OL40: TG517123

CASTLE RISING CASTLE NORFOLK – PE31 6AH

One of the most complete and elaborately decorated Norman keeps in England, surrounded by stupendous earthworks. It was begun in 1138 by the ambitious lord William d'Albini for his wife Adeliza, beautiful widow of Henry I. In the 14th century it became the retirement home of Queen Isabella, widow (and alleged murderer) of Edward II.

Owned and managed by Lord Howard of Rising.

castlerising.co.uk

OPENING TIMES

1 Apr-1 Nov, daily	10am-6pm
	(or dusk if earlier in Oct)
2 Nov-31 Mar, Wed-Sun	10am-4pm
24-26 Dec	Closed

VISIT US

Direction: Located 4 miles NE of King's Lynn off A149

Train: King's Lynn 4½ miles

Bus: Visit traveline.info

Tel: 01553 631330

NON-MEMBERS

Adult **£5.00** | Concession **£4.00**
Child **£3.50** | Family 2 Adults **£15.50**

There will be a premium payable by all visitors, including Members, on special event days – please check castlerising.co.uk for details

ACQ.1958 🍴 ♿ 🐕 🚹 🅿 📷 ⚠

Disabled access (exterior only, toilets).

Dogs allowed on leads (grounds only).

Caution: steep slopes, steep stairs, falling masonry.

MAP PAGE 329 (2G)
OS MAP 132, 250: TF666246

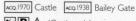

CASTLE ACRE
CASTLE AND BAILEY GATE

—— NORFOLK – PE32 2XB ——

The delightful village of Castle Acre boasts an extraordinary wealth of history.

Situated on the Peddars Way, a major trade and pilgrim route to Thetford, Bromholm Priory and Walsingham, it's a very rare and complete survival of a Norman planned settlement. It includes a castle, town, fine parish church and associated monastery. All this is the work of a powerful Norman baronial family, the Warennes, mainly during the 11th and 12th centuries.

The first William de Warenne founded the castle soon after the Conquest, probably as a stone 'country house'. But during the early 12th century more disturbed conditions prompted its conversion into a strong keep, further defended by stone walls and an immense system of colossal banks and ditches. It offers perhaps the finest medieval castle earthworks anywhere in England.

Meanwhile, the 'planned town' established outside the castle was also protected by earthwork defences with stone gates. The Bailey Gate of c.1200 survives, with the road into the village running between its towers.

You can trace the ancient street layout of this attractive village, lined with flint or brick houses, before exploring both the great castle earthworks and the extensive priory remains.

Pick up a family trail, available from Castle Acre Priory.

OPENING TIMES
Any reasonable daylight hours

VISIT US
Direction: Castle (PE32 2XB) located at SE edge of Castle Acre, 5 miles N of Swaffham. Parking in Pye's Lane. Bailey Gate (PE32 2AG) located in the centre of Castle Acre at the top of Bailey St

Bus: Visit traveline.info

ACQ.1970 Castle   ACQ.1938 Bailey Gate

🐾 P ⚠ (Castle only)

Caution: Gate: beware of traffic.
Castle: steep slopes, steep stairs, failing masonry.

MAP PAGE 329 (2G)
OS MAP 132, 236/238
BAILEY GATE: TF819152
CASTLE: TF819152

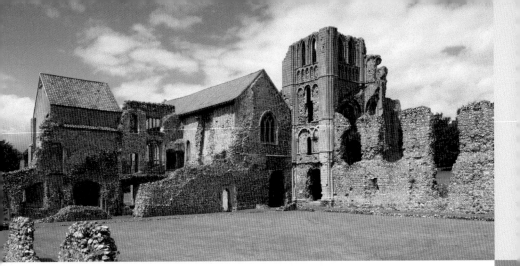

CASTLE ACRE PRIORY

—— NORFOLK – PE32 2XD ——

A family trail and fresh displays offer plenty for you to enjoy at the priory.

Among the best preserved monastic sites in England, the immense size and variety of Castle Acre Priory can't fail to impress. Founded in about 1090 by William de Warenne II, it reflected his family's devotion to the famous French monastery of Cluny. You can see Cluny-style architectural decoration displayed in the beautiful west front of the great 12th-century priory church. Explore beyond and discover the impressive remains of the cloister and monks' living quarters, including a gigantic, two-storey, 24-seater toilet block.

The west range is virtually complete and fully roofed. Its flint-chequered porch and oriel-windowed prior's lodging make a striking group with the church's west front. A mansion in itself, the lodging includes a chamber sumptuously revamped in early Tudor times, with a ceiling painted with Tudor roses. The adjacent prior's chapel displays intriguing traces of medieval wall paintings.

Be sure to leave time to explore the display of archaeological site finds and take an audio tour featuring a 15th-century chant from a Castle Acre songbook.

OPENING TIMES

1 Apr-30 Oct, daily	10am-5pm
31 Oct-31 Mar, Sat-Sun	10am-4pm
24-26 Dec & 1 Jan	Closed

Last entry 30 mins before closing

VISIT US

Direction: ¼ mile W of village of Castle Acre, 5 miles N of Swaffham

Bus: Visit traveline.info

Tel: 01760 755394

NON-MEMBERS

Adult **£9.00** | Concession **£8.10** | Child **£5.40**
Family 2 Adults **£23.40** | Family 1 Adult **£14.40**

ACQ.1929

Disabled access (ground floor and grounds only).

Toilets (a short walk. 50 metres from entrance).

MAP PAGE 329 (2G)
OS MAP 132, 236/238: TF814148

COW TOWER, NORWICH
NORFOLK – NR1 4AA

Among the earliest purpose-built English artillery blockhouses, this brick tower of c. 1398-99 commands a strategic point in Norwich's defences.

External viewing only.

Managed by Norwich City Council.

OPENING TIMES

Exterior only: Any reasonable daylight hours

VISIT US

Direction: In Norwich, near cathedral (approx. ½ mile walk)

Train: Norwich ½ mile

Bus: Visit traveline.info for the latest bus timetables and routes

Tel: 01603 706229

ACQ.1950

MAP PAGE 329 (2J)
OS MAP 134, OL40/237: TG240092

CREAKE ABBEY
NORFOLK – NR21 9LF

CREAKE ABBEY

Set in tranquil countryside, the flint-walled ruins of this Augustinian abbey church tell a sad story of monastic disaster. After a devastating 15th-century fire, it was drastically reduced in size, with arches and windows blocked. Then plague struck, the last abbot died alone, and in 1506 the abbey closed.

Managed by Mr and Mrs A C Scott.

creakeabbey.co.uk

OPENING TIMES

Any reasonable daylight hours

VISIT US

Direction: N of North Creake off B1355

Bus: Visit traveline.info for the latest bus timetables and routes

ACQ.1950 Caution: falling masonry.

MAP PAGE 329 (1G)
OS MAP 132, 251: TF856395

NORTH ELMHAM CHAPEL
NORFOLK – NR20 5JU

A small Norman chapel, probably on the site of the Saxon cathedral of East Anglia. Later converted into a 14th-century fortified mansion by Henry Despenser, warrior-Bishop of Norwich.

Managed by North Elmham Parish Council.

OPENING TIMES

Any reasonable daylight hours

NORTH ELMHAM CHAPEL

VISIT US

Direction: Located 6 miles N of East Dereham on B1110

Train: Wymondham 17 miles

Bus: Visit traveline.info for the latest bus timetables and routes

ACQ.1948

Disabled access to some of the site on gravel paths.

Caution: steep slopes.

MAP PAGE 329 (2H)
OS MAP 132, 238: TF988216

ST OLAVE'S PRIORY
NORFOLK – NR31 9HE

The wonderfully complete, 14th-century, brick-vaulted refectory undercroft – later a cottage occupied until 1902 – of a small Augustinian priory.

OPENING TIMES

Any reasonable daylight hours

VISIT US

Direction: Located 5½ miles SW of the town of Great Yarmouth on A143

Train: Haddiscoe 1¼ miles

Bus: Visit traveline.info for the latest bus timetables and routes

ACQ.1921

Disabled access (exterior only).

Dogs allowed on leads in the grounds only.

Caution: steep stairs.

MAP PAGE 329 (3J)
OS MAP 134, OL40: TM459996

GREAT YARMOUTH ROW HOUSES
AND GREYFRIARS' CLOISTERS

—— NORFOLK – NR30 2RG ——

These unique and vividly presented houses are rare survivors of Yarmouth's once-crowded 'Rows' – narrow alleyways linking the town's main thoroughfares.

Most 'Row houses' were destroyed by Second World War bombing or post-war clearances. These surviving examples are now presented at various stages in their history, leading you into centuries of fishing-port life. There are toys in the children's upstairs bedrooms.

Both Row 111 House and the Old Merchant's House were built in the early 17th century as wealthy merchants' residences, but later sub-divided into tenements. You'll find the Old Merchant's House, which has spectacular Jacobean plaster ceilings, appearing as it was in the 1850s, when fish merchant Simon Fleet occupied half the property, and in the 1890s when the other half housed Martha King's family. Adjacent Row 111 House is shown as in 1942 (just before it suffered a direct hit by an incendiary bomb).

Nearby stands Greyfriars' Cloisters, the remains of a medieval friary later converted into a number of Row dwellings. Traces of their interior features exist on the walls of the Cloister and church, which also display early 14th-century wall paintings.

OPENING TIMES

1 Apr-30 Sep, Fri-Sun	10am-5pm
1 Oct-31 Mar	Closed

Last entry 30 mins before closing

Due to essential conservation works, the Row Houses and Cloisters may be closed. Please check the website before visiting for up-to-date information

VISIT US

Direction: Great Yarmouth, follow signs for Historic Quay

Train: Great Yarmouth ½ mile

Bus: Visit traveline.info for the latest bus timetables and routes

Tel: 01493 857900

NON-MEMBERS

Adult **£6.60** | Concession **£5.90** | Child **£4.00**
Family 2 Adults **£17.20** | Family 1 Adult **£10.60**

Please see our website for guided tours of Greyfriars' Cloisters (may be closed for conservation)

ACQ 1950 | 🐾 | ▢ | 🍴 | 👶 | 🚫 | 📷 | ⚠ | OVP

MAP PAGE 329 (2J)
OS MAP 134, OL40
HOUSES: TG525072
CLOISTERS: TG524073

GRIME'S GRAVES
PREHISTORIC FLINT MINE

——— NORFOLK – IP26 5DE ———

NEW FOR 2022

A new staircase now allows children seven and over to safely enter the mine shaft.

Grime's Graves is the only Neolithic flint mine in Britain open to visitors.

A lunar landscape of over 400 shafts, quarries and spoil dumps, they were first named Grim's Graves by the Anglo-Saxons – meaning the pagan god Grim's quarries, or 'the Devil's holes'. Not until one was excavated in 1868-70 were they identified as flint mines dug over 5,000 years ago, during the later Neolithic and early Bronze Ages.

Prehistoric miners sought the fine quality, jet-black flint floorstone, which occurs some 9 to 12 metres (approximately 33 feet) below surface level. Digging with red deer antler picks, they sank shafts and dug radiating galleries following the seams of flint. Today, you can have the unforgettable experience of descending 9 metres (30 feet) by ladder into one excavated shaft.

Grime's Graves flint was prized for its distinctive colour and easily 'knapped' qualities. Rough-outs of axes and other tools were made here, but then traded on and finished elsewhere. Set amid the unique Breckland heath landscape, Grime's Graves is also a Site of Special Scientific Interest, the habitat of a variety of rare and distinctive plants and animals.

Discover more about Neolithic mining in the introductory exhibition, including a virtual tour of the mines and landscape and touchable reproduction Neolithic tools.

OPENING TIMES
1 Apr-30 Oct, Wed-Sun	10am-5pm

Children must be seven and over to enter the mine shaft

31 Oct-31 Mar	Closed

Last entry 30 mins before closing

VISIT US
Direction: Located 7 miles NW of Thetford off A134

Train: Brandon 3½ miles

Tel: 01842 810656

NON-MEMBERS
Adult **£7.80** | Concession **£7.00**
Child **£4.70** | Family 2 Adults **£20.30**
Family 1 Adult **£12.50**

ACQ.1931 ♿ 🚼 E 👷 📷 🚶 🧍 P 📷
⚠ OVP

Disabled access (exhibition area only; access track rough).

Dogs on leads (restricted areas).

Visitors intending to descend the shaft should wear flat shoes.

MAP PAGE 329 (3G)
OS MAP 144, 229: TL817899

THETFORD, CHURCH OF THE HOLY SEPULCHRE

NORFOLK – IP24 3PW

The only remains in England of a priory church of Canons of the Holy Sepulchre, later used as a barn.

Managed by Thetford Town Council.

OPENING TIMES

All year, daily	10am-5pm
(or dusk, whichever is earlier)	
25 Dec	Closed

VISIT US

Direction: Located on the W side of Thetford on A134

Train: Thetford ¾ mile

Bus: Visit traveline.info for the latest bus timetables and routes

Tel: 01842 754038

ACQ.1977 🐾 ⚠

Caution: falling masonry.

MAP PAGE 329 (3G)
OS MAP 144, 229: TL865831

THETFORD PRIORY

NORFOLK – IP24 1BB

Extensive remains of one of the most important East Anglian monasteries, the Cluniac Priory of Our Lady of Thetford. Founded in the early 12th century, it owed much of its prosperity to a miraculous appearance of the Virgin Mary. Her statue here was discovered to conceal relics

THETFORD PRIORY

of saints and became a magnet for pilgrims. Survivals include church and cloister walls, the impressive shell of the priors' lodging and an almost complete 14th-century gatehouse. Burial place of the earls and dukes of Norfolk for 400 years, it enjoyed their powerful protection. It was almost the last English monastery to be suppressed, in 1540.

Managed by Thetford Town Council.

OPENING TIMES

1 Apr-30 Sep, daily	8am-6pm
1 Oct-31 Mar, daily	8am-4pm
25 Dec	Closed

VISIT US

Direction: Near Thetford station

Train: Thetford ¾ mile

Bus: Visit traveline.info for the latest bus timetables and routes

Tel: 01842 754038

ACQ.1932 ♿ 🐾 ⚠

Disabled access to some areas on paths.

Limited free parking at the entrance to the priory.

Caution: falling masonry.

MAP PAGE 329 (3G)
OS MAP 144, 229: TL865831

THETFORD WARREN LODGE

NORFOLK – IP24 3NE

Probably built c. 1400 by the Prior of Thetford as a refuge from armed poachers. Much later used by local 'warreners', who harvested rabbits here.

THETFORD WARREN LODGE

OPENING TIMES

Exterior only: Any reasonable daylight hours

VISIT US

Direction: Located 2 miles W of Thetford off B1107

Train: Thetford 2½ miles

Bus: Visit traveline.info for the latest bus timetables and routes

ACQ.1948 🐾 P

Parking (not English Heritage).

MAP PAGE 329 (3G)
OS MAP 144, 229: TL839984

WEETING CASTLE

NORFOLK – IP27 0RQ

The ruins of a substantial early medieval moated manor house, built in local flint.

OPENING TIMES

Any reasonable daylight hours. Access via steps

VISIT US

Direction: Located 2 miles N of Brandon off B1106

Train: Brandon 1½ miles

Bus: Visit traveline.info for the latest bus timetables and routes

ACQ.1926 🐾 ⚠

No wheelchair access.

Caution: deep water, falling masonry.

MAP PAGE 329 (3G)
OS MAP 144, 229: TL778891

BURY ST EDMUNDS ABBEY
SUFFOLK – IP33 1UZ

Extensive remains of the wealthiest and most powerful English Benedictine monastery, shrine of St Edmund. They include the Great Gate and Norman Tower and ruins of the immense church.

Managed by West Suffolk District Council.

OPENING TIMES

Apr-May, Mon-Sat	7.30am-6pm	
Sun	9am-6pm	
Jun-Sep, Mon-Sat	7.30am-8pm	
Sun	9am-8pm	
Oct, Mon-Sat	7.30am-6pm	
Sun	9am-6pm	
Nov-Feb, Mon-Sat	7.30am-4.30pm	
Sun	9am-4.30pm	
Mar, Mon-Sat	7.30am-6pm	
Sun	9am-6pm	

The dates/times are guidelines and may vary depending on daylight hours

VISIT US

Direction: E end of town centre

Train: Bury St Edmunds 1 mile

Bus: Visit traveline.info for the latest bus timetables and routes

Tel: 01284 764667

ACQ.1955
Caution: falling masonry.
New guidebook available via website.

MAP PAGE 329 (4G)
OS MAP 155, 211: TL857642

LEISTON ABBEY
SUFFOLK – IP16 4TD

Among Suffolk's most impressive monastic ruins, the mainly 14th-century remains of an abbey of Premonstratensian canons.

Managed by Pro Corda Trust.

OPENING TIMES
Any reasonable daylight hours

VISIT US

Direction: N of Leiston off B1069

Train: Saxmundham 5 miles

Bus: Visit traveline.info for the latest bus timetables and routes

Tel: 01728 831354

ACQ.1964
Caution: steep stairs, falling masonry.

MAP PAGE 329 (4J)
OS MAP 156, 212: TM445642

LINDSEY ST JAMES'S CHAPEL
SUFFOLK – IP7 6QA

A pretty, thatched, 13th-century chapel with lancet windows.

OPENING TIMES
Closed for essential maintenance. Please check website for information

VISIT US

Direction: Located on an unclassified road ½ mile E of Rose Green and 8 miles E of Sudbury

Train: Sudbury 8 miles

Bus: Visit traveline.info for the latest bus timetables and routes

ACQ.1930
Disabled access (single step).

MAP PAGE 329 (4H)
OS MAP 155, 196: TL9784444

OUR EVENTS

Check out our year-long programme of events.

english-heritage.org.uk/events

MOULTON PACKHORSE BRIDGE
SUFFOLK – CB8 8SR

A pretty, four-arched, late medieval bridge spanning the River Kennet on the old route from Cambridge to Bury St Edmunds.

OPENING TIMES
Any reasonable daylight hours

VISIT US

Direction: In Moulton off B1085, 4 miles E of Newmarket

Train: Kennett 2 miles

Bus: Visit traveline.info for the latest bus timetables and routes

ACQ.1977
Caution: beware of traffic.

MAP PAGE 329 (4G)
OS MAP 154, 210/226: TL698645

CHECK ONLINE

Pre-booking for visits to our staffed sites may be required, check our website for the latest guidance.

LANDGUARD FORT

—— SUFFOLK – IP11 3TW ——

Landguard Fort defends the approach to Harwich Harbour, an important haven for shipping. The fort stands near a nature reserve and a busy container port.

An earlier fort here was the site of the last opposed seaborne invasion of England, when the Royal Marines (in their first land battle) repulsed a Dutch attack in 1667. The current polygonal fort was begun in the 18th century and updated in Victorian times, with emplacements for heavy guns and a fortified barrack block. Outside batteries were added in 1901, and in 1951 part of the fort became a Cold War control room.

Guided tours and audio tours of the fort are supplemented by an audio-visual presentation.

Managed by Landguard Fort Trust. landguard.com

The Felixstowe Museum – an award-winning visitor attraction – is next to the fort in a building originally used for harbour defence and submarine mining. (For museum opening times and prices see felixstowemuseum.org or call 01394 674355. 20% discount for Members.)

OPENING TIMES

1 Apr-30 Sep, Thu-Sun	10am-5pm
1-30 Oct, Thu-Sun	10am-4pm
31 Oct-31 Mar	Closed

Last entry 90 minutes before closing. Pre-booked group and education visits are welcome and may be possible outside normal opening times

Check website for school holiday opening hours, which will be published nearer the time

VISIT US

Direction: 1 mile S of Felixstowe town centre – follow signs to Landguard Point

Train: Felixstowe 2½ miles

Bus: Visit traveline.info

Bicycle: The fort lies on National Cycle Route 51 between Ipswich and Harwich

Tel: 01394 675900

NON-MEMBERS

Please check website for details

Free entry for children under 5 and wheelchair users

There may be a premium payable by all visitors, including Members, on event days – please check landguard.com for details

ACQ.1975 🎧 ♿ 🐕 🛡 E 🖼 🅿 📷 ⚠

Disabled access (to most of ground floor).

Caution: CCTV at site, steep stairs.

MAP PAGE 329 (5J)
OS MAP 169, 197: TM284319

FRAMLINGHAM CASTLE

SUFFOLK – IP13 9BP

One of medieval England's finest baronial fortresses, impressive Framlingham Castle offers you intriguing interpretation, hands-on children's activities and a spacious café in a historic setting. You'll discover the stories of medieval aristocrats, a Tudor queen and Georgian poorhouse children.

Framlingham Castle's spectacular walls are more than 10 metres (32 feet) high and 2 metres (6.5 feet) thick, and studded with 13 strong towers. Raised in the 1190s, they were among the first of their kind ever built in England. They proclaim the power and status of the earls and dukes of Norfolk, who owned the fortress for over four centuries.

You can follow the wall-top walk round them to view eight centuries of history from above, guided by a lively audio tour and panels which tell you about the castle's surroundings – the pretty market town, the parkland, the castle's outer earthworks and the Mere, the lake which mirrors the fortress walls. Don't forget to look up at the tall Tudor chimneys which crown every tower, each one decorated in a different brick design. There's a lift for easier access to our exhibition.

The exhibition, 'Power and Poverty', traces how the castle housed both the very richest and the very poorest over the centuries. You'll discover how successive dynasties of Framlingham's owners – the defiant Bigods, the mighty Mowbrays and the scheming Howards of Tudor times – wielded almost kingly power in East Anglia. Mary Tudor famously mustered her supporters here in 1553 before being crowned queen.

Later, in complete contrast, the castle walls sheltered a workhouse for the local poor, which operated until 1839.

The presentation includes Tudor and workhouse display costumes and interactive games, and you can try on hats from a Norman helmet to a workhouse pauper's cap. The 'Who Ate What' game helps you create plates of imitation foods and match them to the people – aristocrats, the very poor or 'everyone else' – who would have eaten them.

If this gives you an appetite, our revamped café serves locally sourced food and Suffolk specialities in a baronial setting with stone walls, round-arched windows and a huge fireplace.

There's plenty more to see and do at Framlingham. The Lanman Museum within the castle displays an intriguing variety of local objects, from kitchenware to a parish coffin. Outside the walls, you can explore the castle's outer defences, including the deep ditch and the grassy outer court between fortress and Mere. Leave time, too, to wander the picture-book market town and admire the impressive tombs of the Howard castle-owners, and that of Henry Fitzroy, Henry VIII's illegitimate son, in the parish church.

OPENING TIMES

1 Apr-30 Jun, daily	10am-5pm
1 Jul-31 Aug, daily	10am-6pm
1 Sep-30 Oct, daily	10am-5pm
31 Oct-23 Dec, Sat-Sun	10am-4pm
2 Jan-10 Feb, Sat-Sun	10am-4pm
11-19 Feb, daily	10am-4pm
20 Feb-31 Mar, Wed-Sun	10am-4pm

Christmas Opening

24-25 Dec	Closed
26 Dec-1 Jan, daily	10am-4pm

Please check website for additional opening times

Last entry 30 mins before closing

VISIT US

Address: Framlingham Castle, Church Street, Framlingham, Suffolk

Direction: In Framlingham on B1116

Train: Wickham Market 6½ miles; Saxmundham 7 miles

Bus: Visit traveline.info for the latest bus timetables and routes

Tel: 0370 333 1181

Local Tourist Information: Woodbridge: 01394 382240

NON-MEMBERS

Adult £12.80 | Concession £11.50
Child £7.60 | Family 2 Adults £33.20
Family 1 Adult £20.40

Disabled access (grounds and ground floor only).

Parking: charges apply to non-members, free for Members with valid car sticker.

MAP PAGE 329 (4J)
OS MAP 156, 212: TM287637

ORFORD CASTLE

—— SUFFOLK – IP12 2ND ——

Discover the unique polygonal tower-keep of Orford Castle, set in a pretty Suffolk coastal town.

Built by Henry II between 1165 and 1173, the castle was intended to curtail the power of turbulent East Anglian barons such as Hugh Bigod of Framlingham Castle. An 18-sided drum with three square turrets, its keep was built to a revolutionary new design. From the roof you can enjoy magnificent views seaward to Orford Ness.

Today, both exterior and interior survive almost intact, allowing you to explore the basement, with its vital well, and the lower and upper halls. Around these polygonal rooms, a maze of passages leads you to the chapel, kitchen and other chambers. Displays and hands-on features reveal how the rooms might have been used. There are multimedia guides, including one for families, and a large model of the castle shows you how it appeared when newly built, with the keep surrounded by a towered curtain wall. Find out about the 'Wild Man of Orford', a mysterious being from the sea allegedly imprisoned here in the 12th century.

In the upper hall, take in the Orford Museum Trust's exhibition, featuring changing displays of local finds, from prehistoric to modern.

OPENING TIMES

1 Apr-30 Oct, daily	10am-5pm
31 Oct-10 Feb, Sat-Sun	10am-4pm
11-19 Feb, daily	10am-4pm
20 Feb-31 Mar, Sat-Sun	10am-4pm
Christmas Opening 24-26 Dec & 1 Jan	Closed

Last entry 30 mins before closing

VISIT US

Direction: In Orford on B1084, 20 miles NE of Ipswich

Train: Wickham Market 8 miles

Bus: Visit traveline.info for the latest bus timetables and routes

Tel: 01394 450472

Local Tourist Information: Woodbridge: 01394 382240

NON-MEMBERS

Adult **£9.00** | Concession **£8.10** | Child **£5.40**
Family 2 Adults **£23.40** | Family 1 Adult **£14.40**

Toilets (close-by in Orford town).

Parking: charges apply to non-members, free for Members with valid English Heritage car sticker.

MAP PAGE 329 (4J)   OS MAP 169, 212: TM419499

SAXTEAD GREEN
POST MILL

—— SUFFOLK – IP13 9QQ ——

Come and admire impressive Saxtead Green Post Mill, back in action with a new set of craftsman-built sails.

In an idyllic village green setting near Framlingham Castle, this striking four-sailed corn-grinding mill is a rare survivor of a post mill, whose whole body turns on its roundhouse base, propelled by wind on a 'fantail'. Originally raised in about 1796, it's been rebuilt three times. It ceased commercial milling in 1947, but remains one of only a handful of Suffolk mills still fully operational.

Its sails have a span of 18.2 metres, but were in poor condition. Working with Suffolk millwright Tim Whiting – one of the few practitioners of a critically endangered craft – we've given it a new set of sails, copied from 1930s photographs. We have installed a replacement structural staircase to the buck house and carried out repairs to the mill and the fantail at the rear of the windmill.

An audio experience enables you to dial up stories of the mill and its millers over the years – just call 0303 003 4000 to listen in.

OPENING TIMES

1 Apr-30 Sep, Fri-Sat & Bank Hols	12pm-5pm
1 Oct-31 Mar	Closed

Last entry 30 mins before closing

VISIT US

Direction: 2½ miles NW of Framlingham on A1120

Train: Wickham Market 9 miles

Bus: Visit traveline.info for the latest bus timetables and routes

Tel: 01728 685789

NON-MEMBERS

Adult **£5.60** | Concession **£5.00** | Child **£3.40**
Family 2 Adults **£14.60** | Family 1 Adult **£9.00**

MAP PAGE 329 (4J)
OS MAP 156, 212: TM253644

WELCOME TO THE

EAST
MIDLANDS

Kirby Hall, Northamptonshire

East Midlands

West Yorkshire

East Riding

South Yorkshire

North Lincolnshire

North East Lincolnshire

Glossop

7

Buxton
Bakewell
1
Chesterfield
5
8
3
2
6
4
9

24

Worksop

23
14
Gainsborough

Market Rasen

Lincolnshire

15
Lincoln

13
Skegness

17

16

Boston

Mansfield

Nottinghamshire

Derby

Derbyshire

Nottingham

Grantham

Spalding

Staffordshire

10
Loughborough

12
11
Leicester

Leicestershire

Oakham

Rutland

25
21
18

Corby

20

Market
Harborough
22
Kettering

Northamptonshire

19

Daventry

Northampton

Brackley

West Midlands

Warwickshire

Norfolk

Cambridgeshire

Bedfordshire

Essex

Buckinghamshire

Hertfordshire

Gloucestershire

Oxfordshire

Peak District Old Stones Way

38 miles | 3-4 days

From the rock fortress of Carl Wark you can see your destination of Minninglow hill – this is ancient landscape design on a vast and beautiful scale. Feel the connection between places relating to burial, ritual and celebration from successive ages over thousands of years.

Discover English Heritage sites along the pilgrimage route

A Nine Ladies Stone Circle *(p.180)*

B Arbor Low Stone Circle and Gib Hill Barrow *(p.180)*

In partnership with

the **British Pilgrimage Trust**

View more details and a downloadable version of this route at english-heritage.org.uk/pilgrimage

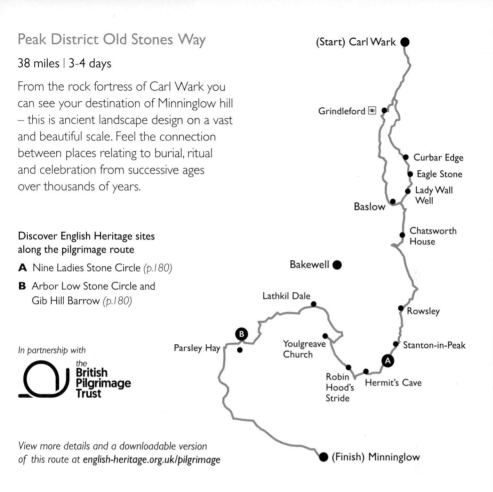

(Start) Carl Wark

Grindleford

Curbar Edge
Eagle Stone
Lady Wall Well
Baslow

Chatsworth House

Bakewell

Lathkil Dale

Rowsley

Parsley Hay

Youlgreave Church

Stanton-in-Peak

B

A

Robin Hood's Stride

Hermit's Cave

(Finish) Minninglow

ARBOR LOW STONE CIRCLE AND GIB HILL BARROW

DERBYSHIRE – DE45 1JS

An important Neolithic henge atmospherically set amid moorland. Within an earthen bank, some fifty recumbent slabs surround a central stone 'cove'. Gib Hill is a burial mound.

Please note: Access charge of £1 per person to use path across private land to the stone circle.

Managed by Peak District National Park Authority.

OPENING TIMES

Any reasonable daylight hours

Access through private land, for which the landowner issues a charge of £1 per person

VISIT US

Direction: ½ mile E of A515, 2 miles S of Monyash

Train: Buxton 10 miles

Bus: Visit **traveline.info** for the latest bus timetables and routes

Tel: 01629 816200

ACQ.1884

Beware – cattle may be grazing.

MAP PAGE 330 (2E)
OS MAP 119, OL24: SK160636

BOLSOVER CUNDY HOUSE

DERBYSHIRE – S44 6BQ

This charming cottage-like 17th-century conduit house, with vaulted stone-slab roof, once supplied water to Bolsover Castle.

OPENING TIMES

Exterior only: Any reasonable daylight hours

VISIT US

Direction: Off M1 at junction 29A, follow signs for Bolsover Castle. Between junctions of Craggs Rd and Houfton Rd with Bolsover Hill, Bolsover, 6 miles E of Chesterfield on A362

Train: Chesterfield 6 miles or Langwith – Whaley Thorns 4½ miles

Bus: Visit **traveline.info** for the latest bus timetables and routes

Tel: 01246 822844 (Bolsover Castle)

ACQ.1945

MAP PAGE 331 (2F)
OS MAP 120, 269: SK471709

HOB HURST'S HOUSE

DERBYSHIRE – DE4 2NT

A square prehistoric burial mound with earthwork ditch and bank, amid remote moorland. Named after a local goblin.

Managed by Peak District National Park Authority.

OPENING TIMES

Any reasonable daylight hours

Access is across moorland with gates and stiles

VISIT US

Direction: On open moorland from unclassified road off B5057, 9 miles W of Chesterfield

Train: Chesterfield 9 miles

Bus: Visit **traveline.info** for the latest bus timetables and routes

Tel: 01629 816200

ACQ.1884

MAP PAGE 330 (2E)
OS MAP 119, OL24: SK287692

NINE LADIES STONE CIRCLE

DERBYSHIRE – DE4 2LS

A small Bronze Age stone circle, traditionally believed to represent nine ladies turned to stone.

Managed by Peak District National Park Authority.

OPENING TIMES

Any reasonable daylight hours

Access is through fields and woodland with gates and stiles

VISIT US

Direction: From an unclassified road off A6, 5 miles SE of Bakewell

Train: Matlock 4½ miles

Bus: Visit **traveline.info** for the latest bus timetables and routes

Tel: 01629 816200

ACQ.1883

MAP PAGE 330 (2E)
OS MAP 119, OL24: SK249635

HARDWICK OLD HALL DERBYSHIRE – S44 5QJ

SUTTON SCARSDALE HALL

DERBYSHIRE – S44 5UR

The spectacular hilltop shell of Sutton Scarsdale Hall tells the story of the rise and fall of a great mansion. It was built in 1724-29 for the fourth Earl of Scarsdale, employing the very finest craftsmen, but its immense cost almost bankrupted his heirs. Eventually, in 1919, its lavish interiors were stripped out and sold; several rooms still survive in American museums. Having narrowly escaped demolition, the impressive roofless shell is still being conserved.

A rare opportunity to explore the 'bare bones' of a towering Elizabethan mansion, built by the formidable Bess of Hardwick. Daughter of an impoverished local squire, Bess rose via four increasingly advantageous marriages to become Countess of Shrewsbury, and perhaps the richest woman in England. Built on the site of her birthplace, the Old Hall proclaimed her success. Before it was finished, she began the even grander Hardwick Hall nearby.

Though the Old Hall is now roofless, you can still ascend through four storeys to admire lavishly decorated plasterwork and overmantels in the former state rooms, and explore the basement kitchen and service rooms. There are fine views of Hardwick Hall and the surrounding countryside, an audio tour and a revealing ground floor exhibition.

Managed by English Heritage and owned by the National Trust.

OPENING TIMES

A major conservation project is under way, so access will be limited. Please check the website for details

VISIT US

Direction: 8 miles SE of Chesterfield, off A6175 (J29 of M1)

Train: Chesterfield 8 miles

Bus: Visit traveline.info for the latest bus timetables and routes

Tel: 01246 850431

NON-MEMBERS

Adult £9.00 | Concession £8.10
Child £5.40 | Family 2 Adults £23.40
Family 1 Adult £14.40

ACQ.1959 🎧 ✕ E ⊡ ⧊ ⬆ P 🖼
⚠ OVP

MAP PAGE 331 (2F)
OS MAP 120, 269: SK462637

CHECK ONLINE

Check our website for latest pre-booking guidance.

OPENING TIMES

Exterior only:

Summer, daily	10am-6pm
Winter, daily	10am-4pm
24-26 Dec & 1 Jan	Closed

Due to a major conservation project, the hall is currently inaccessible. The grounds remain open. Please check the website for further details

VISIT US

Direction: Between Chesterfield and Bolsover, 1½ miles S of Arkwright Town

Train: Chesterfield 5 miles

Bus: Visit traveline.info

ACQ.1971 ♿ ✕ P 🖼 ⚠

Caution: falling masonry.

MAP PAGE 331 (2F)
OS MAP 120, 269: SK442689

BOLSOVER CASTLE

DERBYSHIRE – S44 6PR

Exquisitely restored to recreate its past glories, Bolsover Castle was the fantasy hilltop pleasure palace of a horse-mad Cavalier playboy. This unique Stuart showpiece displays some of the most lavishly decorated rooms anywhere in England, a wonderfully recreated period garden, an astonishing riding school and amazing views. Be transported to a lost age of aristocratic extravagance, brought to life by fantastically costumed storytellers.

Our imaginative yet carefully researched re-presentation brings to life the golden days of the fairytale Stuart mansion and its larger-than-life creator, William Cavendish. You'll find there's plenty to see and do.

Bolsover Castle was always something special. Neither a fortress nor a conventional country house, it was designed purely to impress, entertain and intrigue visitors, particularly King Charles I and his court in 1634. Replacing a now-vanished medieval hilltop fortress, its site was carefully chosen both to dominate the landscape for many miles around and to astonish visitors with unrivalled panoramas.

Bolsover is again dazzling visitors. Explore the playfully pinnacled and battlemented 'Little Castle', the core of the mansion and focus of its magic. Begun by Sir Charles Cavendish in 1612, this Stuart plutocrat's fantasy was completed, decorated and furnished regardless of expense by his son William – playboy, poet, courtier and later Royalist general and Duke of Newcastle. There's a wealth of details to enjoy; the original exquisitely carved fireplaces, painted panelling and above all the astonishing

array of dramatic murals (recently saved as part of our Members' wall paintings appeal). Absorb the atmosphere of the Star Chamber and Marble Closet with their striking replica tapestries, satin wall-hangings and red velvet upholstery. Interactive 'cabinets of curiosity' reveal how the rooms, including the extraordinary 'Elysium Closet' with its painted ceiling and frieze of naked Classical gods and goddesses, were used to intrigue and impress noble visitors. It's well worth exploring the whole building, from its top-floor bedchambers to its cavernous basement kitchen complex.

Outside you can stroll the wall walk around the Fountain Garden, where Stuart courtiers promenaded to see and be seen. Designed around a statue of a naked Venus – goddess of love and pleasure – emerging from her bath, the enchanting garden has been attentively recreated, with borders planted with over 5,000 flowers and plants fashionable in Bolsover's heyday. Investigate the secluded chamber set into the garden wall, once the scene of intimate banquets for the chosen few. Enjoy truly astonishing vistas over the surrounding countryside beyond.

DON'T MISS

Immersing yourself in tales of Bolsover told by our fantastically costumed storytellers in the Little Castle. Meet the Storyteller, the castle personified, and encounter William and Margaret Cavendish, Stuart owners of the castle, whose extravagant outfits mirror their flamboyant lives and careers.

The easy-to-use handheld multimedia guide helps you experience Bolsover Castle at whatever level of detail you choose.

Narrated by actor Rupert Penry-Jones, the touchscreen guide lets you select from 'playlets', videos, reconstructions of room interiors and interviews with experts explaining how this captivating pleasure house operated. Don't miss exploring the dramatic roofless shell of the enormous Terrace Range, once the site of yet another set of sumptuous state rooms.

There's plenty more to discover at Bolsover. William Cavendish's passion for training horses is reflected in the vast indoor Riding House and the great Stables, where you'll find a stylish interactive exhibition (including a replica 17th-century saddle for children to try).

Children have their own entertainment too. A play area inspired by the castle's battlements and towers is ideally sited next to the tearoom's outdoor seating. In the Little Castle both children and adults can dress up in theatrical costumes and take the stage, echoing 'Love's Welcome at Bolsover', the masque performed here for Charles I and Queen Henrietta Maria at the zenith of the castle's now-revived glory.

Stop off at the tearoom, with indoor and outdoor seating and fantastic views towards the Riding House, for a refreshing break while exploring the site.

OPENING TIMES

1 Apr-30 Oct, daily	10am-5pm
31 Oct-23 Dec, Sat-Sun	10am-4pm
2 Jan-18 Feb, Sat-Sun	10am-4pm
19 Feb-31 Mar, daily	10am-4pm
Christmas Opening	
24-25 Dec	Closed
26 Dec-1 Jan, daily	10am-4pm

Last entry 30 mins before closing

VISIT US

Address: Bolsover Castle, Castle Street, Bolsover, Derbyshire S44 6PR

Direction: In Bolsover, 6 miles E of Chesterfield on A632. Off M1 at junction 29A (signposted)

Train: Chesterfield 6 miles

Bus: Visit traveline.info for the latest bus timetables and routes

Tel: 01246 822844

Local Tourist Information: Chesterfield: 01246 345777

NON-MEMBERS

Adult £14.20 | Concession £12.80
Child £8.50 | Family 2 Adults £36.90
Family 1 Adult £22.70

The coach drop-off point is in the council car park opposite.

There is good access to the grounds, but please note that the Little Castle is not accessible to wheelchairs.

MAP PAGE 331 (2F)
OS MAP 120, 269: SK470707

PEVERIL CASTLE DERBYSHIRE – S33 8WQ

Towering high above the pretty Peak District market town of Castleton, Peveril is among the most spectacularly sited castles in England.

Climbing the steep path from the visitor centre (there are benches along the way) you might be surprised that this is the easiest access to the castle. Reaching the top, you'll discover that it's defended on the other sides by sheer drops into Cave Dale and Peak Cavern Gorge. These natural defences encouraged William the Conqueror's trusted knight William Peverell to raise one of the first stone castles in England here, very soon after 1066. Look out for the characteristic early Norman zig-zag herringbone masonry in the curtain walls.

A century later, in the 1170s, the great royal fortress builder Henry II further strengthened the castle, adding the hallmark keep on the hill summit. Still rising almost to its original height, it's entered for security at first floor level; its main chamber is equipped with a garderobe toilet draining into the chasm below – a real 'loo with a view'.

Breathtaking views over the Peak District's hills and valleys are the great reward for venturing up to this wonderfully positioned castle. In the visitor centre at the foot of the hill you'll find a model of the original fortress, and displays revealing how Peveril was for

centuries the hub of the Forest of the Peak, a jealously guarded royal hunting preserve.

🎬 *The Princess Bride* (1987).

OPENING TIMES

1 Apr-30 Oct, daily	10am-5pm
31 Oct-17 Feb, Sat-Sun	10am-4pm
18-26 Feb, daily	10am-4pm
27 Feb-31 Mar, Sat-Sun	10am-4pm
24-26 Dec & 1 Jan	Closed

Last entry 45 mins before closing

VISIT US

Direction: Via the marketplace in Castleton; 15 miles W of Sheffield on A6187

Train: Hope 2½ miles

Bus: Visit traveline.info for the latest bus timetables and routes

Tel: 01433 620613

Local Tourist Information: 01433 620679

NON-MEMBERS

Peak (28 May-31 Aug, Sat-Sun and Bank Holidays)
Adult £9.00 | Concession £8.10
Child £5.40 | Family 2 Adults £23.40
Family 1 Adult £14.40

Standard (1 Apr-27 May and Sep-Oct, Sat-Sun and Bank Holidays; 28 May-31 Aug, Mon-Fri)
Adult £8.40 | Concession £7.60
Child £5.00 | Family 2 Adults £21.80
Family 1 Adult £13.40

Off-peak (1 Apr-27 May and Sep-Oct, Mon-Fri and Nov-Mar)
Adult £7.80 | Concession £7.00
Child £4.70 | Family 2 Adults £20.30
Family 1 Adult £12.50

ACQ.1932 ⬚ 🐾 ⚲ 📷 🧍 👶 **P** 📷
⚠ OVP

Wheelchair access to visitor centre only.

Parking (in town).

Caution: moderately challenging 10-15 mins uphill walk to castle from visitor centre.

MAP PAGE 330 (2E)
OS MAP 110, OL1: SK149826

WINGFIELD MANOR
DERBYSHIRE – DE55 7NH

The vast ruins of a palatial medieval manor house, built in the 1440s for Ralph, Lord Cromwell, Treasurer of England.

Please note: Wingfield Manor is part of a working farm. Please respect the owner's privacy at all times. No public access.

OPENING TIMES

Currently no access during conservation project. Please check website for details

VISIT US

Direction: 17 miles N of Derby; 11 miles S of Chesterfield on B5035; ½ mile S of South Wingfield. From M1 junction 28, W on A38, A615 (Matlock Road) at Alfreton, 1½ miles and turn onto B5035

Train: Alfreton 4 miles

Bus: Visit traveline.info for the latest bus timetables and routes

Tel: 0370 333 1181 to book (Customer Services)

NON-MEMBERS

Adult £9.00 | Concession £8.10
Child £5.40 | Family 2 Adults £23.40
Family 1 Adult £14.40

ACQ.1960 🚫 ⚠

Parking (none on site or in gateway).

MAP PAGE 331 (3F)
OS MAP 119, 269: SK374548

ASHBY DE LA ZOUCH CASTLE

LEICESTERSHIRE – LE65 1BR

Ashby de la Zouch Castle forms the backdrop to the famous jousting scenes in Sir Walter Scott's classic novel, *Ivanhoe*.

The castle began as a manor house in the 12th century, and achieved castle status in the 15th century. Between 1474 and his execution by Richard Duke of Gloucester, later Richard III, in 1483, Edward IV's friend Lord Hastings added the chapel and the impressive keep-like Hastings Tower – a castle within a castle. For fine views, climb 24 metres (78 feet) to the top of the tower.

Later, the castle hosted many royal visitors, including Henry VII, Mary Queen of Scots, James I and Charles I. A Royalist stronghold during the Civil War, Ashby finally fell to Parliament in 1646, and was then made unusable. You can still explore an underground passage from the kitchen to the tower, probably created during the Civil War.

OPENING TIMES

1 Apr-30 Oct, Wed-Sun & Bank Hols	10am-5pm
31 Oct-10 Feb, Sat-Sun	10am-4pm
11-19 Feb, Wed-Sun	10am-4pm
20 Feb-31 Mar, Sat-Sun	10am-4pm
24-26 Dec & 1 Jan	Closed

Last entry 30 mins before closing

VISIT US

Direction: In Ashby de la Zouch, 12 miles S of Derby on A511

Train: Burton on Trent 9 miles

Bus: Visit traveline.info for the latest bus timetables and routes

Tel: 01530 413343

Local Tourist Information: 01530 411767

NON-MEMBERS

Adult £7.80 | Concession £7.00 | Child £4.70
Family 2 Adults £20.30 | Family 1 Adult £12.50

Disabled access (grounds only).

Disabled only parking, please use the town centre car parks (charges apply).

MAP PAGE 331 (4F)   OS MAP 128, 245: SK361166

JEWRY WALL
LEICESTERSHIRE – LE1 4LB

Among the most massive survivals of Roman masonry in Britain, this wall of a town-centre Roman bath house complex still stands over 9 metres (30 feet) high. The baths were completed by about AD 160.

Managed by Leicester City Council.

OPENING TIMES

Access to the site is currently closed during refurbishment of the Jewry Wall Museum

Exterior viewable from adjacent footpath

VISIT US

Direction: In St Nicholas Street, W of Church of St Nicholas

Train: Leicester ¾ mile

Bus: Visit traveline.info for the latest bus timetables and routes

ACQ 1920 ☂ P

Parking (by museum, within St Nicholas Circle).

MAP PAGE 331 (4F)
OS MAP 140, 233: SK582045

DON'T FORGET

Remember to take your membership card.

KIRBY MUXLOE CASTLE   LEICESTERSHIRE – LE9 2DH

The picturesque moated remains, including the fine gatehouse and a complete corner tower, of a largely brick-built fortified mansion conserved by English Heritage. Begun in 1480 by Lord Hastings, a leading supporter and close friend of Edward IV, the 'castle' was constructed in the most up-to-date style in the fashionable new brick building material, and cosmetically equipped for artillery defence with gunports, some of them 'dummies'. But at a council meeting in 1483 the future king Richard III suddenly denounced his former ally Hastings as a traitor. He had Hastings immediately beheaded and the showpiece mansion was never finished.

OPENING TIMES

| 1 Apr-30 Sep, Sat-Sun & Bank Hol Mon | 10am-5pm |
| 1 Oct -31 Mar | Closed |

Last entry 30 mins before closing

VISIT US

Direction: 4 miles W of Leicester off B5380; close to M1 junction 21A, northbound exit only

Train: Leicester 5 miles

Bus: Visit traveline.info for the latest bus timetables and routes

Tel: 0116 238 6886

NON-MEMBERS

Adult **£6.60** | Concession **£5.90**
Child **£4.00** | Family 2 Adults **£17.20**
Family 1 Adult **£10.60**

ACQ 1912 ☂ ⌂ P ⚠ OVP

Small car park available on site.

Please note: this site is cash only and is unable to accept card payments.

MAP PAGE 331 (4F)
OS MAP 140, 233: SK524046

GAINSBOROUGH OLD HALL

LINCOLNSHIRE – DN21 2NB

It's well worth venturing off the beaten track to Gainsborough Old Hall, one of the biggest and best-preserved yet least known medieval manor houses in England. Transformed interpretation now helps you trace its amazingly varied history during five and a half centuries at the core of Gainsborough's life.

Lavishly constructed in timber framing and fine brickwork, this imposing mansion was largely built during the later 15th century by Sir Thomas Burgh, the leading Lincolnshire Yorkist. Richard III stayed here in 1483, and Henry VIII and his ill-fated fifth wife, Catherine Howard, in 1541. Developed into a fashionable Jacobean residence by the wealthy and very Protestant Hickman family, it subsequently fell on hard times. Parts of it served as a theatre and preaching hall, crammed tenements for the poorest people, workshops and even a pub, before it became the hub of fashionable Victorian social life, eventually secured for the future by the people of Gainsborough.

There's a lot to see here, so allow plenty of time. Highlights include the magnificent medieval great hall – later a raucous Georgian theatre – and the finest medieval kitchen complex anywhere in England, with stupendous fireplaces and everything needed for the biggest of feasts. View bedchambers, lodgings for lords and paupers and the Victorian Assembly Rooms in the former great chamber. Climb the high brick tower for views over the town and the river Trent, explored by pictorial panels. Don't miss a stroll round the hall's impressive exterior, and take a break in the open-to-all tearoom, with indoor and outdoor seating.

🎬 *Peterloo* (2018).

OPENING TIMES

1 Apr-30 Oct, daily	10am-5pm
31 Oct-10 Feb, Sat-Sun	10am-4pm
11-19 Feb, daily	10am-4pm
20 Feb-31 Mar, Sat-Sun	10am-4pm
24-26 Dec & 1 Jan	Closed

Last entry 30 mins before closing

The site may close on Fri and Sat between May and Oct for weddings – please phone site to check for latest details

VISIT US

Direction: In Parnell Road, Gainsborough, opposite the library

Train: Gainsborough Central ½ mile, Gainsborough Lea Road 1 mile

Bus: Visit traveline.info for the latest bus timetables and routes

Tel: 01427 677348

NON-MEMBERS

Adult **£10.00** | Concession **£9.00** | Child **£6.00** Family 2 Adults **£26.00** | Family 1 Adult **£16.00** Free entry for children under 5

Admission price payable by all visitors, including Members, on occasional special event days

15% discount on rates for groups of 11 or more paying a lump sum

Disabled access (most of ground floor).

Assistance dogs only within the house. Dogs on leads permitted in tearoom and gift shop.

No dedicated parking at site. Free parking (max 1 hour) in surrounding streets, and longer-term paid parking at Riverside car park, 100 metres away.

New guidebook.

MAP PAGE 331 (1G) OS MAP 112/121, 280: SK813900

BOLINGBROKE CASTLE

LINCOLNSHIRE – PE23 4HH

Remains of a once-impressive, multi-towered 13th-century castle, begun in the 1220s by Ranulf, Earl of Chester and Lincoln. Famous as the birthplace in 1367 of Henry of Bolingbroke, the future King Henry IV. A Civil War Royalist base, it was besieged and taken in 1643 by Oliver Cromwell, and reduced to ruin.

Managed by Heritage Lincolnshire.

OPENING TIMES

Any reasonable daylight hours

VISIT US

Direction: In Old Bolingbroke, 16 miles N of Boston off A16

Train: Thorpe Culvert 9 miles

Bus: Visit traveline.info for the latest bus timetables and routes

Tel: 01529 461499

ACQ.1949 ⚓ 🚂 ⚠ Caution: deep water. Please take care around castle moat.

MAP PAGE 331 (2J)
OS MAP 122, 273: TF349650

LINCOLN MEDIEVAL BISHOPS' PALACE

LINCOLNSHIRE – LN2 1PU

These intriguing remains of a medieval bishops' palace stand in the shadow of Lincoln Cathedral, in the heart of the ancient city.

They're currently benefiting from a major conservation project. Using a mix of modern technology and traditional

LINCOLN MEDIEVAL BISHOPS' PALACE

methods, we're conserving and consolidating the delicate and important stonework throughout the site. This will ensure that the palace is accessible for many generations to come. Reopens March 2023.

OPENING TIMES

A major conservation project is under way, so access to the palace will be limited. Please check the website for details

VISIT US

Direction: On the south side of Lincoln Cathedral. From Exchequer Gate, follow the wall to your right to the doorway directly opposite cathedral south porch, then take Chesney Gate tunnelled walkway. Entrance to the left down the pathway

Train: Lincoln 1 mile

Bus: Visit traveline.info

NON-MEMBERS

Adult **£7.80** | Concession **£7.00**
Child **£4.70** | Family 2 Adults **£20.30**
Family 1 Adult **£12.50**

ACQ.1954 ⚠

MAP PAGE 331 (2H)
OS MAP 121, 272: SK978717

SIBSEY TRADER WINDMILL

LINCOLNSHIRE – PE22 0SY

This six-storey Victorian mill is undergoing major conservation. Repairs to the brick mill tower have been completed and the millwright is now working on a new cap and fantail before new sails are installed. We hope to re-open the mill, though not yet in working order, during 2022. Please be sure to check our website before planning a visit. The mill shop, selling a wide variety of flours and grains, will be open on some weekends, and new information boards explaining the mill works are planned.

SIBSEY TRADER WINDMILL

Managed by Ian Ansell.

sibseytraderwindmill.co.uk

OPENING TIMES

A major conservation project is under way. Please check the website for details

VISIT US

Direction: ½ mile W of Sibsey off A16, 5 miles N of Boston

Train: Boston 5 miles

Bus: Visit traveline.info for the latest bus timetables and routes

Tel: 01205 460647/07718 320449

NON-MEMBERS

Please check website for details

ACQ.1975 ♿ 🚶 🚻 ⊗ P 🏪 ⚠ OVP

Disabled access (exterior only).

Caution: steep stairs.

MAP PAGE 331 (3J)
OS MAP 122, 261: TF345510

TATTERSHALL COLLEGE

LINCOLNSHIRE – LN4 4LG

Remains of a grammar school for church choristers, founded in the mid-15th century by Ralph, Lord Cromwell, builder of Wingfield Manor (p.185) and nearby Tattershall Castle (National Trust).

Managed by Heritage Lincolnshire.

OPENING TIMES

Any reasonable daylight hours

Likely to be closed for part of 2022, pending planned conservation works. Please see website for details

VISIT US

Direction: In Tattershall, 14 miles NE of Sleaford on A153

Train: Ruskington 10 miles

Bus: Visit traveline.info for the latest bus timetables and routes

Tel: 01529 461499

ACQ.1972 ⚓

MAP PAGE 331 (2H)
OS MAP 122, 261: TF213578

KIRBY HALL

NORTHAMPTONSHIRE – NN17 3EN

Magnificent Kirby Hall is one of England's greatest Elizabethan and 17th-century houses. Imaginative new interactive displays help you trace its rise, fall and rescue through 450 years – and experience a royal visit.

Standing in splendid isolation amid rolling countryside, Kirby Hall offers visitors an unforgettable experience, not to be missed. For though its finest staterooms survive impressively complete, much of this vast mansion is now a dramatic roofless shell, intriguing to explore. Its rich decoration and ambitious architecture set successive owners at the forefront of new ideas about design and aristocratic lifestyle.

Begun in 1570 for local landowner Sir Humphrey Stafford, Kirby's inner courtyard displays the pioneering use of Classical-style features never previously seen in English mansions. Soon afterwards the house was bought by Sir Christopher Hatton, who first attracted Queen Elizabeth I's favour by his dancing and eventually became her Lord Chancellor. He added an outer forecourt and a wing of lavishly regal staterooms, lit by noble double-height bow windows. The third Sir Christopher Hatton modernised the mansion during the 1630s, and a fourth Sir Christopher added the great garden, now strikingly recreated as it appeared in the late 17th century.

New displays in the staterooms trace the story of Kirby's rise and fall, from its foundation to its abandonment in the 19th century and eventual rescue after 1930, when it became the first major mansion taken into state care. There's also an intriguing array of site finds, along with examples of the panelling, wallpapers and other decorative features which once graced Kirby's interiors. You'll find out about the mansion's people across the centuries, including the black servant James Chappell, who heroically rescued the fourth Sir Christopher and his daughters from disaster before apparently becoming landlord of the local pub.

You can also experience a royal visit. Though the first Sir Christopher waited in vain to welcome Queen Elizabeth on one of her 'progresses', King James I visited his successors no fewer than nine times. A tapestry trail draws you into the excitement of a regal stay, and interactives let you discover what you look like in aristocratic 17th century clothes, and judge who 'takes the chair' as the most important person present. In the best bedchamber you can even try out a theatrical recreation of a grand royal bed, inspired by one recorded here in 1619.

The comprehensive new audio tour enhances your visit, and there's a new family activity trail featuring Edmund, one of Kirby Hall's famous resident peacocks.

Owned by the Earl of Winchilsea and managed by English Heritage.

APETHORPE PALACE NORTHAMPTONSHIRE – PE8 5DJ

OPENING TIMES

1 Apr-30 Oct, Wed-Sun	10am-5pm
31 Oct-10 Feb, Sat-Sun	10am-4pm
11-19 Feb, daily	10am-4pm
20 Feb-31 Mar, Sat-Sun	10am-4pm
24-26 Dec & 1 Jan	Closed

Last entry 30 mins before closing

VISIT US

Direction: On an unclassified road off A43, 4 miles NE of Corby

Train: Corby 4 miles; Kettering 11 miles

Bus: Visit traveline.info for the latest bus timetables and routes

Tel: 01536 203230

NON-MEMBERS

Adult **£10.00** I Concession **£9.00**
Child **£6.00**
Family 2 Adults **£26.00**
Family 1 Adult **£16.00**

ACQ.1930 🎧👩‍🦽🔨Ⓔ❋🏠👤
👤🅿🖼📷⚠

Disabled access (grounds, gardens and ground floor only).

Dogs on leads (restricted areas only).

Please note: there is no tearoom at Kirby Hall, but plenty of places to picnic.

MAP PAGE 331 (5G)
OS MAP 141, 224: SP926927

🎬 *Mansfield Park* (1999).

Visitors have a unique opportunity to discover stately Apethorpe Palace, owned by Elizabeth I and favourite royal residence of James I and Charles I.

Among England's greatest stately homes, Apethorpe Palace holds a particularly important place in history because of its ownership by, and role in entertaining, Tudor and Stuart monarchs.

Elizabeth I once owned the building, which she had inherited from Henry VIII. For a period, Apethorpe was a royal palace lived in regularly by James I and Charles I.

James I so loved Apethorpe that he personally contributed to its extension, to make it more suitable for his 'princely recreation' and 'commodious entertainment', particularly for hunting in the nearby royal forest of Rockingham. The resulting series of state rooms, including the King's Bedchamber and the impressive long gallery, is one of the most complete to survive from the Jacobean period.

Apethorpe Palace has a private owner who is committed to opening the gardens and the state rooms to the public.

Please note: There are lots of stairs, and no resting/seating points available. Children under 16 must be accompanied by an adult. We are unable to admit children under 5.

OPENING TIMES

Open by pre-booked guided tour only (charge applies). See website or call Customer Services for dates and booking information

VISIT US

Direction: Located off the A43 towards King's Cliffe. If entering Apethorpe via King's Cliffe Road, advance to Laundry Lane, not the High Street. If entering via Bridge St, pass the stone cross and turn left into Laundry Lane

Train: 14 miles from Peterborough. Trains via Kings Cross to Peterborough (approx. 45 mins)

Bus: Visit traveline.info for the latest bus timetables and routes

Tel: 0370 333 1181

NON-MEMBERS

Please check the website for prices

ACQ.2004 🅿

Access via narrow residential lane – please observe 10mph speed limit at all times.

MAP PAGE 331 (5H)
OS MAP 141, 224/234: TL023954

CHICHELE COLLEGE

NORTHAMPTONSHIRE – NN10 8DX

The remains of a residence for priests serving the parish church, founded by locally born Henry Chichele, Archbishop of Canterbury 1414-43. Often exhibits local artists' work.

Managed by Higham Ferrers Tourism, Business and Community Partnership.

OPENING TIMES

Garden: Please check website for current information

Interior: Open during events and exhibitions – please check website for details

VISIT US

Direction: College Street, Higham Ferrers

Train: Wellingborough 5 miles

Bus: Visit traveline.info for the latest bus timetables and routes

ACQ.1949 🚻 🖼 ⚠

Dogs on leads (grounds only).

Caution: falling masonry.

MAP PAGE 331 (5H)
OS MAP 153, 224: SP960687

ELEANOR CROSS, GEDDINGTON

NORTHAMPTONSHIRE – NN14 1AD

This stately triangular cross is the finest survivor of the 'Eleanor Crosses', which marked the places where the body of Eleanor of Castile, wife of Edward I, rested on its way to Westminster Abbey.

OPENING TIMES

Viewing from adjacent highway. Any reasonable daylight hours

VISIT US

Direction: In Geddington, off A43 between Kettering and Corby

Train: Kettering 4 miles

Bus: Visit traveline.info

ACQ.1915 🚻 ⚠ Caution: beware of traffic.

MAP PAGE 331 (5G)
OS MAP 141, 224: SP894830

RUSHTON TRIANGULAR LODGE

NORTHAMPTONSHIRE – NN14 1RP

The extraordinary creation of an extraordinary Elizabethan, this intriguing triangular folly was built in 1593-97 by Sir Thomas Tresham, father of one of the Gunpowder Plotters.

Tresham was a staunch Roman Catholic, often fined or imprisoned for his faith. His lodge testifies to his defiant Catholicism, but also to his obsession with individualistic buildings, symbolism and numbers – particularly three. All its features come in threes, symbolising the Holy Trinity. There are three floors, trefoil windows and three sides each 33⅓-feet-long, with three triangular gables. Inscribed over the door is 'Tres Testimonium Dant' ('there are three that bear witness'), a Biblical reference to the Trinity. It's also a pun on Tresham's name; his wife called him 'Good Tres', so the inscription could also mean 'Tres bears witness'.

OPENING TIMES

1 Apr-30 Oct, Fri-Sun	10am-5pm
31 Oct-31 Mar	Closed

Last entry 30 mins before closing

Due to essential maintenance work Rushton Triangular Lodge may be closed. Please check the website before visiting to find the most up-to-date information

VISIT US

Direction: 1 mile W of Rushton, on unclassified road; 1 mile from Desborough on A6

Train: Kettering 5 miles

Bus: Visit traveline.info for the latest bus timetables and routes

Tel: 01536 710761

NON-MEMBERS

Adult £5.60 | Concession £5.00 Child £3.40 | Family 2 Adults £14.60 Family 1 Adult £9.00

ACQ.1951 🚻 🖼 P 🖨 OVP

Dogs on leads (restricted areas only).

Parking in lay-by on opposite side of road to entrance.

MAP PAGE 331 (5G)
OS MAP 141, 224: SP830831

NOTTINGHAMSHIRE

MATTERSEY PRIORY

NOTTINGHAMSHIRE – DN10 5HN

Remote remains (mainly the refectory) of a tiny priory housing just six Gilbertine canons – the only wholly English monastic order. Sculpted panels from here are now in the village church.

OPENING TIMES

Daily   9am-5pm or dusk if earlier

VISIT US

Direction: Approx. 1 mile from Mattersey village. Park in village, then walk from church along Abbey Road (bridleway). Access is by landowner's permission through private land. **Please note:** no vehicular access to site

Train: Retford 7 miles

Bus: Visit traveline.info

Tel: 01604 735464

ACQ.1913 🚻 ⚠

Access to the site is over a stile and there may be animals grazing.

MAP PAGE 331 (1G)
OS MAP 112/120, 280: SK703896

RUFFORD ABBEY

NOTTINGHAMSHIRE – NG22 9DF

England's best-preserved remains of a Cistercian abbey west cloister range, dating from c. 1170. Incorporated into part of a 17th-century and later mansion, in Rufford Country Park.

Owned by Nottinghamshire County Council and managed by Parkwood Outdoors.

OPENING TIMES

See **parkwoodoutdoors.co.uk/ centre/rufford-abbey** for full details

25 Dec	Closed

VISIT US

Direction: 2 miles S of Ollerton off A614

Train: Mansfield 8 miles

Bus: Visit **traveline.info** for the latest bus timetables and routes

Tel: 01623 821338

Parking (charge applies – not managed by English Heritage).

Shops in Stable Block.

Caution: falling masonry.

MAP PAGE 331 (2G)
OS MAP 120, 270: SK646648W

LYDDINGTON BEDE HOUSE   RUTLAND – LE15 9LZ

Set beside the church in a picturesque ironstone-built village, Lyddington Bede House originated as the late medieval wing of a palace of the Bishops of Lincoln.

By 1600 it had passed to Sir Thomas Cecil, son of Queen Elizabeth's chief minister. He converted it into an almshouse for twelve poor 'bedesmen' over 30 years old and two women (who had to be over 45), all guaranteed free of lunacy, leprosy or the French pox. It continued as an almshouse until the 1930s.

You can explore the bedesmen's rooms, with their tiny windows and fireplaces, view a fine timbered roof, and admire the bishops' great chamber on the first floor, with its beautiful carved Tudor cornice. Interpretation includes audio boxes where you can hear letters read by the bedesmen. A bedesman's and a bedeswoman's room have been recreated as they appeared in Victorian times.

OPENING TIMES

1 Apr-30 Oct, Wed-Sun	10am-5pm
31 Oct-31 Mar	Closed

Last entry 30 mins before closing

VISIT US

Direction: In Lyddington, 6 miles N of Corby; 1 mile E of A6003, next to the church

Train: Oakham 7 miles

Bus: Visit **traveline.info**

Tel: 01572 822438

NON-MEMBERS

Adult **£7.80** I Concession **£7.00**
Child **£4.70** I Family 2 Adults **£20.30**
Family 1 Adult **£12.50**

Dogs on leads (restricted areas only).

MAP PAGE 331 (4G)
OS MAP 141, 234: SP876870

WELCOME TO THE

WEST MIDLANDS

Discover English Heritage sites along the pilgrimage route

A Wenlock Priory (p.207)
B Langley Chapel (p.204)
C Acton Burnell Castle (p.201)

In partnership with

the
**British
Pilgrimage
Trust**

The Abbesses' Way

20 miles | 2-3 days

Make pilgrimage from St Milburga's Wenlock Priory, through the rolling Shropshire landscape to the shrine of St Winefride at Shrewsbury Abbey.

View more details and a downloadable version of this route at **english-heritage.org.uk/pilgrimage**

GOODRICH CASTLE

HEREFORDSHIRE – HR9 6HY

Goodrich is the perfect medieval castle. Refreshed interpretation and a fun family game offer you even more reasons to visit this strikingly well-preserved baronial fortress.

Set in beautiful wooded country, Goodrich Castle guarded a strategic crossing of the River Wye. The earliest fortress here – 'Godric's Castle' – was begun in the late 11th century by an English landowner called Godric. A generation later, the de Clare family added the well-preserved little Norman keep which still stands at the core of the castle. Then, after ownership by William the Marshal (renowned as 'the Greatest Knight'), the castle was rebuilt in the most up-to-date style by King Edward I's uncle William de Valence, Earl of Pembroke.

This late 13th-century castle is revealed as you walk up the gentle slope from the ticket office. Still almost completely walled, it has massive round towers reinforced by distinctive 'spur buttresses', the latest fashion in castle building. It's surrounded by a rock-cut ditch, which you'll cross by a once-fortified bridge modelled on one at the Tower of London – another symbol of William's almost-royal status. Passing through the heavily defended gatehouse, you'll find the courtyard crowded with buildings.

Goodrich, in fact, boasts one of the most complete sets of medieval living quarters surviving in any English castle. From rare surviving records, we know a lot about how these were used by William's widow Countess Joan. She often stayed here, packing nearly 200 servants, staff and guests into the castle.

Pick up the family game from the ticket office and you can join her household as you explore the castle. The game features nine cartoon characters ranging from Countess Joan herself to the baker's assistant. You can choose how they might have answered questions – or make up your own cheeky replies. Adventurous (and reasonably fit) visitors can venture into the pitch-dark dungeon, or climb the steep narrow stairway to the keep top for breathtaking views over the castle and its surroundings. Don't miss the chapel, with its two striking modern stained-glass windows.

In the courtyard you'll also meet 'Roaring Meg', the only surviving Civil War mortar in England. During Goodrich's greatest crisis, the two-month siege of 1646, it lobbed deadly exploding 'bombs' into the Royalist-held castle, eventually forcing its surrender. One struck and buried the well, where excavations have produced a fascinating array of finds, from Civil War weapons to everyday household objects. You'll find some displayed in the ticket office exhibition.

Before returning for a break in the tearoom (which has indoor and outdoor seating), it's worth walking right round the castle's dry moat. It's a great place to picnic, and the frowning walls above you are a reminder of how strong Goodrich was. Look out for the garderobe tower which housed multiple medieval loos – spot the aperture at its base, which allowed the 'gong farmer' to clear the cesspit.

OPENING TIMES

1 Apr-30 Oct, daily	10am-5pm
31 Oct-17 Feb, Sat-Sun	10am-4pm
18-26 Feb, daily	10am-4pm
27 Feb-31 Mar, Wed-Sun	10am-4pm

Christmas Opening

| 24-26 Dec & 1 Jan | Closed |

Last entry 30 mins before closing

VISIT US

Address: Goodrich Castle, Castle Lane, Goodrich, Ross-on-Wye, Herefordshire HR9 6HY

Direction: 5 miles S of Ross-on-Wye off A40

Bus: Visit traveline.info

Tel: 01600 890538

NON-MEMBERS

Peak (28 May-31 Aug, Sat-Sun and Bank Holidays)
Adult £11.70 | Concession £10.50
Child £7.00 | Family 2 Adults £30.40
Family 1 Adult £18.70

Standard (1 Apr-27 May and Sep-Oct, Sat-Sun and Bank Holidays; 28 May-31 Aug, Mon-Fri)
Adult £10.80 | Concession £9.70
Child £6.50 | Family 2 Adults £28.10
Family 1 Adult £17.30

Off-peak (1 Apr-27 May and Sep-Oct, Mon-Fri and Nov-Mar)
Adult £10.00 | Concession £9.00
Child £6.00 | Family 2 Adults £26.00
Family 1 Adult £16.00

Disabled access (limited, please call for details or ask the Visitor Centre on arrival).

Caution: the stairs to the keep top are steep, dark and narrow.

The tearoom will close 30 minutes before the site closes.

Parking: charges apply to non-members, free for Members with valid car sticker.

MAP PAGE 330 (7C)
OS MAP 162, OL14: SO577200

ARTHUR'S STONE

HEREFORDSHIRE – HR3 6AX

Ridge-top Neolithic chambered tomb made of great stone slabs, with spectacular views over the Golden Valley.

According to legend, King Arthur killed a giant here; certainly Charles I picnicked here in 1645.

OPENING TIMES

Any reasonable daylight hours

VISIT US

Direction: 7 miles E of Hay-on-Wye via B4348, signposted from Dorstone off steep minor road to Bredwardine

Train: Hereford 16 miles

Bus: Visit traveline.info for the latest bus timetables and routes

ACQ.1909

Parking in village of Dorstone. Very limited parking on site.

Please do not climb on the stones. Walk from Dorstone village approx. 1km.

Caution: unguarded drops.

> MAP PAGE 330 (6B)
> OS MAP 148/161, OL13/201:
> SO319431

EDVIN LOACH OLD CHURCH

HEREFORDSHIRE – HR7 4PW

Ruins of a small early Norman church, displaying striking herringbone work masonry. Stands within the earthworks of a motte-and-bailey castle, with a pretty Victorian church beside it.

OPENING TIMES

Any reasonable daylight hours

VISIT US

Direction: 4 miles N of Bromyard via B4203, then narrow lanes signposted Edvin Loach. Look for EH sign after Steeples Farm. **WARNING:** track to church is very uneven, drive with care

Bus: Visit traveline.info for the latest bus timetables and routes

ACQ.1980

> MAP PAGE 330 (6C)
> OS MAP 149, 202: SO663584

LONGTOWN CASTLE

HEREFORDSHIRE – HR2 0LE

A powerful 12th-century round keep on a steep mound dominates this Welsh Border castle, whose outer defences probably originated as a Roman fort. Set in the beautiful Olchon Valley, with the Black Mountains as a backdrop. See longtowncastles.com for recent discoveries here.

Managed in association with Longtown Village Pride.

OPENING TIMES

Any reasonable daylight hours

VISIT US

Direction: In Longtown village, accessible by minor roads from Hay-on-Wye

Bus: Visit traveline.info for the latest bus timetables and routes

ACQ.1973

Parking on roadside.

Garden available for picnics.

Caution: steep stairs.

> MAP PAGE 330 (7B)
> OS MAP 161, OL13: SO321291

ROTHERWAS CHAPEL

HEREFORDSHIRE – HR2 6LD

The family chapel of the Roman Catholic Bodenham family. The originally simple medieval building has a fine Elizabethan timber roof, a rebuilt 18th-century tower, and striking Victorian interior decoration and furnishings by the Pugins.

ROTHERWAS CHAPEL

Managed in association with the Friends of Rotherwas Chapel.

OPENING TIMES

Key available from the Herefordshire Archive and Records Centre. herefordshire.gov.uk/archives
Tel: 01432 260750
Mon-Fri and second Sat of every month   10am-4pm

VISIT US

Direction: 1½ miles SE of Hereford on B4399, left into Chapel Road

Train: Hereford 3½ miles

Bus: Visit traveline.info for the latest bus timetables and routes

ACQ.1928

Parking at Herefordshire Archive & Records Centre, 800m away.

Disabled access (ground floor only – one step).

Caution: steep stairs.

> MAP PAGE 330 (6C)
> OS MAP 149, 189: SO536383

WIGMORE CASTLE

HEREFORDSHIRE – HR6 9UB

Among the most unusual ruins in England, this stronghold of the turbulent medieval Mortimer family is now maintained as a romantic ruin and conserved for its wildlife habitats. Many of its part-buried fortifications survive, including its towering keep-mound.

OPENING TIMES

Any reasonable daylight hours

WIGMORE CASTLE

VISIT US

Direction: Located 8 miles W of Ludlow on A4110. Accessible via footpath ¾ mile from the village on Mortimer Way

Train: Bucknell 6 miles, Ludlow 10 miles

Bus: Visit traveline.info for the latest bus timetables and routes

[ACQ.1995] 🎍 P ⚠

Parking at Wigmore Village Hall. Toilets in the village hall are open from Easter to October half-term, inclusive. There is a disabled toilet with ramp access.

Caution: the site contains steep steps, which are hazardous in icy and wet conditions. Children must stay under close control. Please do not climb on the walls or banks. Strong footwear is recommended.

MAP PAGE 330 (5B)
OS MAP 137/148, 203: SO408693

SHROPSHIRE

ACTON BURNELL CASTLE

SHROPSHIRE – SY5 7PF

The dramatic battlemented red sandstone shell of one of the earliest medieval English fortified mansions, in an atmospheric wooded setting by an attractive Shropshire village. Begun after 1284 by Bishop Robert Burnell, a local man who rose to prominence as King Edward I's Lord Chancellor, its large windows demonstrate that it was designed for show rather than defence. It once contained the lavish private

apartments at the core of a much larger house, where King Edward stayed in 1283, holding a famous Parliament nearby. Bishop Burnell's impressive church stands beside it.

OPENING TIMES

Any reasonable daylight hours

VISIT US

Direction: Located in Acton Burnell, signposted from A49, 8 miles S of Shrewsbury

Train: Shrewsbury or Church Stretton, both 8 miles

Bus: Visit traveline.info for the latest bus timetables and routes

[ACQ.1930] ♿ 🎍 P ⚠

Please do not climb on the walls.
Car park is closed at dusk.

MAP PAGE 330 (4C)
OS MAP 126, 241: SJ534019

BUILDWAS ABBEY

SHROPSHIRE – TF8 7BW

Impressive ruins of a Cistercian abbey, including its unusually unaltered 12th-century church, beautiful vaulted chapter house and crypt chapel.

In a wooded Severn-side setting, near the Iron Bridge (p.205) and Wenlock Priory (p.207).

OPENING TIMES

1 Apr-30 Oct, daily	10am-5pm
31 Oct-31 Mar, daily	10am-4pm
24-26, 31 Dec & 1 Jan	Closed

BUILDWAS ABBEY

VISIT US

Direction: On S bank of River Severn on A4169, 2 miles W of Ironbridge

Train: Telford Central 6 miles

Bus: Visit traveline.info for the latest bus timetables and routes

[ACQ.1925] ♿ 🎍 🖵 P ⚠

Disabled access is limited.

Parking: charges apply to non-members, free for Members with valid car sticker.

Caution: unguarded drops, falling masonry. Please do not climb on the walls.

MAP PAGE 330 (4C)
OS MAP 127, 242: SJ643043

CANTLOP BRIDGE

SHROPSHIRE – SY5 7DD

A single-span, cast-iron road bridge over the Cound Brook. Possibly designed and certainly approved by the great engineer Thomas Telford, who was instrumental in shaping industrial Shropshire and the West Midlands.

OPENING TIMES

Any reasonable daylight hours

VISIT US

Direction: ¾ mile SW of Berrington on an unclassified road off A458

Train: Shrewsbury 5 miles

Bus: Visit traveline.info for the latest bus timetables and routes

[ACQ.1977] ♿ 🎍 P ⚠

Parking in lay-by.

Caution: deep water, sheer drop into water.

MAP PAGE 330 (4C)
OS MAP 126, 241: SJ517062

BOSCOBEL HOUSE AND THE ROYAL OAK

SHROPSHIRE – ST19 9AR

Boscobel House and its Royal Oak tree played a starring role in English history, hiding the young Charles II from his Cromwellian pursuers. Now our family-friendly 'Hide and Seek' re-presentation transforms visits to the house and its surroundings. It brings to life both the king's hairsbreadth escape and Boscobel's later life as a busy Victorian farm.

Originally surrounded by dense woodland, Boscobel House was ostensibly a hunting lodge, but also a secret hiding place for persecuted Catholics. So it was an ideal refuge for the 21-year-old Charles II, fleeing for his life from Cromwellian troopers after his Civil War defeat at Worcester in 1651.

Imaginative interactive interpretation in the house – backed up on selected days by storytellers in period costume – leads you through the king's 'Hide and Seek' visit. Pick up an electronic candle, which conjures up sights and sounds as you explore the rooms. You'll discover how he hid for fourteen hours in the 'Royal Oak' tree before spending a cramped night in a still visible priest's hole in the house. Interactives help families to seek the king's hiding place, and puzzle out the crucial choices faced by ordinary men and women during the turbulent Civil War period.

You'll also find the house's extensive surroundings looking more as they did when Charles took refuge here. Following a contemporary illustration, we've strikingly revived the 1651 style of the gardens, complete with period box hedging and flowers and the newly recreated 'pretty arbour

upon a mount' where Charles briefly relaxed. From here you can see dozens of young oak trees recently planted near the veteran Royal Oak, beginning to restore its original woodland setting.

More new features tempt children to play historical hide-and-seek. There's a winding willow tunnel to explore near the gardens, and the tree-themed playground includes a tunnel, aerial walkway, slide, basket swing and willow pod. It's conveniently sited near the revamped tearoom in a former stable, with indoor and outdoor seating.

There are farm animals to meet, too, helping to vividly revive Boscobel's later life as a Victorian farm. You can also discover the stables, barn, smithy, earth closet privies and other atmospheric farm buildings. Models and audios suggest how they were used, and who used them.

QR codes around the site help you to delve deeper into its history.

The descendant of the original Royal Oak stands near the house, and a pretty 20-minute country walk takes you to White Ladies Priory (p.206), another of Charles II's hiding places.

DON'T MISS

Meeting real rare breed farm animals, recalling those which lived at Victorian Boscobel farm. There are chickens, ducks, charming Tamworth pigs and Shropshire and Coloured Ryeland sheep. Younger children won't want to miss the imaginative tree-themed Hide and Seek playground, already a firm favourite.

OPENING TIMES

1 Apr-30 Oct, daily	10am-5pm
31 Oct-17 Feb, Sat-Sun	10am-4pm
18-26 Feb, daily	10am-4pm
27 Feb-31 Mar, Wed-Sun	10am-4pm

Christmas Opening

24-26 Dec & 1 Jan	Closed

Last entry 1 hour before closing

VISIT US

Address: Brewood, Bishop's Wood, Shropshire ST19 9AR

Direction: 8 miles NW of Wolverhampton. On minor road off A41 Whitchurch road, north of M54 Junction 3. Turn right at Bell Inn, then after 3 miles right again at Bishop's Wood Village Hall

Train: Cosford 3 miles

Bus: Visit traveline.info for the latest bus timetables and routes

Tel: 01902 850244

NON-MEMBERS

Adult £11.20 | Concession £10.10
Child £6.60 | Family 2 Adults £29.00
Family 1 Adult £17.80

Dogs on leads (grounds only).

Parking (coaches welcome but must book with site in advance).

Disabled access limited. For visitors with mobility issues, free tablets available at the shop offer a virtual tour of the house.

New guidebook.

MAP PAGE 330 (4D)
OS MAP 127, 242: SJ838082

CLUN CASTLE

SHROPSHIRE – SY7 8JT

Dramatic riverside ruins and earthworks of a Welsh Border castle, its tall 13th-century keep unusually set on the side of its mound. Panels tell the story of the castle and adjacent town.

OPENING TIMES

Any reasonable daylight hours

VISIT US

Direction: In Clun, off A488, 18 miles W of Ludlow

Train: Hopton Heath 6½ miles; Knighton 6½ miles

Bus: Visit traveline.info for the latest bus timetables and routes

ACQ.1991 ☒ 🐄 P 🏞 ⚠

Toilets available in car park (not managed by English Heritage).

Caution: steep slopes, sheer drop into water.

MAP PAGE 330 (5B)
OS MAP 137, 201: SO299809

LANGLEY CHAPEL

SHROPSHIRE – SY5 7HU

LANGLEY CHAPEL

Experience what churches looked like before the Victorians. This uniquely unaltered chapel, amid remote countryside, has a perfect set of rustic Jacobean furnishings, including gentry box pews, canopied pulpit and musicians' pew.

OPENING TIMES

1 Apr-30 Oct, daily	10am-6pm
31 Oct-31 Mar, daily	10am-4pm
24-26 Dec & 1 Jan	Closed

VISIT US

Direction: 9½ miles S of Shrewsbury and 1½ miles S of Acton Burnell, on an unclassified narrow road. Signposted from Acton Burnell

Train: Shrewsbury 7½ miles

Bus: Visit traveline.info for the latest bus timetables and routes

ACQ.1914 ☒ P

Very limited parking (2 cars).

MAP PAGE 330 (4C)
OS MAP 126/127/138, 217/241: SJ538001

LILLESHALL ABBEY

SHROPSHIRE – TF10 9HW

Extensive Augustinian abbey ruins, in a deeply rural setting. Much of the church survives, unusually viewable from gallery level, along with an elaborate processional doorway.

OPENING TIMES

1 Apr-30 Sep, daily	10am-6pm
1 Oct-31 Mar, daily	10am-4pm
24-26 Dec & 1 Jan	Closed

VISIT US

Direction: On an unclassified road off A518, 4 miles N of Oakengates

Train: Oakengates 4½ miles

Bus: Visit traveline.info for the latest bus timetables and routes

ACQ.1950 ♿ ☒ 🏞 P ⚠

Disabled access (kissing gate only).

Guidebook available from online shop.

1 Nov-31 Mar, parking on roadside only with access via kissing gate.

Caution: steep stairs.

Please do not climb on the walls.

MAP PAGE 330 (4C)
OS MAP 127, 242: SJ738142

HAUGHMOND ABBEY   SHROPSHIRE – SY4 4RW

Extensive remains of an Augustinian abbey, including its abbots' quarters and cloister. The chapter house displays rich 12th- and 14th-century carving and a fine timber roof.

OPENING TIMES

1 Apr-30 Oct, daily	10am-6pm
31 Oct-31 Mar, daily	10am-4pm
24-26 Dec & 1 Jan	Closed

VISIT US

Direction: Located 3 miles NE of Shrewsbury off B5062

Train: Shrewsbury 3½ miles

Bus: Visit traveline.info

ACQ.1931 ♿ ☒ 🏞 P ⚠

Disabled access is limited.

Guidebook available from online shop.

Please do not climb on the walls.

MAP PAGE 330 (4C)
OS MAP 126, 241: SJ542152

IRON BRIDGE

------- SHROPSHIRE – TF8 7JP -------

This famous structure is the world's very first iron bridge, an iconic symbol of the Industrial Revolution. Our £3.6m conservation project has safeguarded the bridge for future generations.

Britain's best-known industrial monument was erected over the River Severn in 1779. It gave its name to spectacular wooded Ironbridge Gorge, once an industrial powerhouse and the cradle of the Industrial Revolution. Ironbridge Gorge is now a World Heritage Site.

In the early 18th century, Abraham Darby I pioneered the process of using coke made from local coal to smelt iron ore. Expansion was hampered by the lack of a bridge over the Severn here, and any bridge had to be a single span to allow barge traffic. Abraham Darby III cast the bridge in his Coalbrookdale foundry, using 378 tons of iron, at a cost of over £6,000. A crucial turning point in design and engineering, this testament to the achievements of Shropshire ironmasters remained in use by traffic until 1934.

Over the 240 years since it was built, the bridge suffered many stresses, some dating from its original construction. Ground movement in the surrounding gorge, countless floods and even an earthquake in 1896 had left the historic structure under threat, placing stresses on the ironwork and leading to cracking. Our major conservation project has repaired and protected the bridge for the future. Among changes is the colour of the bridge, restored to its original dark red-brown after samples of the earliest historic paintwork were discovered as part of the project.

For more information about the conservation project, visit english-heritage.org.uk/visit/places/iron-bridge/project-iron-bridge/

OPENING TIMES
Any reasonable daylight hours

VISIT US
Direction: Adjacent to A4169

Train: Telford Central 5 miles

Bus: Visit traveline.info for the latest bus timetables and routes

ACQ.1975   👤 👍 🅿

Parking (charge applies). Car park not managed by English Heritage.

MAP PAGE 330 (4C)
OS MAP 127, 242: SJ672034

MITCHELL'S FOLD STONE CIRCLE

SHROPSHIRE – SY15 6DE

Neolithic stone circle, the focus of many legends, set amid dramatic moorland. It once consisted of some 30 stones – 15 are still visible.

OPENING TIMES

Any reasonable daylight hours

VISIT US

Direction: 16 miles SW of Shrewsbury, on unclassified road off A488

Train: Welshpool 10 miles

Bus: Visit traveline.info for the latest bus timetables and routes

ACQ.1915

Parking in lay-by at end of track – no vehicular access onto the moor.

MAP PAGE 330 (4B)
OS MAP 137, 216: SO304984

CHECK ONLINE

Pre-booking for visits to our staffed sites may be required, check our website for the latest guidance.

MORETON CORBET CASTLE

SHROPSHIRE – SY4 4DW

Ruins of the castle and Tudor mansion of the Corbets, dominated by the theatrical shell of an Elizabethan wing, devastated during the Civil War.

OPENING TIMES

Any reasonable daylight hours

VISIT US

Direction: In Moreton Corbet off B5063 (a turning off A49), 7 miles NE of Shrewsbury

Train: Yorton 4 miles

Bus: Visit traveline.info for the latest bus timetables and routes

ACQ.1939

Disabled access is limited.

Guidebook available from online shop.

Caution: hidden drops.

Please do not climb on the walls.

MAP PAGE 330 (4C)
OS MAP 126, 241: SJ561231

OLD OSWESTRY HILLFORT

SHROPSHIRE – SY11 1DR

Among the most hugely impressive Iron Age hillforts on the Welsh Borders, covering 40 acres, with formidable multiple ramparts.

OPENING TIMES

Any reasonable daylight hours

VISIT US

Direction: 1 mile N of Oswestry, off an unclassified road off A483

OLD OSWESTRY HILLFORT

Train: Gobowen 2 miles

Bus: Visit traveline.info for the latest bus timetables and routes

ACQ.1946

Parking at top of Gateacre Ave.

Dogs on leads (restricted areas only).

Caution: steep slopes.

MAP PAGE 330 (3B)
OS MAP 126, 240/258: SJ295310

WHITE LADIES PRIORY

SHROPSHIRE – WV8 1QZ

Ruined Norman church of a nunnery of 'white ladies', later part of a vanished mansion. Charles II rested here in 1651 before seeking refuge at nearby Boscobel House (p.202).

Best reached via a footpath from Boscobel House (approximately 20 minutes' walk).

OPENING TIMES

Any reasonable daylight hours

VISIT US

Direction: Located 1 mile SW of Boscobel House off an unclassified road between A41 and A5; 8 miles NW of Wolverhampton

Train: Cosford 2½ miles

Bus: Visit traveline.info for the latest bus timetables and routes

ACQ.1938

Toilet facilities, café and shop available at Boscobel House.

Very limited roadside parking. Other parking at Boscobel House.

Caution: CCTV at site.

MAP PAGE 330 (4D)
OS MAP 217, 242: SJ826076

WENLOCK PRIORY

SHROPSHIRE – TF13 6HS

The tranquil ruins of Wenlock Priory are picturesquely sited on the fringe of Much Wenlock.

An Anglo-Saxon monastery was founded here by King Merewalh of Mercia, whose abbess daughter Milburga became a saint. Her relics were miraculously rediscovered here in 1101, attracting both pilgrims and prosperity.

By then Wenlock had been refounded as a Norman Cluniac priory. Its impressive remains reflect everywhere the Cluniac love of elaborate decoration. Parts of the great 13th-century church still stand high; and there is a replica of an unusual monks' washing fountain with 12th-century carvings. The priory's greatest glory is the extravagantly decorated chapter house, its walls bedecked with interlocking round arches on multiple carved columns.

Set in a topiary-filled garden, against the backdrop of the monastic infirmary wing, later converted into a mansion and still a private residence.

OPENING TIMES

1 Apr-30 Oct, daily	10am-5pm
31 Oct-17 Feb, Sat-Sun	10am-4pm
18-26 Feb, daily	10am-4pm
27 Feb-31 Mar, Sat-Sun	10am-4pm
24-26 Dec & 1 Jan	Closed

Last entry 30 mins before closing

VISIT US

Direction: In Much Wenlock

Train: Telford Central 9 miles

Bus: Visit traveline.info for the latest bus timetables and routes

Tel: 01952 727466

NON-MEMBERS

Adult £7.80 | Concession £7.00 | Child £4.70
Family 2 Adults £20.30 | Family 1 Adult £12.50

ACQ.1964 🎧 📷 ♿ ✕ ✿ 🛍 🚹 P 📷 OVP

Parking: charges apply to non-members, free for Members with valid English Heritage car sticker.

MAP PAGE 330 (4C)
OS MAP 127/138, 217/242: SJ625001

STOKESAY CASTLE

SHROPSHIRE – SY7 9AH

Stokesay Castle is the finest and best-preserved fortified medieval manor house in England. Unobtrusive interpretation and a children's riddle quest help you to explore the history and legends of this atmospherically unaltered survival from the Middle Ages.

A treasure bypassed by time, the moated manor, timber-framed gatehouse and parish church make an unforgettably picturesque group. Though 'builded like a castle', Stokesay was really a lightly defended mansion, designed for comfort and show as well as security. Lawrence of Ludlow, the wealthiest wool merchant in England, began rebuilding it in about 1285. Tree-ring dating proves that work was completed by 1291, with the same team of carpenters used throughout. Amazingly, the dating also revealed that Stokesay has changed very little since; there are few places in England where you can see so much unaltered medieval timberwork.

So that you can discover Stokesay's story while still experiencing its unspoiled atmosphere, we've discreetly installed information panels into period-style features, showing how the rooms were used. There's also an absorbing audio tour. Families can follow an intriguing puzzle quest, inspired by the legend of two giants who lived on wooded hills flanking the castle. Riddles and clues tucked away throughout the castle help you track down the giants' lost key.

There's plenty to see here. In the magnificent open-hearthed great hall you can admire a fine timber roof and shuttered gable windows, and even climb an original 13th-century staircase with treads cut from whole tree trunks. This leads to the three-storey north tower, featuring a room with a medieval tiled floor and a spacious second-floor guest chamber. On the other side of the hall is a 'solar' (private apartment) block and the tall south tower – the most defensible and castle-like part of the house – offering wonderful views when you climb via tiers of rooms to its battlements.

The solar block includes one of the few later additions to Stokesay, a magnificent panelled chamber. It's dominated by a fireplace with a richly carved overmantel, where you can just trace original painting in five colours. This was created in about 1641, at the same time as the delightful castle gatehouse, timber-framed and embellished in the lavish Welsh Marches style. Look out for the 'Stokesay dragons' and charming carvings of Adam and Eve.

Outside, you can enjoy the courtyard garden, replanted in the Edwardian cottage garden style of 1908. Don't miss a walk round the dry moat for impressive exterior views of the castle walls and the north tower's overhanging timber-framed 'jetty', and look into the adjacent parish church with its unusually unchanged 17th-century interior (not managed by English Heritage). Just outside the castle, the attractive cottage tearoom is open to all and is dog friendly. It has an outdoor play space and additional outdoor seating with views of the surrounding Welsh Border hills.

OPENING TIMES

1 Apr-30 Oct, daily	10am-5pm
31 Oct-17 Feb, Sat-Sun	10am-4pm
18-26 Feb, daily	10am-4pm
27 Feb-31 Mar, Wed-Sun	10am-4pm

Christmas Opening
24-26 Dec & 1 Jan   Closed

Last entry 30 mins before closing

VISIT US

Address: Stokesay Castle,
Nr Craven Arms, Shropshire

Direction: 7 miles NW of Ludlow
off A49

Train: Craven Arms 1 mile

Bus: Visit **traveline.info** for the latest bus timetables and routes

Tel: 01588 672544

Local Tourist Information:
Ludlow: 01584 875053

NON-MEMBERS

Adult £10.00 | Concession £9.00
Child £6.00 | Family 2 Adults £26.00
Family 1 Adult £16.00

Disabled access (call site for details).

Dogs allowed within the grounds on a lead but not allowed within the castle.

Entrance to the courtyard is through a historic gate. Unsuitable for motorised scooters and unassisted wheelchair users. Cottage tearoom fully accessible.

Cottage tearoom is outside the castle and open to all. It closes 30 minutes before castle.

Parking: charges apply to non-members, free for Members with valid car sticker.

Caution: some steep unlit staircases within the castle, especially in the south tower.

MAP PAGE 330 (5B)
OS MAP 137/148, 203: SO436815

WROXETER ROMAN CITY

SHROPSHIRE – SY5 6PJ

Discover how the Romans lived 2,000 years ago at Wroxeter (or Viroconium) – once the fourth largest city in Roman Britain, with up to 5,000 citizens. Eventually covering some 180 acres, it was equal in size to Pompeii in Italy.

Wroxeter began as a legionary fortress and developed into a thriving civilian city, populated by traders and retired soldiers. Today its ruins stand in open fields. The most impressive features are the remains of the 2nd-century municipal baths and the huge wall dividing them from the exercise hall, once in the heart of the city.

The audio tour describes how Wroxeter worked in its heyday, and you can explore a wealth of site finds in the fascinating museum. The military weapons and equipment, fashion accessories and medical instruments reveal details of the citizens' everyday life. Trace the city's rise, flourishing, post-Roman survival and eventual abandonment through the vivid interpretation.

Be sure to see the on-site recreation of a Roman townhouse, complete with painted rooms including dining room, bedroom and bath suite and replicas of Roman furniture. Inspired by houses excavated here, it was built using traditional methods as interpreted by six modern builders for the Channel 4 series *Rome Wasn't Built in a Day*.

Rome Wasn't Built in a Day (2011); *I am Patrick* (2020)

OPENING TIMES

1 Apr-30 Oct, daily	10am-5pm
31 Oct-31 Mar, Sat-Sun	10am-4pm
24-26 Dec & 1 Jan	Closed

Last entry 30 mins before closing

Please note: the site museum will be closed from 19 Sep 2022 for major re-presentation. Remainder of site open as usual, and please check the website for up-to-date information.

VISIT US

Direction: 5 miles SE of Shrewsbury, on a minor road signposted from the B4380

Train: Shrewsbury 5½ miles; Wellington Telford West 6 miles

Bus: Visit **traveline.info** for the latest bus timetables and routes

Tel: 01743 761330

NON-MEMBERS

Adult **£9.00** | Concession **£8.10** | Child **£5.40**
Family 2 Adults **£23.40** | Family 1 Adult **£14.40**

ACQ. 1947 OVP

An education room is available for schools.

Light refreshments are available.

MAP PAGE 330 (4C)
OS MAP 126, 241: SJ565087

CROXDEN ABBEY STAFFORDSHIRE – ST14 5JG

OPENING TIMES

1 Apr-30 Oct, daily	10am-5pm
31 Oct-31 Mar, daily	10am-4pm
24-26, 31 Dec & 1 Jan	Closed

VISIT US

Direction: 5 miles NW of Uttoxeter off A522

Train: Uttoxeter 6 miles

Bus: Visit traveline.info for the latest bus timetables and routes

ACQ.1936   🛈 🖈 P ⚠

Limited parking.

Caution: unguarded drops.

Please do not climb on the walls.

MAP PAGE 330 (3E)
OS MAP 128, 259: SK066397

The impressive ruins of an abbey of Cistercian 'white monks', once prosperous from sheep farming. They include the towering west walls and tall lancet windows of its 13th-century church, its infirmary and 14th-century abbot's lodging. Information panels and a decorative stonework display tell the story of Croxden's spectacular architecture.

WALL ROMAN SITE (LETOCETUM) STAFFORDSHIRE – WS14 0AW

OPENING TIMES

Open Air Site
Any reasonable daylight hours

Museum
26-27 Mar, 16-18, 30 Apr,
1-2, 14-15, 28-29 May,
11-12, 25-26 Jun, 16-17, 30-31 Jul,
6-7, 13-14, 20-21, 27-29 Aug,
10-11, 24-25 Sep, 15-16, 29-30 Oct
11am-4pm

VISIT US

Direction: Off Eastbound A5 at Wall, near Lichfield

Train: Shenstone 1½ miles

Bus: Visit traveline.info

ACQ.1949 🖈 🖀 🛉 🛉 🖾 P 🚻 ⚠

Parking (not English Heritage).

Toilet facilities are available during museum opening hours.

Caution: beware of traffic.

Please do not climb on the walls.

MAP PAGE 330 (4E)
OS MAP 139, 244: SK098066

An important staging post on Watling Street, the Roman military road to North Wales, Wall provided overnight accommodation for travelling Roman officials and imperial messengers. It displays foundations of an inn and bath house, with excavated finds in the on-site museum.

Managed by English Heritage for the National Trust, with thanks to the Friends of Letocetum.

KENILWORTH CASTLE AND ELIZABETHAN GARDEN

WARWICKSHIRE – CV8 1NG

Spend a royal day out among the delights of spectacular Kenilworth Castle. Hear tales of the castle from our costumed storytellers, climb to lofty viewing platforms for a 'queen's-eye view' of the castle and its surroundings and experience the refreshed Elizabethan Garden.

A vast medieval fortress which endured an epic siege and later became an Elizabethan palace, Kenilworth Castle is among Britain's biggest historic sites. Extensive developments highlight Kenilworth's famous associations with Queen Elizabeth I and her favourite, Robert Dudley.

Spanning more than nine centuries, Kenilworth's varied buildings reflect its long connection with English monarchs. Henry I's treasurer began the massive Norman keep in the 1120s, Henry II made Kenilworth a royal castle and King John greatly strengthened it. Thus it could withstand the longest siege in medieval English history in 1266, when rebellious barons held out here for six months. In the impressively timbered Tudor stables, which also house the tearoom, you can see trebuchet balls from the siege in the interactive display of the castle's history.

John of Gaunt, Duke of Lancaster, rebuilt Kenilworth's inner court, beginning the castle's transition into a favoured residence of the Lancastrian and early Tudor kings. You can still admire the shell of Gaunt's 14th-century Great Hall. By Henry VIII's time it was already renowned for its 'many fair chambers'. The scene was set for Kenilworth's greatest period of fame.

This began when Queen Elizabeth I's childhood friend, Robert Dudley, Earl of Leicester, took possession of the castle in 1563. He then lavished fortunes on converting it into a great showpiece mansion, designed to receive the queen and her court on their ceremonial 'progresses' around England. You can see striking evidence of his transformation everywhere at Kenilworth, including the tall, mansion-sized 'Leicester's Building' designed specifically for the queen's use.

Viewing platforms within Leicester's Building allow you to climb 18 metres (59 feet) to the level of the queen's apartments. Here you can admire fantastic views over the castle and surrounding countryside, once enjoyed only by Elizabeth and her highest-ranking courtiers. Interpretation helps you imagine this miniature palace in its heyday.

Leicester's Gatehouse is the imposing entrance to his transformed 'wonder-house'. Discover its lower floor chambers recreated as they might have appeared in the 1930s. On its top floor, take in an exhibition telling the story of Elizabeth I's relationship with Dudley and her four visits to his castle.

NEW FOR 2022

On selected days, come and hear tales of Kenilworth Castle from our costumed storytellers. Encounter an Elizabethan lady-in-waiting, talk to our mischievous Jester or meet the Bear with Ragged Staff in the gardens, revealing the stories behind the flowers and plants and explaining why he is the badge of Warwickshire.

THE ELIZABETHAN GARDEN

On the most famous of these visits, in July 1575, Elizabeth stayed for 19 days. Dudley not only entertained her royally throughout, he also created a fabulous garden especially for her visit. This garden was lost for centuries, but in 2009 we brought it back to life, basing our meticulous recreation on careful archaeological research and the survival of an eye-witness description by a courtier, who sneaked a visit while the queen was out hunting. It presents the most complete evocation of an Elizabethan garden anywhere in the world and opens a window on the period's most enduring love story – that of Elizabeth I and her favourite, Robert Dudley.

Among the glories of the garden you'll discover a Renaissance aviary, plant beds full of scent, colour and fruit, and an imposing fountain carved from Carrara marble. The rejuvenated garden features refreshed paths, flower beds and woodwork, and a garden gate. Families can play Tudor garden games, and there's even a step to give little ones a better view of the birds in the aviary.

The 'Speed and Power' exhibition in the gatehouse celebrates Coventry-based motoring and aviation pioneer John Siddeley, first Baron Kenilworth, who gave the castle to the nation in 1938. Exhibits celebrate his cars and planes, and there's a family room where families can play together.

OPENING TIMES

1 Apr-30 Jun, daily	10am-5pm
1 Jul-31 Aug, daily	10am-6pm
1 Sep-30 Oct, daily	10am-5pm
31 Oct-23 Dec, Sat-Sun	10am-4pm
2 Jan-17 Feb, Sat-Sun	10am-4pm
18-26 Feb, daily	10am-4pm
27 Feb-31 Mar, Wed-Sun	10am-4pm
Christmas Opening	
24-25 Dec	Closed
26 Dec-1 Jan, daily	10am-4pm
Last entry 30 mins before closing	

VISIT US

Address: Kenilworth Castle, Castle Green, off Castle Road, Kenilworth, Warwickshire CV8 1NG

Direction: In Kenilworth off A46. Clearly signposted from the town centre, off B4103

Train: Kenilworth 1 mile

Bus: Visit traveline.info for the latest bus timetables and routes

Tel: 01926 852078

Local Tourist Information:
Kenilworth: 0300 555 8171

NON-MEMBERS

Peak (28 May-31 Aug, Sat-Sun and Bank Holidays)
Adult £16.50 | Concession £14.90
Child £9.90 | Family 2 Adults £42.90
Family 1 Adult £26.40

Standard (1 Apr-27 May and Sep-Oct, Sat-Sun and Bank Holidays; 28 May-31 Aug, Mon-Fri)
Adult £15.30 | Concession £13.80
Child £9.20 | Family 2 Adults £39.80
Family 1 Adult £24.50

Off-peak (1 Apr-27 May and Sep-Oct, Mon-Fri and Nov-Mar)
Adult £14.20 | Concession £12.80
Child £8.50 | Family 2 Adults £36.90
Family 1 Adult £22.70

Audio tours available (English, French, German and a children's version). Audio tours not available on special event days.

Tearoom open as per site, closing 30 minutes before the site closes.

Parking: charges apply to non-members, free for Members with valid car sticker.

MAP PAGE 330 (5E)
OS MAP 140, 221: SP278723

J.W. EVANS SILVER FACTORY BIRMINGHAM – B1 3EA

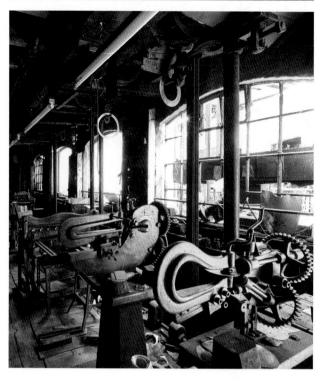

HALESOWEN ABBEY
WEST MIDLANDS – B62 8RJ

Remains of an abbey founded by King John in the 13th century.

OPENING TIMES
Open to view from the public footpath only

VISIT US
Directions: Off A456, ½ mile W of J3, M5

Train: Old Hill 2½ miles

Bus: Visit traveline.info

ACQ.1976

MAP PAGE 330 (5D)
OS MAP 139, 219: SO975828

WORCESTERSHIRE

LEIGH COURT BARN
WORCESTERSHIRE – WR6 5LB

An outstanding display of medieval carpentry, this huge 14th-century timber-framed barn is the largest cruck-framed structure in Britain, 46 metres (150 feet) long.

OPENING TIMES

1 Apr-30 Sep, Thu-Sun & Bank Hols	10am-6pm
1 Oct-31 Mar, Thu-Sun	10am-4pm
24-26 Dec & 1 Jan	Closed

VISIT US
Direction: 5 miles west of Worcester, on minor road signposted from A4103 at Bransford roundabout. Footpath to barn signposted at gateway to Leigh Court (private), next to church

Train: Worcester Foregate Street 5 miles

Bus: Visit traveline.info

ACQ.1990

Very limited parking on roadside verges near church.

Access via kissing gate.

MAP PAGE 330 (6D)
OS MAP 150, 204: SO783535

One of the most complete surviving historic factories in Birmingham's Jewellery Quarter, established in 1881. Behind the frontage of terraced houses, the workshops retain their dies for silverware manufacture, working equipment, stock and business records. English Heritage rescued the factory in 2008. Pre-booked guided tours only.

OPENING TIMES
Pre-booked tours only. For dates and booking please go to our website. Free for members and £11.20 non-members

VISIT US
Direction: 54-57 Albion Street, ½ mile from city centre

Train: Birmingham New Street or Birmingham Snow Hill ½ mile

Bus: Visit traveline.info

Tel: 0370 333 1181

ACQ.2008

MAP PAGE 330 (5E)
OS MAP 139, 220: SP062870

WITLEY COURT AND GARDENS

WORCESTERSHIRE – WR6 6JT

Inspire the whole family with a day out at Witley Court. Explore the Victorian country house mansion amid vast and beautiful grounds. Experience the legendary Perseus and Andromeda fountain, admire the colourful formal gardens, wander enchanted woodland walks, and try out the imaginative wilderness play area.

In its late-Victorian heyday Witley Court was staffed by over a hundred servants. It hosted lavish house parties attended by the Prince of Wales – later Edward VII – and his opulent friends, while at Christmas the ballroom's tree was hung with jewellery for female guests. The house fell into decline after the First World War and was accidentally burnt to a roofless shell in 1937. Wander through its dramatic Italianate ruins and you can still conjure up images of its glamorous past.

We've recreated the mansion's colourful formal gardens, originally laid out from the 1850s by leading landscape designer William Andrews Nesfield. The East Parterre, with its Flora Fountain, imitates embroidery, while the elegant South Parterre focuses on the astonishing Perseus and Andromeda fountain.

One of Europe's greatest fountains, this dramatically depicts the legendary Greek hero Perseus swooping down on his winged horse Pegasus to rescue the beautiful Andromeda, chained to a rock as a sacrifice to a sea monster. Its central jet reaches a height of up to 30 metres, complemented by nearly 30 more jets hidden among shells, sea nymphs and dolphins. Fully restored to working order, between April and October it fires on the hour from 11am until an hour before closing – a sight and sound not to be missed.

Wend your way up to the mansion through Witley's paradise of wild gardens, with their winding paths, rustic bridges, surprise lake vistas, trees and flowering shrubs from all over the world. Enchanting woodland walks are signposted for you, including a lakeside path to the Victorian boathouse: they offer glimpses of the park's abundant wildlife. Near the visitor centre is an 'organic' wilderness play area for children. With lots of exciting activities for different age groups, it's sure to fire their imaginations. The centrepiece is a tree house, reached by a wobbly bridge. A section for younger children includes a nest-like basket swing and wooden animal rides. There's also an adventure area with a scramble net and rope walks. However many visits they make, children will have a different experience every time they come.

Leave time to visit Great Witley Church, attached to the mansion, with its golden dome and gleaming gilded baroque interior. There's a tearoom near the church. (Please note: church and tearoom not managed by English Heritage.)

STAY WITH US

The substantial **Pool House** holiday cottage can sleep up to eight people, and has its own well-screened garden with sheltered dining terrace.

See p.16 for details on staying at **Witley** and our other holiday cottages.

OPENING TIMES

1 Apr-30 Oct, daily	10am-5pm
31 Oct-17 Feb, Sat-Sun	10am-4pm
18-26 Feb, daily	10am-4pm
27 Feb-31 Mar, Wed-Sun	10am-4pm

Christmas Opening
24-26 Dec & 1 Jan   Closed

Last entry 1 hour before closing

VISIT US

Address: Witley Court, Worcester Road, Great Witley, Worcestershire WR6 6JT

Direction: 10 miles NW of Worcester on A443

Train: Droitwich Spa 8½ miles

Bus: Visit traveline.info for the latest bus timetables and routes

Tel: 01299 896636

Local Tourist Information: Worcester: 01905 726311

NON-MEMBERS

Adult **£10.00** | Concession **£9.00**
Child **£6.00** | Family 2 Adults **£26.00**
Family 1 Adult **£16.00**

ACQ.1972

Disabled access (exterior and grounds only). A terrain guide is available on the website.

Tearoom (seasonal): Easter-31 October (not managed by English Heritage).

Parking: charges apply to non-members, free for Members with valid car sticker.

MAP PAGE 330 (6D)
OS MAP 138/150, 204: SO769649

WELCOME TO

YORKSHIRE AND THE HUMBER

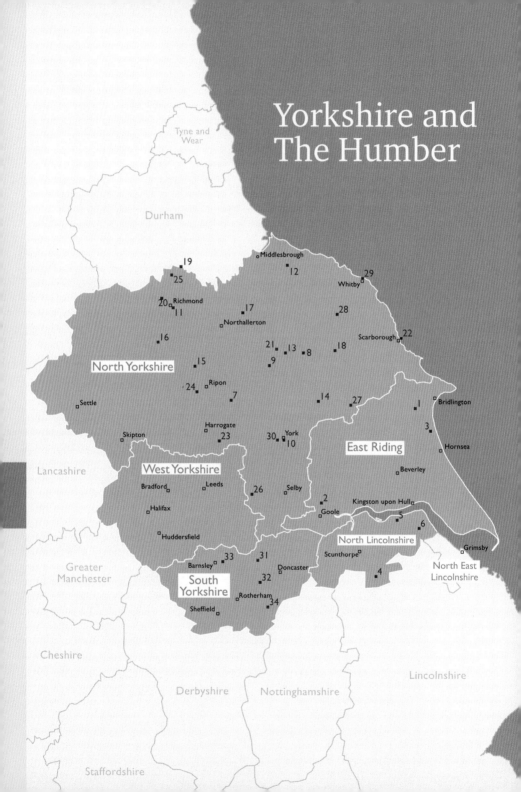

Yorkshire and The Humber

Tyne and Wear

Durham

Lancashire

Greater Manchester

Cheshire

Staffordshire

Derbyshire

Nottinghamshire

Lincolnshire

North Yorkshire

West Yorkshire

South Yorkshire

East Riding

North Lincolnshire

North East Lincolnshire

Middlesbrough

19

25

20 Richmond
11

16

Northallerton

17

12

Whitby

29

28

Scarborough 22

21 13 8
9

18

15

24 Ripon

7

14

27

1 Bridlington

Settle

Harrogate

23

3

Hornsea

Skipton

30 York
10

Bradford Leeds

26 Selby

Beverley

Kingston upon Hull

Halifax

2
Goole

5

6

Huddersfield

Barnsley 33 31

32

Rotherham

34

Doncaster

Scunthorpe

4

Grimsby

Sheffield

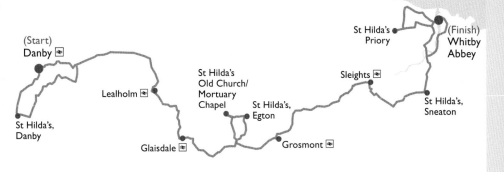

St Hilda's Priory

(Finish) Whitby Abbey

(Start) Danby

St Hilda's Old Church/ Mortuary Chapel

Sleights

Lealholm

St Hilda's, Egton

St Hilda's, Sneaton

St Hilda's, Danby

Glaisdale

Grosmont

In partnership with

the British Pilgrimage Trust

Discover English Heritage sites along the pilgrimage route

Whitby Abbey (p.242)

View more details and a downloadable version of this route at english-heritage.org.uk/pilgrimage

St Hilda's Way 22 miles | 2 days

Get to know St Hild – the abbess who hosted the famous Synod of Whitby, and also an Anglo-Saxon princess, spiritual leader, arts enthusiast and peacemaker. She trained five male bishops, and it is said that seabirds in Whitby still dip their wings in honour of her.

Simply follow this route along the River Esk through the North Yorkshire Moors and feel the ancientness of an almost untouched landscape – humans have never exercised full dominance here. The paths feel old, the rivers timeless, the pace slow. The places dedicated to Hilda will do the rest, possibly inspiring a quiet devotion to someone we can imagine but never fully understand.

BURTON AGNES MANOR HOUSE

EAST RIDING OF YORKSHIRE
– YO25 4NB

A medieval manor house interior, with an atmospheric vaulted Norman undercroft and a 15th-century roof. Encased in brick walls in the 18th century, when it became a laundry.

OPENING TIMES

1 Apr-30 Oct, daily	11am-5pm
31 Oct-31 Mar	Closed

The nearby Burton Agnes Hall and Gardens are privately owned and are not managed by English Heritage. Entrance to the Manor House remains free but access is via the Hall and Gardens: please tell Hall staff that you are visiting the Manor House

VISIT US

Direction: In Burton Agnes village, 5 miles SW of Bridlington on A166

Train: Nafferton 5 miles

Bus: Visit traveline.info for the latest bus timetables and routes

ACQ.1948 🛉🛉🛉 P 🖾 🍴 🖎 ⚠

Parking (in Hall and Gardens car park).

Caution: steep stairs.

MAP PAGE 333 (3J)
OS MAP 101, 295: TA102632

HOWDEN MINSTER

EAST RIDING OF YORKSHIRE
– DN14 7BS

HOWDEN MINSTER

The ruins of an elaborately decorated 14th-century chancel and chapter house (exterior viewing only), attached to the working 'minster' parish church of Howden.

OPENING TIMES

Any reasonable daylight hours

24-26, 31 Dec & 1 Jan	Closed

VISIT US

Direction: In Howden, 23 miles W of Kingston Upon Hull, 25 miles SE of York, near the junction of A63 and A614

Train: Howden 1½ miles

Bus: Visit traveline.info for the latest bus timetables and routes

ACQ.1971 🛉 P

Parking (on-street parking nearby – pay and display).

MAP PAGE 333 (4H)
OS MAP 105/106, 291: SE748283

SKIPSEA CASTLE

EAST RIDING OF YORKSHIRE
– YO25 8TH

Impressive earthworks of a huge Norman motte-and-bailey castle and settlement, perhaps dating from the 1070s and among the first built in Yorkshire. It's been controversially suggested, however, that the immense motte – 85 metres in diameter and 13 metres tall – is actually a reused Iron Age burial mound. If so, it would be unique in Britain.

OPENING TIMES

Any reasonable daylight hours

VISIT US

Direction: Located 8 miles S of Bridlington, W of Skipsea village

Train: Bridlington 9 miles

SKIPSEA CASTLE

Bus: Visit traveline.info for the latest bus timetables and routes

ACQ.1911 🐕 🛉 ⚠

Dogs on leads (restricted areas only).

Waterproof footwear recommended.

Caution: steep slopes.

MAP PAGE 333 (3J)
OS MAP 107, 295: TA162551

GAINSTHORPE MEDIEVAL VILLAGE

NORTH LINCOLNSHIRE – DN21 4JH

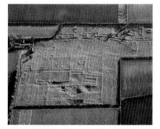

One of the best-preserved deserted medieval villages in England, clearly visible as a complex of grassy humps. According to legend, the village was inhabited by thieves and was demolished by locals who could tolerate them no more.

OPENING TIMES

Any reasonable daylight hours

VISIT US

Direction: Located on minor road W of A15 – towards Cleatham; S of Hibaldstow; 5 miles SW of Brigg

Train: Kirton Lindsey 3 miles

Bus: Visit traveline.info for the latest bus timetables and routes

ACQ.1974 🛉 🖛 ⚠

Access via grazing field.

Beware – livestock may be grazing on site.

MAP PAGE 333 (5H)
OS MAP 112, 281: SE954011

THORNTON ABBEY
& GATEHOUSE

NORTH LINCOLNSHIRE – DN39 6TU

Among the most extraordinary medieval buildings in England, Thornton Abbey's ornate gatehouse is worth travelling a long way to see.

This largest and most magnificent of all English monastic gatehouses was raised around the 1380s. An early example of large-scale English building in brick, it's bedecked with an extravaganza of turrets, sculpture and carved figures. Within the entrance arch, look out for the original 14th-century doors and medieval graffiti of sailing ships.

Though it's also lavishly equipped with arrow loops and other castle-like features, the gatehouse was built principally for show rather than defence. It proclaimed the wool-trade-based wealth and power of one of the richest Augustinian monasteries in England.

You can explore the gatehouse's intriguing interior, with its two floors of passageways and stairways, 'garderobe' toilets, tiny chambers and two big rooms, one probably housing the abbot's law courts. Now this 'great chamber' displays a wealth of carvings from the ruins, along with an exhibition tracing Thornton Abbey's history, including Henry VIII's visit, the abbey's brief rebirth as a Tudor 'college', and its role in huge Victorian temperance rallies. There's a further display of site finds and tactile features in the small ground level visitor centre.

Don't miss the tranquil remains of the abbey itself, notably two beautifully decorated walls of the octagonal chapter house of 1282-1308. Full of fascinating features to discover, they're also an ideal place to picnic and relax.

St Peter's Church, Barton-upon-Humber (see p.224) is nearby.

OPENING TIMES

Major conservation works are planned. Please check the website prior to visit

VISIT US

Direction: 18 miles NE of Scunthorpe, on a road N of A160; 7 miles SE of the Humber Bridge, on a road E of A1077

Train: Thornton Abbey ¼ mile

Bus: Visit traveline.info

Tel: 01469 541445

NON-MEMBERS

Adult **£7.80** | Concession **£7.00**
Child **£4.70** | Family 2 Adults **£20.30**
Family 1 Adult **£12.50**

Disabled access (except gatehouse interior and part of ruins).

Caution: steep narrow stairs within gatehouse. No dogs allowed as livestock may be grazing around ruins.

MAP PAGE 333 (4J)
OS MAP 113, 284: TA118189

ST PETER'S CHURCH

BARTON-UPON-HUMBER

—— NORTH LINCOLNSHIRE – DN18 5EX ——

An archaeological as well as an architectural treasure, this famous Anglo-Saxon church reveals a thousand fascinating years of the 'Buried Lives' of its people.

The oldest parts of the church, its striking Anglo-Saxon tower and adjacent baptistery, were built in the early 11th century. Look out for the tower's characteristically Saxon triangular-headed windows and decoration with thin stone strips – a feature echoing Saxon timber buildings. In medieval times the church was progressively enlarged, eventually reaching six times its original size: its upper tier of big 15th-century windows fills it with light.

Declared redundant in 1972, the church and churchyard were comprehensively excavated. The remains of nearly 3,000 people were recovered, as well as perfectly preserved medieval coffins. Well preserved by waterlogged ground, they span the thousand years between Anglo-Saxon and Victorian times. Research on them is vividly presented in the Buried Lives display, where you can trace the effects of historic disease, diet and surgery, witness family tragedies and the sometimes mysterious objects buried with bodies, and discover how and why medieval children and adults grew at differing rates from their modern descendants.

Thornton Abbey and Gatehouse (see p.223) is not far away.

OPENING TIMES

1 Apr-30 Sep, Sun & Bank Hols	10am-3pm
1 Oct-31 Mar	Closed

Last entry 30 mins before closing

VISIT US

Direction: Off Beck Hill, near Barton-upon-Humber town centre

Train: Barton-upon-Humber ½ mile

Bus: Visit traveline.info for the latest bus timetables and routes

Tel: 01652 632516
Thornton Abbey: 01469 541445

NON-MEMBERS

Adult **£5.60** | Concession **£5.00**
Child **£3.40** | Family 2 Adults **£14.60**
Family 1 Adult **£9.00**

ACQ.1923 [icons] OVP

Limited parking in adjacent street.

MAP PAGE 333 (4J)
OS MAP 107, 112, 281: TA035219

NORTH YORKSHIRE

ALDBOROUGH ROMAN TOWN
NORTH YORKSHIRE – YO51 9ES

Beneath the picturesque village of Aldborough lies the Roman town of Isurium Brigantum, administrative capital of the Brigantes, the largest tribal confederation in Britain. Remains of its defences are visible amid towering pine trees in a Victorian garden, and two fine Roman mosaics – evidence of the town's prosperity – are displayed within charming period buildings. The recently refreshed site museum displays an outstanding collection of Roman finds tracing three centuries of archaeology at Isurium, including important recent discoveries. Updated information panels help to guide you round the site.

OPENING TIMES

1 Apr-30 Sep, Fri-Sun & Bank Hols	10am-5pm
1 Oct-31 Mar	Closed

Last entry 30 mins before closing

Please check website for details of Friends of Roman Aldborough tours

VISIT US

Direction: In Aldborough, ¾ mile SE of Boroughbridge on a minor road off B6265; within 1 mile of junction of A1 and A6055

Train: Cattal 7½ miles

Bus: Visit traveline.info for the latest bus timetables and routes

Tel: 01423 322768

NON-MEMBERS

Adult **£5.60** I Concession **£5.00**
Child **£3.40** I Family 2 Adults **£14.60**
Family 1 Adult **£9.00**

ACQ.1952

Dogs on leads (restricted areas only).

Limited parking on adjacent street.

MAP PAGE 333 (3F)
OS MAP 299, 99: SE405662

BYLAND ABBEY   NORTH YORKSHIRE – YO61 4BD

Admire the stately ruins of Byland Abbey, one of Yorkshire's greatest Cistercian monasteries.

Set against a backdrop of wooded hills, Byland was planned to the grandest of designs. The immense church, which today dominates the ruins, was the most ambitious Cistercian church in 12th-century Europe, and helped to pioneer the new Gothic style of architecture in northern England. You can trace the transition today in the combination of round Norman and pointed Gothic arches, and the towering west front. Decorative tiled floors still adorn many parts of the church.

You can also explore the remains of the monastic buildings, which originally housed some 300 monks and lay brothers, later reduced to just 14 by plague and Scots raiders.

Refreshments available at adjacent Abbey Inn, please see website for details.

OPENING TIMES

1 Apr-30 Sep, daily	10am-6pm
1-30 Oct, daily	10am-5pm
31 Oct-31 Mar, daily	10am-4pm
24-26, 31 Dec & 1 Jan	Closed

Last entry 30 mins before closing

Please see website for opening times of the small site museum

VISIT US

Direction: 2 miles S of A170, between Thirsk and Helmsley; near Coxwold village

Train: Thirsk 10 miles

Bus: Visit traveline.info

ACQ.1921

Parking (adjacent to Abbey Inn).

Toilets and Restaurant at Abbey Inn.

Caution: falling masonry.

MAP PAGE 333 (2G)
OS MAP 100, OL26/299: SE549789

CLIFFORD'S TOWER, YORK

NORTH YORKSHIRE – YO1 9SA

Crowning a Norman motte, Clifford's Tower is the largest remaining building of York Castle, northern England's greatest medieval royal fortress. Today, it offers unrivalled views over the ancient city. Our new multisensory experience makes the tower's history and interior more accessible than they've been for centuries, bringing its dramatic and sometimes tragic story to life as never before.

The transformed experience of visiting Clifford's Tower begins at the base of the motte. A new arrival forecourt designed to welcome visitors now includes permanent seating, a large-scale bronze timeline and a tactile site map. An innovative three-wheeled electric Piaggio offers fly-through animated views of the tower interior, admission tickets and guidebooks. To make climbing the tower steps easier, three well-spaced resting places off the central stairway have been created. For visitors unable to access the tower, a new virtual tour, accessible via the English Heritage website, can guide you through the site.

As York Castle's keep, Clifford's Tower was commissioned by King Henry III in 1244. Its architecture followed an elaborate four-lobed plan, which is unique in England. The tower proclaimed royal power over the city from the 13th century until its interior was gutted by a supposedly accidental fire and explosion in 1684.

Reflecting its four-lobed plan, user-friendly, multisensory interpretation within the tower explores four key periods of its history. You'll discover how William the Conqueror devastated the city during his brutal Harrying of the North, and how York's Jewish community tragically committed mass suicide in the tower's timber predecessor in 1190, to escape massacre by a mob. Then learn

how the present tower was rebuilt in stone and became the focus of royal government during the long Anglo-Scottish wars. In Tudor times, Robert Aske, leader of the 'Pilgrimage of Grace', was hung in chains from the tower; during the Civil War Siege of York in 1644 it became a platform for Royalist heavy guns, before the fire of 1684 finally destroyed the interior. Later, the tower became a romantic ruin concealed for a century behind prison walls.

All text information is available in audio and has been translated into a number of languages, available via QR codes. Enjoy audio stories of York Castle and Clifford's Tower told by fictional characters from its history, and immerse yourself in the historic soundscape as it transports you back to life in past centuries.

New internal stairs and suspended walkways allow you to explore the first floor level. There you can enjoy features inaccessible since the 17th century, including the ingeniously flushed royal 'garderobe' medieval lavatory. At the top of the tower the new timber deck viewing platform offers safe access to 360-degree panoramas over the city of York and beyond. Illustrated information panels will help you identify significant landmarks and buildings, including Baile Hill, the site of York's second Norman castle, and reveal how these related to Clifford's Tower through nearly a thousand years of history.

DON'T MISS

Hearing recorded stories from York Castle and Clifford's Tower's history, from a woman devastated and made homeless during the clearing of land to build York Castle; a Jewish citizen whose family members died during the tragedy of 1190; a medieval builder; a young girl recounting rumours about the cause of the fire of 1684; and a Victorian visitor to the ruined tower. All the actors are from York and reflect the city's continuing pride in the tower.

OPENING TIMES

1 Apr-30 Oct, daily	10am-6pm
31 Oct-31 Mar, daily	10am-4pm
24-25 Dec	Closed

Last entry 30 mins before closing

Please see our website english-heritage.org.uk/cliffords for up-to-date information and opening times

VISIT US

Address: Tower Street, York, North Yorkshire YO1 9SA

Direction: Tower St, York

Train: York 1 mile

Bus: Visit traveline.info for the latest bus timetables and routes

Tel: 01904 646940

Local Tourist Information: York: 01904 550099

NON-MEMBERS

Adult **£9.00** | Concession **£8.10**
Child **£5.40** | Family 2 Adults **£23.40**
Family 1 Adult **£14.40**

ACQ 1915 🖐 💻 ⊗ **P** ⚠ OVP

Parking (charged, not managed by English Heritage).

Caution: access via steep steps.

New guidebook.

MAP PAGE 333 (3G)
OS MAP 105, 290: SE605515

BEADLAM ROMAN VILLA

NORTH YORKSHIRE – YO62 7TD

A small number of bookable guided tours of Beadlam Roman Villa will be available in 2022. Set in a riverside meadow below the southern fringe of the North York Moors, Beadlam is one of the most northerly Roman villas in Britain which can be seen above ground. Low walls of the north range of a villa complex are visible. This contained eight domestic rooms, some heated by hypocausts, and was fronted by a veranda. Remains of the east and west ranges (which included a bath suite) exist below ground. Though possibly begun earlier, the villa was mainly in use during the third and fourth centuries AD. A mosaic from the villa is in Helmsley Archaeology Store (p.230).

OPENING TIMES

Please check the website for guided tour dates and bookings

VISIT US

Direction: Between Helmsley and Beadlam, off A170: full directions provided on booking

ACQ.1972

No parking near villa. No facilities at site. No access except on pre-booked tours.

Beware – livestock may be grazing on site.

MAP PAGE 333 (2G)
OS MAP 100, OL26: SE634841

DON'T FORGET

Remember to take your membership card.

EASBY ABBEY

NORTH YORKSHIRE – DL10 7EU

Impressive ruins of a Premonstratensian abbey, set by the River Swale. They include a lavishly appointed refectory of c. 1300 and extensive monastic buildings. The neighbouring parish church displays outstanding 13th-century wall paintings.

Easby can also be reached via a pleasant walk from Richmond Castle (p.236).

OPENING TIMES

1 Apr-30 Sep, daily	10am-6pm
1-30 Oct, daily	10am-5pm
31 Oct-31 Mar, daily	10am-4pm
24-26, 31 Dec & 1 Jan	Closed

VISIT US

Direction: 1 mile SE of Richmond, off B6271

Bus: Visit traveline.info for the latest bus timetables and routes

ACQ.1930

Caution: unguarded drops.

MAP PAGE 333 (2F)
OS MAP 92, 304: NZ185003

GISBOROUGH PRIORY

NORTH YORKSHIRE – TS14 6HG

The ruins of an Augustinian priory founded in 1119 by the Bruce family, afterwards Kings of Scotland. The dramatic east end wall of the church is one of the finest examples of late 13th-century architecture in England. Substantial pier bases, a knight's grave slab and the remains of the 12th-century gatehouse hint at the priory's former grandeur.

We are grateful to the Gisborough Priory Project, who manage the site and the adjoining historic woodland gardens. For more details see gisboroughprioryproject.org.uk

OPENING TIMES

1 Apr-6 Nov, Wed-Sun & Bank Hols	10am-4pm
7 Nov-28 Feb	Closed
1-31 Mar, Wed-Sun	10am-4pm

VISIT US

Direction: Church Street Guisborough, next to the parish church

Train: Marske 4½ miles

Bus: Visit traveline.info for the latest bus timetables and routes

Tel: 07391 351757
The number is manned by volunteers but any messages left will be responded to as soon as possible

ACQ.1932

Parking and toilets in town.

MAP PAGE 333 (1G)
OS MAP 94, OL26/306: NZ617160

KIRKHAM PRIORY

NORTH YORKSHIRE – YO60 7TD

The picturesque ruins of Kirkham Priory stand in an idyllic setting beside the River Derwent. They played an important part in rehearsals for the D-Day landings.

Celebrating its 900th anniversary in 2022, this priory of Augustinian canons was founded in 1122 by Walter Espec of Helmsley Castle, who later also founded Rievaulx Abbey. The heraldry of the lords of Helmsley bedecks the richly embellished priory gatehouse, along with worn figures of St George and the Dragon and David and Goliath.

Ranged across a riverside slope, the priory's extensive ruins testify to its medieval size and wealth. Remains of a tall east end window recall the vanished magnificence of its church, but much more survives of the cloister buildings. Look out for the finely carved 13th-century 'laver', where the canons washed before entering their refectory through an elaborately sculpted 12th-century doorway.

During the Second World War, the site was a focus of training for the D-Day invasion. Tanks due to land on the Normandy beaches tested their waterproofing in the Derwent and a pool created between ruins and river, while troops tried out scrambling nets hung on the priory walls. Winston Churchill and King George VI paid a top-secret visit to Kirkham to view the preparations.

OPENING TIMES

1 Apr-30 Jun, Wed-Sun & Bank Hols	10am-5pm
1 Jul-31 Aug, daily	10am-5pm
1 Sep-30 Oct, Wed-Sun	10am-5pm
31 Oct-31 Mar	Closed

Last entry 30 mins before closing

VISIT US

Direction: 5 miles SW of Malton, on a minor road off A64

Train: Malton 6 miles

Bus: Visit traveline.info

Tel: 01653 618768

NON-MEMBERS

Peak (28 May-31 Aug, Sat-Sun and Bank Holidays)
Adult £6.80 | Concession £6.10 | Child £4.10
Family 2 Adults £17.70 | Family 1 Adult £10.90

Standard (1 Apr-27 May and Sep-Oct, Sat-Sun and Bank Holidays; 28 May-31 Aug, Mon-Fri)
Adult £6.20 | Concession £5.60 | Child £3.70
Family 2 Adults £16.10 | Family 1 Adult £9.90

Off-peak (1 Apr-27 May and Sep-Oct, Mon-Fri and Nov-Mar)
Adult £5.60 | Concession £5.00 | Child £3.40
Family 2 Adults £14.60 | Family 1 Adult £9.00

ACQ.1927 ♿ ☕ 🏪 ♿ 🖥 🚹 ♿ P 📷 📷 ⚠ OVP

MAP PAGE 333 (3H)   OS MAP 100, 300: SE736658

HELMSLEY CASTLE

NORTH YORKSHIRE – YO62 5AB

Set beside an attractive market town, Helmsley Castle was in turn a formidable medieval fortress, an Elizabethan mansion, a besieged stronghold and a romantic ruin. Discover how life was lived here in war and peace.

The spectacular double banks and ditches surrounding the castle were created in the mid-1100s for its founder Walter Espec, a Norman baron of 'immense stature... with a voice like a trumpet'. Renowned for piety as well as soldiering, he also founded Kirkham Priory (p.229) and nearby Rievaulx Abbey (p.238).

Walter's successors, the de Roos family, raised the castle's impressive stonework defences between the late 12th and 14th centuries. They include the strong south barbican through which you enter the castle and the tall, keep-like east tower which still dominates Helmsley town, as it was always intended to do. Later the medieval west range was converted into a luxurious Elizabethan mansion by the Manners family; you can admire some of its fine timber panelling and elaborate plasterwork (look out for mermaids and dolphins) within its upper storey.

Yet Helmsley remained a powerful stronghold. In 1644, during its first and last military challenge, the castle's garrison of 200 Royalists held out for three months against a stronger force of cannon-armed Parliamentarians, marching out with the honours of war only when starved into surrender. Thereafter its defences were systematically made unusable, though the mansion remained intact: you can still see rubble from the part-demolished east tower lying in the castle ditch. Finally abandoned as a residence in the early 18th century, the castle became a romantic 'eye-catcher' ruin in the designed landscape of nearby Duncombe Park.

Extensive displays of site-finds in the mansion – from a Civil War mortar bomb to tableware and a 17th-century aristocratic chamber pot – combine with models and interactives to explore life in the castle through five centuries of war and peace. Don't miss a walk along the embankment between the castle ditches (accessible from the north barbican). This offers fine views of the fortress exterior, the adjacent parkland and the restored Helmsley Walled Garden (not managed by English Heritage), as well as the chance in season to spot some of the castle's abundant wild flowers and wildlife.

From April-October, you can also book a free monthly expert-guided tour of Helmsley Archaeology Store, housing fascinating artefacts from English Heritage's sites in northern England. See english-heritage.org.uk/visit/places/helmsley-castle/helmsley-archaeology-store. Call 0370 333 1181 to pre-book.

Rievaulx (p.238) and Byland (p.225) are both nearby. Rievaulx can be reached on foot via the Cleveland Way National Trail. Approx. 1½ hours (2½ miles) each way. Strong footwear is required.

OPENING TIMES

1 Apr-30 Oct, daily	10am-5pm
31 Oct-10 Feb, Fri-Sun	10am-4pm
11-19 Feb, daily	10am-4pm
20 Feb-31 Mar, Fri-Sun	10am-4pm
24-26 Dec & 1 Jan	Closed

Last entry 30 mins before closing

Conservation work will be taking place to the west range during the year, which may involve limited access to part of site – check website for details

Helmsley Archaeology Store Tours
For tour times and dates, please check our Helmsley Archaeology Store web page. Booking essential, call Customer Services on 0370 333 1181

Tours are free to Members and non-members and are led by the Collections Curators

VISIT US

Address: Helmsley Castle, Castlegate, Helmsley, North Yorkshire YO62 5AB

Direction: Near the town centre; follow brown signs to long stay car park

Bus: Visit traveline.info for the latest bus timetables and routes

Tel: 01439 770442

NON-MEMBERS

Peak (28 May-31 Aug, Sat-Sun and Bank Holidays)
Adult £10.50 | Concession £9.50
Child £6.30 | Family 2 Adults £27.30
Family 1 Adult £16.80

Standard (1 Apr-27 May and Sep-Oct, Sat-Sun and Bank Holidays; 28 May-31 Aug, Mon-Fri)
Adult £9.70 | Concession £8.70
Child £5.80 | Family 2 Adults £25.20
Family 1 Adult £15.50

Off-peak (1 Apr-27 May and Sep-Oct, Mon-Fri and Nov-Mar)
Adult £9.00 | Concession £8.10
Child £5.40 | Family 2 Adults £23.40
Family 1 Adult £14.40

Audio tours.

Parking: large car park adjacent to castle entrance. Charge payable by all visitors (not managed by English Heritage).

Toilets (in car park and town centre).

MAP PAGE 333 (2G)
OS MAP 100, OL26: SE611836

MARMION TOWER

NORTH YORKSHIRE – HG4 5JQ

Fine 15th-century gatehouse of a vanished riverside manor house, with a beautiful oriel window. Monuments of the Marmion family owners grace the adjacent church.

OPENING TIMES

1 Apr-30 Sep, daily	10am-6pm
1-30 Oct, daily	10am-5pm
31 Oct-31 Mar, daily	10am-4pm
24-26, 31 Dec & 1 Jan	Closed

VISIT US

Direction: On A6108 in West Tanfield

Train: Thirsk 10 miles

Bus: Visit traveline.info for the latest bus timetables and routes

ACQ 1976 🐕

MAP PAGE 333 (2F)
OS MAP 99, 298: SE268787

PIERCEBRIDGE ROMAN BRIDGE

NORTH YORKSHIRE – DL2 3SW

Stonework foundations of a bridge, now marooned in a field, which once led to Piercebridge Roman Fort.

OPENING TIMES

Any reasonable daylight hours

VISIT US

Direction: At Piercebridge; 4 miles W of Darlington, on B6275

Train: Darlington 5 miles

Bus: Visit traveline.info for the latest bus timetables and routes

ACQ 1975 🐕 ⚠

Parking available at nearby George Hotel. May infrequently be restricted when hosting large functions. Not managed by English Heritage.

MAP PAGE 333 (1F)
OS MAP 93, 304: NZ214155

PICKERING CASTLE

NORTH YORKSHIRE – YO18 7AX

Impressive ruins of a medieval royal castle, on the fringe of an attractive moors-edge market town. A classic example of how early earth-and-timber castles were progressively rebuilt in stone, its core is a high and steep-sided Norman 'motte' mound surrounded by a ditch. Among the earliest in northern England, this was raised by William the Conqueror during his devastating Harrying of the North in 1069-70. It was later crowned by a stone shell keep, and you can climb the motte stairway for panoramic views over the surrounding countryside. During the 13th and 14th centuries the castle's timber outer defences were replaced by stone curtain walls. Three of their imposing towers stand almost to full height: the Mill Tower housed a prison. Discover more about the castle's story in the chapel exhibition, and look out for its abundant wildlife – kestrels sometimes nest here.

OPENING TIMES

1 Apr-30 Oct, daily	10am-5pm
31 Oct-31 Mar	Closed

Last entry 30 mins before closing

VISIT US

Direction: In Pickering; 15 miles SW of Scarborough

PICKERING CASTLE

Train: Malton (9 miles) or Pickering (North Yorkshire Moors Railway) ¼ mile

Bus: Visit traveline.info for the latest bus timetables and routes

Tel: 01751 474989

NON-MEMBERS

Adult **£6.60** | Concession **£5.90**
Child **£4.00** | Family 2 Adults **£17.20**
Family 1 Adult **£10.60**

ACQ 1926 👤 🐕 🏪 E 🖐 🏠 🚹 🚻
P 🏠 📷 ⚠ OVP

Disabled access (except motte).

Caution: steep drops.

MAP PAGE 333 (2H)
OS MAP 100, OL27: SE799845

ST MARY'S CHURCH, STUDLEY ROYAL

NORTH YORKSHIRE – HG4 3DY

Magnificent High Victorian Anglican church, designed in the 1870s by the flamboyant architect William Burges. Its extravagantly decorated interior survives unaltered.

Owned by English Heritage and managed by the National Trust as part of the Fountains Abbey and Studley Royal Estate (see p.308).

OPENING TIMES

1 Apr-30 Sep, daily	12pm-4pm
1 Oct-31 Mar	Closed

Some additional opening may be available in Mar and Oct. Please see website for details

VISIT US

Direction: Located 2½ miles W of Ripon, off B6265; in the grounds of the Studley Royal Estate

Bus: Visit traveline.info for the latest bus timetables and routes

Tel: 01765 608888

ACQ 1975 👤 🚳 P

Parking (at visitor centre or Studley Royal).

MAP PAGE 333 (3F)
OS MAP 99, 298/299: SE275693

MIDDLEHAM CASTLE

—— NORTH YORKSHIRE – DL8 4QG ——

One of Yorkshire's most impressive medieval fortresses, Middleham Castle became the northern power base of King Richard III. It stands in an attractive Wensleydale market town.

The castle's core is the immense Norman keep, among the biggest in England. Three storeys high, it was probably built during the 1170s. Around this keep the powerful Neville family, Earls of Westmorland and of Warwick, progressively constructed three ranges of luxurious lodgings. By the mid-15th century the castle had turned into a fortified palace – 'the Windsor of the North'. Though roofless, most of the castle's buildings survive, including a multi-storey latrine tower and the remains of a later horse-powered mill, making Middleham a rewarding place to explore.

Though there is no firm evidence that Richard III lived here as a child, he may have visited as a teenager in the guardianship of 'Warwick the Kingmaker'. But in the 1470s Richard certainly made Middleham the focus of his growing power in the north, taking over the castle after Warwick's death and marrying his daughter Anne. The couple's only son, Edward of Middleham, was born and died here, aged no more than 10.

Enjoy views over Wensleydale from the keep's viewing platform. In a small exhibition about the castle's past you'll see a replica of the famous Middleham Jewel, a 15th-century gold and sapphire pendant found nearby. Engraved with religious images and magic words, it may have belonged to Richard's mother-in-law, Anne Beauchamp.

Children's games are available for the family to enjoy.

OPENING TIMES

1 Apr-30 Oct, daily	10am-5pm
31 Oct-31 Mar, Sat-Sun	10am-4pm
24-26 Dec & 1 Jan	Closed
Last entry 30 mins before closing	

VISIT US

Direction: Located at Middleham, 2 miles S of Leyburn on A6108

Train: Leyburn (Wensleydale Railway) 2 miles

Bus: Visit traveline.info for the latest bus timetables and routes

Tel: 01969 623899

Local Tourist Information: Leyburn: 01969 623069

NON-MEMBERS

Adult **£7.80** | Concession **£7.00**
Child **£4.70** | Family 2 Adults **£20.30**
Family 1 Adult **£12.50**

ACQ 1926

Disabled access (except keep).

MAP PAGE 333 (2F)
OS MAP 99, OL30: SE127876

MOUNT GRACE PRIORY, HOUSE AND GARDENS

NORTH YORKSHIRE – DL6 3JG

There's something for everyone to enjoy on a day out at Mount Grace. You'll find the rejuvenated Arts and Crafts gardens maturing beautifully and wilder spaces to wander, as well as an Arts and Crafts mansion and the most strikingly unusual of all our medieval monasteries.

Picturesquely set against the wooded Cleveland Hills, Mount Grace Priory was the last of the great Yorkshire monasteries, founded in 1398. Five centuries later, its ruins were bought by wealthy industrialist Sir Lowthian Bell, patron of the Arts and Crafts movement. Following the movement's principles of craftsmanship, natural materials and simplicity, he refurbished a 17th-century mansion adapted from the priory's guest house, fronting it with terraced gardens.

Masterminded by celebrity garden designer Chris Beardshaw, these award-winning Arts and Crafts gardens are now maturing. You can wander the terraces with their richly planted herbaceous borders, cross a newly built bridge to the Moat Island, and walk through a wildflower meadow to the Monks' Pond. Individual pamphlets for each season highlight garden and wildlife changes throughout the year. Collect a children's explorer pack, and go hunting for Priory Stoat badges dotted around the site. The Orchard Café, open to all, is set by an orchard recreated with local varieties of fruit trees.

Within the mansion, you'll see how Sir Lowthian sensitively combined 17th-century features with Arts and Crafts remodelling. Rooms have been dressed as they might have appeared in 1901. Don't miss the attics, which were nurseries

for the Bell children in the 1920s and 30s. Sir Lowthian's granddaughter Gertrude Bell, the famous adventurer, archaeologist and Middle East diplomat, knew and loved Mount Grace.

The mansion also houses a fascinating display about medieval Mount Grace Priory, best-preserved of the few English Carthusian monasteries. Stepping into its extensive ruins, you'll notice how they differ radically from conventional monasteries. Unlike other monks who lived and worshipped communally, the austere and much-respected Carthusians were semi-hermits. Each monk lived in solitude in one of the cottage-like cells ranged round the immense Great Cloister.

One of these two-storeyed cells – a private monastery in itself – is recreated as it appeared in the 15th century. It contains a living room, study and bedroom-chapel and workshop. An L-shaped hatch allowed servants to pass in the monk's frugal meat-free meals without seeing him. The monk's walled garden has a toilet, flushed by an ingenious plumbing system which channelled water to each cell. The garden has been replanted, and you'll discover which plants the hermit-monks grew for food, healing and contemplation.

Owned by the National Trust, maintained and managed by English Heritage.

STAY WITH US

Prior's Lodge sleeps four, with views over the mansion's garden in one direction, the monastic ruins in the other.

See p.16 for details on staying at **Mount Grace** and our other holiday cottages.

OPENING TIMES

1 Apr-30 Oct, daily	10am-5pm
31 Oct-10 Feb, Sat-Sun	10am-4pm
11-19 Feb, daily	10am-4pm
20 Feb-31 Mar, Wed-Sun	10am-4pm
24-26 Dec & 1 Jan	Closed

Last entry 30 mins before closing

During the winter, the attics may close early due to low light levels

VISIT US

Address: Staddlebridge, Northallerton, North Yorkshire DL6 3JG

Direction: 12 miles N of Thirsk, and 6 miles NE of Northallerton, signposted from A19

Train: Northallerton 6 miles

Tel: 01609 883494

Local Tourist Information:
Thirsk: 01845 522755

NON-MEMBERS

Adult **£11.20** | Concession **£10.10**
Child **£6.60** | Family 2 Adults **£29.00**
Family 1 Adult **£17.80**

National Trust members admitted free, except on event days

ACQ.1955

Parking: charges apply to non-members, free for Members with valid car sticker. Parking fee applies to National Trust members.

Dogs on leads (grounds only).

MAP PAGE 333 (2G)
OS MAP 99, OL26: SE449985

RICHMOND CASTLE

—— NORTH YORKSHIRE – DL10 4QW ——

Dominating a picturesque Dales market town, impressive Richmond Castle is among the oldest Norman stone fortresses in England. An extensive exhibition and imaginative interactives help you enjoy your visit.

Colourful displays highlight the many intriguing characters who made the castle's long story, from its 11th-century founder Count Alan the Red to the Conscientious Objectors who suffered here for refusing to fight in the First World War. You'll discover how generations of aristocrats, knights, soldiers and servants defended and lived in the castle. Find out how it inspired myths and legends, try your hand at designing heraldry, and enjoy the children's dressing-up box.

The Non-Combatant Corps was based here in 1916. You can hear the voices of those who wouldn't carry weapons, and the 'absolutists' who refused all war work – including the 'Richmond 16', sent to France and threatened with execution. A touchscreen presentation explores the poignant graffiti they left on their cell walls, proclaiming their pacifist beliefs and remembering loved ones.

Interactive displays and challenges tempt families to explore the great fortress, ranged round a vast grassy space. Don't miss the impressive ruins of Scolland's Hall and tiny St Nicholas's Chapel, among the oldest Norman domestic buildings in England. Try out the fun 'Seats of Power' feature inside the towering 100ft (30 metre) high 12th-century keep, and climb to the roof for amazing panoramic vistas over the castle, the ancient town and the Yorkshire Dales. Our orientation toposcopes help you explore the views.

OPENING TIMES

1 Apr-30 Oct, daily	10am-5pm
31 Oct-10 Feb, Sat-Sun	10am-4pm
11-19 Feb, daily	10am-4pm
20 Feb-31 Mar, Sat-Sun	10am-4pm
24-26 Dec & 1 Jan	Closed

Last entry 30 mins before closing

VISIT US

Direction: In Richmond, just off the market place

Bus: Visit traveline.info for the latest bus timetables and routes

Tel: 01748 822493

NON-MEMBERS

Adult **£7.80** | Concession **£7.00**
Child **£4.70** | Family 2 Adults **£20.30**
Family 1 Adult **£12.50**

ACQ.1916

Disc parking (2 hours free in market place – not managed by English Heritage).

Disabled parking available at site on request, or in market place.

MAP PAGE 333 (2F)
OS MAP 92, 304: NZ172007

SPOFFORTH CASTLE
NORTH YORKSHIRE – HG3 1DA

The ruined hall and chamber of a fortified medieval manor house of the powerful Percy family, rebuilt in the 15th century. Its undercroft is cut into a rocky outcrop.

Managed by Spofforth-with-Stockeld Parish Council.

OPENING TIMES

1 Apr-30 Sep, daily	10am-6pm
1 Oct-31 Mar, daily	10am-4pm
24-26, 31 Dec & 1 Jan	Closed

VISIT US

Direction: 3½ miles SE of Harrogate, off A661 at Spofforth

Train: Pannal 4 miles

Bus: Visit traveline.info for the latest bus timetables and routes

ACQ.1924

Dogs on leads (restricted areas only).

MAP PAGE 333 (3F)
OS MAP 104, 289: SE36051

STANWICK IRON AGE FORTIFICATIONS
NORTH YORKSHIRE – DL11 7RU

A reconstructed portion of the ramparts of the huge Iron Age power centre of the Brigantes, the most important tribe in pre-Roman northern Britain. Its defences were once some 4 miles long. The Brigantian capital later moved to Aldborough Roman Town (see p.225).

STANWICK IRON AGE FORTIFICATIONS

OPENING TIMES
Any reasonable daylight hours

VISIT US

Direction: Located on a minor road off A6274, at Forcett Village

Train: Darlington 10 miles

Bus: Visit traveline.info for the latest bus timetables and routes

ACQ.1953

Dogs on leads (restricted areas only).

Caution: deep water, steep slopes.

MAP PAGE 333 (1F)
OS MAP 92, 304: NZ179124

STEETON HALL GATEWAY
NORTH YORKSHIRE – LS25 5PD

A fine example of a small, well-preserved manorial gatehouse dating from the 14th century.

OPENING TIMES

Exterior only: Any reasonable daylight hours

VISIT US

Direction: Located 4 miles NE of Castleford, on a minor road off A162 at South Milford

Train: South Milford 1 mile

Bus: Visit traveline.info for the latest bus timetables and routes

ACQ.1948

Dogs on leads (restricted areas only).

MAP PAGE 333 (4G)
OS MAP 105, 290: SE484314

WHARRAM PERCY DESERTED MEDIEVAL VILLAGE
NORTH YORKSHIRE – YO17 9TN

Europe's best-known deserted medieval village, in a remote Wolds valley. Continuously occupied for six centuries, Wharram was abandoned by c. 1527. Above the substantial church ruins and mill pond, the outlines of many houses are traceable on a grassy plateau. Graphic panels recreate their original appearance.

Download a free audio tour from our website.

OPENING TIMES
Any reasonable daylight hours

VISIT US

Direction: 6 miles SE of Malton, on minor road from B1248; ½ mile S of Wharram-le-Street. Park in car park, then ¾ mile walk via uneven track, steep in places. Site also accessible on foot via Wolds Way footpath. Sturdy and waterproof footwear required. Parts of site slope steeply, and farm livestock likely to be present on site and access path

Train: Malton 8 miles

Bus: Visit traveline.info for the latest bus timetables and routes

ACQ.1972

Please note: site is hazardous in snowy conditions.

Beware – cattle may be grazing.

Parking: charges apply to non-members, free for Members with valid car sticker.

Caution: deep water, steep slopes, falling masonry.

MAP PAGE 333 (3H)
OS MAP 100, 300: SE859644

RIEVAULX ABBEY

NORTH YORKSHIRE – YO62 5LB

Rievaulx Abbey offers a host of exciting discoveries. Set in a tranquil wooded valley, the stately ruins are enhanced by many attractions. A welcoming café, site museum and audio tour trail help visitors of all ages enjoy the most impressive and extensive monastic remains in Britain.

'High hills surround the valley, clothed by trees and encircling it like a crown'; this 12th-century description of Rievaulx's setting still applies today. Here, in 1132, just twelve monks of the new Cistercian order, which was revolutionising monasticism in western Europe, founded an abbey, 'far from the haunts of men'. It became one of the wealthiest monasteries in medieval England. By the 1160s a peak of around 640 monks were living here, attracted by the holiness of Abbot Aelred. After his death the monks successfully sought his canonisation, rebuilding the east end of the church in the new Early English style of Gothic architecture to house his shrine.

Surviving almost to its full height, the east end of this church still serenely dominates the ruins. You can also explore the maze of monastic buildings where the white-robed Cistercian choir monks and their brown-clad lay brothers lived, worked and cared for their sick. The audio tour and pictorial interpretation panels help you find the site's highlights, like the refectory – the finest example in Britain – where the monks ate their largely vegetarian meals. You can also seek out intriguing features like the warming house sink where the monks did their laundry, the monks' toilets, and the tannery where they prepared leather in vats of urine.

Discover lots more about life at Rievaulx in the must-see museum. Here a wonderful display of artefacts ranges from beautifully carved stonework (including a tiger hunt using a mirror to distract the prey), via building tools, writing equipment and a 'scourge' whip for monastic penance, to everyday items like 'patten' footwear for muddy weather. A screen presentation illustrates major chapters in Rievaulx's story, including its suppression by Henry VIII in 1538. The 'Shattered Remains' display recalls the wholesale destruction at this time, before Rievaulx's later rebirth as a supremely romantic ruin, a delight to visit.

You can take a break from exploring in the imaginatively designed café. Soak up views of the abbey as you sample a wide range of Yorkshire dishes. There's indoor and outdoor seating, picnic tables, and a big shop offering local products, so allow plenty of time for your visit to Rievaulx Abbey, one of England's most fascinating and atmospheric monastic ruins.

You can also reach Rievaulx from Helmsley Castle (p.230) on foot, via the Cleveland Way. Approx. 1½ hours (2½ miles) each way. Strong footwear required. Byland Abbey (p.225), another great Yorkshire Cistercian monastery, is within easy driving distance.

🎬 *Transformers: The Last Knight* (2017).

STAY WITH US

Enjoy the peace and tranquillity of Rievaulx after it closes to the public when you stay in the *Refectory Cottage*. Sleeps 4.

See p.16 for details on staying at Rievaulx and our other holiday cottages.

NEW FOR 2022

The Rye Valley Abbey exhibition explores the relationship between Rievaulx (which means 'Rye valley') Abbey and the river Rye, through images and artefacts. Presented in partnership with the Ryevitalise Landscape Partnership Scheme, supported by the National Lottery Heritage Fund. See the website for launch dates and further details.

OPENING TIMES

1 Apr-30 Oct, daily	10am-5pm
31 Oct-10 Feb, Wed-Sun	10am-4pm
11 Feb-31 Mar, daily	10am-4pm

Christmas Opening

24-25 Dec	Closed
26 Dec-1 Jan, daily	10am-4pm

Last entry 30 mins before closing

Café open to abbey closing time

VISIT US

Address: Rievaulx Abbey, Rievaulx, Nr Helmsley, N. Yorks YO62 5LB

Direction: In Rievaulx; 2¼ miles N of Helmsley, on minor road off B1257

Bus: Visit traveline.info for the latest bus timetables and routes

Tel: 01439 798228

NON-MEMBERS

Peak (28 May-31 Aug, Sat-Sun and Bank Holidays)
Adult £13.20 | Concession £11.90
Child £7.90 | Family 2 Adults £34.30
Family 1 Adult £21.10

Standard (1 Apr-27 May and Sep-Oct, Sat-Sun and Bank Holidays; 28 May-31 Aug, Mon-Fri)
Adult £12.20 | Concession £11.00
Child £7.30 | Family 2 Adults £31.70
Family 1 Adult £19.50

Off-peak (1 Apr-27 May and Sep-Oct, Mon-Fri and Nov-Mar)
Adult £11.20 | Concession £10.10
Child £6.60 | Family 2 Adults £29.00
Family 1 Adult £17.80

Parking: charges apply to non-members, free for Members with valid English Heritage car sticker.

MAP PAGE 333 (2G)
OS MAP 100, OL26: SE577850

SCARBOROUGH CASTLE

NORTH YORKSHIRE – YO11 1HY

Battered by siege and attack but still majestic, Scarborough Castle crowns a spectacular headland with a 3,000 year story, amazing views – and 16 acres of history to explore.

Soaring between the two bays of the famous seaside resort, with steep drops on three sides, the headland is a natural stronghold, reachable only by a slender neck of land. It attracted prehistoric, Roman, Saxon and perhaps Viking settlers, and the medieval castle made it almost impregnable. As you approach the castle via the strongly fortified barbican and narrow bridge, the only way in, you'll soon see why it was so hard to attack, defying medieval barons, Tudor rebels and Civil War besiegers. Dominating the fortress stands Henry II's 12th-century Great Tower keep, with one side sheered away by Parliamentarian heavy cannon in 1645. But even then the besiegers couldn't get in, and the garrison had to be starved out.

In the Master Gunner's House, you can trace the headland's long history through site-finds, from a replica Bronze Age sword via Civil War cannonballs to the nose-cap of a shell fired at Scarborough in 1914 during a bombardment by audacious German warships, which shocked the whole nation.

Leave plenty of time to explore the vast grassy headland – bigger than 12 football pitches – and discover its many historic features. It is maintained as a gigantic wildflower meadow, where in high summer you may even spot orchids. On the cliff edge furthest from the keep you'll find the remains of a Roman signal station, one of a chain of beacon towers which gave warning of Saxon coastal raids in the 4th century AD. An Anglo-Saxon church built on its site may have stood here when the Viking King Harald Hardrada seized the headland in 1066, hurling down blazing timbers to fire the town below.

You can follow the long and many-towered curtain wall, which King John built to guard the slope facing towards the harbour. Scarborough was among the busiest east-coast ports in medieval England, making the castle which protected it one of the most important in Yorkshire. Within the ditched Inner Bailey, the heart of the castle, a lofty viewing platform offers you amazing views over the town, the harbour, and the great sweep of South Bay. You'll also get wonderful views – over the narrow castle approach and North Bay – from the platform within the Great Tower, with its tiers of round-topped Norman windows. Dominating the castle and the landscape for miles around, it's one of the finest keeps raised by the champion royal castle-builder King Henry II.

With the finest coastal views in Yorkshire, so much history and such a vast area to explore or play in, Scarborough Castle offers the ideal family day out. Take a break from exploring at our Coffee Shed, serving barista coffee.

Guided tours with staff or volunteers are available most weekends throughout the year and on some summer weekdays, at no additional charge. Please call site in advance for confirmation.

Scarborough (2019).

OPENING TIMES

1 Apr-30 Oct, daily	10am-5pm
31 Oct-23 Dec, Sat-Sun	10am-4pm
2 Jan-10 Feb, Sat-Sun	10am-4pm
11-19 Feb, daily	10am-4pm
20 Feb-31 Mar, Wed-Sun	10am-4pm

Christmas Opening

24-25 Dec	Closed
26 Dec-1 Jan, daily	10am-4pm

Last entry 30 mins before closing

Please note: coffee shop closes 30 mins before castle. During winter, opening times of coffee shop may vary

VISIT US

Address: Castle Road, Scarborough, North Yorkshire YO11 1HY

Direction: Castle Road, E of the town centre

Train: Scarborough 1 mile

Bus: Visit traveline.info for the latest bus timetables and routes

Tel: 01723 372451

Local Tourist Information: Scarborough: 01723 383636

NON-MEMBERS

Adult **£9.00** | Concession **£8.10** | Child **£5.40**
Family 2 Adults **£23.40** | Family 1 Adult **£14.40**

ACQ.1920

No public parking (very limited parking for Blue Badge holders only, please enquire in advance of visit, especially on event days).

MAP PAGE 333 (2J)   OS MAP 101, 301: TA050892

WHITBY ABBEY

NORTH YORKSHIRE – YO22 4JT

Crowned by the hauntingly spectacular Gothic ruins of Whitby Abbey, the headland towering above the picturesque fishing port has been inspiring visitors and artists for 1,500 years. Our recent revamp helps you experience this iconic place in new ways – including a new audio guide downloadable to your smartphone.

Hosting in turn St Hild's Anglo-Saxon monastery, a great medieval abbey and a 17th-century seat of power, the headland is the focus of many stories and legends. Here the cowherd-poet Caedmon was miraculously inspired, and here a visit by Victorian novelist Bram Stoker spawned the notorious fictional vampire, Count Dracula.

On the vast grassy headland loom the ruins of the great abbey church, built in the Early English Gothic style in the 13th century. Battered by time, weather and war, they're still immensely impressive and atmospheric. Our unique Ammonite Quest helps families and groups of friends explore the headland together. Collect an ammonite device and a lanyard information swatch from the visitor centre and (optionally) download a free Live Beacon app to your smartphone. Flashing coloured lights and pulses reveal where key artefacts in the museum were originally found, and when you're walking over the sites of now-vanished abbey buildings.

The visitor centre is sited in Abbey House, the 17th-century mansion of the Cholmley family. Imaginatively themed and dramatically lit, its first floor museum introduces you to the headland, its people and their stories, from prehistory to the present day. It houses a treasury of original artefacts, from Anglo-Saxon crosses and magic charms to elaborate medieval carvings and Victorian paintings. The displays trace how the Anglo-Saxon monastery, famous for holiness and learning, was destroyed by Vikings, refounded soon after the Norman Conquest and eventually superseded by a great mansion. Adult and child-level listening posts, peep-holes and animations tell the headland's many stories: how Hild turned snakes to stone 'ammonites', how Caedmon became a poet, how the lost abbey bells are still heard beneath the waves, and how a real shipwreck at Whitby helped spark off the Dracula tale. There's even a first edition of the famous novel, signed by Bram Stoker himself.

The spacious shop offers an amazing range of products, from folklore and history books to vampire blood cordials and Goth-style bat-patterned parasols. You'll also find a coffee shop, open to all, in the reimagined courtyard fronting the visitor centre.

If you've never visited Whitby Abbey, now's the time to come. If you've visited before, you'll find the experience of rediscovery greatly enhanced and deepened.

Please note: from the Whitby harbour area, you can reach the abbey directly on foot via the famous 199 'church steps'. Alternatively, a well-signposted road leads from the town outskirts to the abbey.

🖼 *Dracula* (2020).

NEW FOR 2022

2022 marks the 125th anniversary of the publication of Bram Stoker's famous Victorian Gothic novel, *Dracula*. Published on the 26 May 1897, it was an immediate success, becoming one of the biggest-selling novels of all time. Never out of print and translated into many languages, it has also inspired over 200 feature films. Many of its most dramatic episodes are set in Whitby, and a programme of activities to celebrate its anniversary will take place at Whitby Abbey during the summer of 2022. Please check the website for more details.

OPENING TIMES

1 Apr-30 Oct, daily	10am-5pm
31 Oct-10 Feb, Wed-Sun	10am-4pm
11 Feb-31 Mar, daily	10am-4pm

Christmas Opening

24-25 Dec	Closed

Last entry 30 mins before closing

Café open until site closing time

VISIT US

Address: Whitby Abbey, Abbey Lane, Whitby, North Yorkshire YO22 4JT

Direction: On cliff top, E of Whitby

Train: Whitby ½ mile

Bus: Visit traveline.info for the latest bus timetables and routes

Tel: 01947 603568

Local Tourist Information: 01723 383636

NON-MEMBERS

Adult **£11.20** | Concession **£10.10**
Child **£6.60** | Family 2 Adults **£29.00**
Family 1 Adult **£17.80**

ACQ.1920 🎧 ♿ 🐕 🎁 🏪 🚹 🚹 📮 **P**
🎪 📷 🛍 ⚠ OVP

Disabled access (south entrance parking, charged).

Parking not managed by English Heritage (charge payable).

Toilets situated in the car park are not operated by English Heritage (charge payable).

Tearooms not managed by English Heritage.

MAP PAGE 333 (1H)
OS MAP 94, OL27: NZ903112

WHEELDALE ROMAN ROAD

NORTH YORKSHIRE –YO22 5AP

An enigmatic mile-long stretch of stone trackway amid wild and beautiful moorland. Usually identified as a Roman road, it may actually be medieval, or even a prehistoric boundary marker.

OPENING TIMES

Any reasonable daylight hours

VISIT US

Direction: Approximately 4 miles SW of Goathland via moorland roads (Wheeldale Road). 7 miles SW of Whitby

Train: Goathland (North Yorkshire Moors Rly) (4 miles) or Newtondale Halt (then 3 mile forest walk)

Bus: Visit traveline.info for the latest bus timetables and routes

Local Tourist Information: Pickering: 01751 473791

ACQ.1912 🐕 🐄 ⚠

Parking on roadside.

Stout footwear essential if walking track.

Livestock may be present.

MAP PAGE 333 (2H)
OS MAP 94/100, OL27: SE806977

DON'T FORGET

Remember to take your membership card with you when visiting one of our sites.

And, don't forget to display your English Heritage car sticker – it gives you free parking at many of our sites.

See p.6-8 for details of planning your visit.

YORK COLD WAR BUNKER

NORTH YORKSHIRE – YO24 4HT

For 30 years the volunteers of the Royal Observer Corps watched for nuclear Armageddon here. At a time of crisis 60 men and women would be entombed within 'No 20 Group Control', ready to plot nuclear explosions and radioactive fallout across Yorkshire. Within the brutal concrete exterior is a chilling Cold War time capsule, where original monitoring and communications equipment sits alongside the necessities of life; a canteen, a dormitory and support systems designed to last just 30 days.

Visits are by guided tour, enhanced by a striking 10-minute film (PG rated) telling the story of the Cold War.

OPENING TIMES

1 Apr-31 Oct, Fri-Sun & Bank Hols	10am-5pm
1 Nov-31 Mar, Sat-Sun	10am-4pm
24-26 Dec & 1 Jan	Closed

Please visit the website to book your tour. Tours last approximately one hour

Weekdays: Admission for schools and groups only. Booking 14 days in advance, minimum fee applies

VISIT US

Direction: Monument Close, off Acomb Road (B1224), turning opposite Hobgate, approx. 2 miles from York city centre

Train: York 1¼ miles

Bus: Visit traveline.info for the latest bus timetables and routes

Tel: 01904 646940

Local Tourist Information: York: 01904 555670

NON-MEMBERS

Adult **£10.00** | Concession **£9.00**
Child **£6.00** | Family 2 Adults **£26.00**
Family 1 Adult **£16.00**

ACQ2001 🦽 ♿ 🎬 📺 🚶 🚻 🎫 P
📷 OVP

MAP PAGE 333 (3G)
OS MAP 105, 290: SE580515

CONISBROUGH CASTLE

SOUTH YORKSHIRE – DN12 3BU

Step into the inspirational setting of Walter Scott's *Ivanhoe* novel. This most unusual medieval fortress has been brought to life by a spectacular and highly imaginative makeover funded by the Heritage Lottery Fund.

The design of Conisbrough Castle's tall cylindrical keep, ringed with six great turret buttresses, is unique in Britain. Probably begun in the 1170s, it was later reinforced by a turreted outer wall. It proclaims the ambition, power and wealth of its builders: Hamelin Plantagenet, illegitimate half-brother of King Henry II, and his wife, the formidable Lady Isabel de Warenne, heiress of Conisbrough.

You can explore the whole fully roofed and floored keep, with its three big chambers and lovely miniature chapel, guided by larger-than-life wall-projected figures of Hamelin, Isabel and their steward. Climbing to the roof, you'll find wonderful all-round vistas over the surrounding countryside.

Graphic novel style interpretation, featuring builders, servants, ladies-in-waiting and squires from the castle's history, offers vivid guidance around the whole fortress. Don't miss the fascinating introductory exhibition, including many excavated site finds. It traces Conisbrough's history from its beginnings to the present day. A striking cutaway model, with moving figures, offers a virtual tour of the keep if you don't wish to ascend its stairways.

OPENING TIMES

1 Apr-30 Oct, daily	10am-5pm
31 Oct-10 Feb, Sat-Sun	10am-4pm
11-19 Feb, daily	10am-4pm
20 Feb-31 Mar, Sat-Sun	10am-4pm
24-26 Dec & 1 Jan	Closed

Last entry 30 mins before closing

VISIT US

Direction: Located NE of Conisbrough town centre off A630; 4½ miles SW of Doncaster

Train: Conisbrough ½ mile

Bus: Visit traveline.info for the latest bus timetables and routes

Tel: 01709 863329

NON-MEMBERS

Adult **£7.80** | Concession **£7.00** | Child **£4.70**
Family 2 Adults **£20.30** | Family 1 Adult **£12.50**

ACQ.1950 ♿ 🐕 🍴 🛡 E ♀ ♂ 📷 ⚠ OVP

Dogs on leads (in grounds only).

Disabled parking available outside the visitor centre.

No disabled access to or within the keep, due to steep stairways.

An interactive device is available for visitors unable to access the keep, allowing them to explore the building and meet characters.

Access limited to some areas.

MAP PAGE 333 (5G)
OS MAP 111, 279: SK515989

BRODSWORTH HALL AND GARDENS

SOUTH YORKSHIRE – DN5 7XJ

Few places in England can match Brodsworth Hall.
In this grand yet gently time-worn Victorian mansion
you can experience life in a country house as it really was.
Now we've not only revived even more of its delightful
Victorian garden features, but also uncovered the hidden
story of Brodsworth's links with the slave trade.

'Conserved as found' when English Heritage took over, Brodsworth still reflects its original opulence, but also reveals how its owners and servants weathered the changes and challenges of the 20th century. It's a house full of surprises.

Brodsworth Hall was built in the 1860s by the fabulously wealthy Charles Sabine Augustus Thellusson, and occupied by his family for over 120 years. The grand rooms on the ground floor recall the house's Victorian heyday, with glittering chandeliers and marble statues.

As you look closer, you can see the changes wrought by time. The last resident, the indomitable Sylvia Grant-Dalton, fought a losing battle against subsidence and leaking roofs. Following her death in 1988, we took the bold decision to conserve the interiors as they were found, rather than restoring them. The house remains as she used it, making do and mending with dwindling funds and ever fewer servants. Some of the bedrooms were modernised over the years, and contain furnishings dating from the 1860s to the 1980s. Other rooms fell out of use, though most of the Victorian servants' furnishings have survived.

Downstairs, the cavernous kitchen with its stupendous cooking range was deserted for a cosier room with an Aga range cooker. Beside the Aga rests the battered armchair of the last cook-housekeeper, Emily Chester. Displays reveal more about the Thellusson family, their servants, and how they lived together.

THE AWARD-WINNING GARDENS

Brodsworth's extensive gardens have been restored to their original splendour as 'a collection of grand gardens in miniature'. Romantic views from the restored summerhouse take in both the formal gardens and the pleasure grounds. Stroll through the statue walks, the fern dell grotto and the beautiful wild rose dell.

In spring, snowdrops, daffodils and bluebells put on a fantastic show. In summer, colourful formal bedding and roses contrast strikingly with the sculptural topiary and ferns. After the brilliant autumn colours fade, you can admire the extensive collection of Victorian hollies throughout the winter. On summer Sunday afternoons, enjoy the best of Yorkshire's brass bands from the garden terraces.

DON'T
MISS

Although the current Brodsworth Hall and Gardens were built and developed after the abolition of slavery, their creation was partly funded by wealth inherited from an earlier owner of the estate, Peter Thellusson, who had profited from enslavement.

A thought-provoking exhibition addresses this part of Brodsworth's history in a balanced and engaging way. It includes wire sculptures produced by internationally significant artist Carl Gabriel, and a poem by the award-winning poet Malika Booker. Runs until November 2022.

MORE REVIVED GARDEN FEATURES

We've been progressively reviving forgotten features of Brodsworth's gardens, including the charming 1864 garden 'privy' toilet and the rare survival of a Victorian game larder. We've strikingly restored the Target Range to its Edwardian glory as a mosaic of brilliantly planted beds and intricate paving. Now we've also restored the Eyecatcher, a ruined Classical-style structure designed to draw the eye along the Target Range, and the Target House, a picturesque chalet-roofed summerhouse where the family rested from archery, which displays new interpretation.

A FAMILY-FRIENDLY PROPERTY

The hall and gardens are welcoming whatever your age. There's an outdoor play area, and families can make the most of events and activities in the garden. Everyone can enjoy the tearoom in the Servants' Wing, or watch the local croquet club in action. Inside the hall, friendly and knowledgeable volunteer room stewards will share stories from Brodsworth's past.

🎬 *Darkest Hour* (2017); *Testament of Youth* (2014); *The Thirteenth Tale* (2013); ITV series *Victoria*.

OPENING TIMES

House & Servants' Wing
House is open for general admission from 11am-4pm.
No flash photography allowed

1 Apr-30 Oct, daily	11am-5pm
31 Oct-31 Mar*	Closed

Garden and Tearooms
1 Apr-30 Oct, daily	10am-5pm
31 Oct-23 Dec, Sat-Sun*	10am-4pm
24-25 Dec	Closed
26 Dec-1 Jan, daily	10am-4pm
27 Dec-10 Feb, Sat-Sun*	10am-4pm
11-19 Feb, daily*	10am-4pm
20 Feb-31 Mar, Wed-Sun*	10am-4pm

Last entry 30 mins before closing

*Servants' Wing open weekends and school holidays during this period   11am-2pm

Mobility Around the Site
Prams and back carriers for babies are not allowed in the hall, small padded pushchairs are available instead. For visitors with mobility needs, an electric buggy operates a shuttle service from the car park. Benches throughout the gardens, although steps and steep slopes limit access to some areas. The hall has ramps and seats, and a lift to the first floor

VISIT US
Address: Brodsworth Hall and Gardens, Brodsworth, Doncaster, South Yorkshire DN5 7XJ
Please note: some satellite navigation systems give multiple locations for the postcode. To avoid confusion, please follow the brown signs in the local area

Direction: In Brodsworth, 5 miles NW of Doncaster off A635 Barnsley Road; from junction 37 of A1(M)

Train: South Elmsall 4 miles; Moorthorpe 4½ miles; Doncaster 5½ miles; Adwick Le Street 3 miles

Bus: Visit traveline.info for the latest bus timetables and routes

Tel: 01302 722598

Local Tourist Information: Doncaster: 01302 734309

NON-MEMBERS
House and Gardens
Adult **£14.20** I Concession **£12.80**
Child **£8.50** I Family 2 Adults **£36.90**
Family 1 Adult **£22.70**

Winter
Adult **£9.90** I Concession **£8.90**
Child **£5.90** I Family 2 Adults **£25.70**
Family 1 Adult **£15.80**

MAP PAGE 333 (5G)
OS MAP 111, 279: SE506070

MONK BRETTON PRIORY SOUTH YORKSHIRE – S71 5QD

The substantial ruins of a Cluniac monastery, later absorbed into the Benedictine order, with an unusually well-marked ground plan, almost complete west range and 15th-century gatehouse.

OPENING TIMES

1 Apr 2022- 31 Mar 2023, daily (managed by a keykeeper)	10am-3pm
24-26, 31 Dec & 1 Jan	Closed

VISIT US

Direction: Located 1 mile E of Barnsley town centre, off A633

Train: Barnsley 2½ miles

Bus: Visit traveline.info for the latest bus timetables and routes

NON-MEMBERS

Charges may apply on event days

ACQ.1932

Caution: CCTV at site.

MAP PAGE 333 (5F)
OS MAP 110/111, 278: SE373065

ROCHE ABBEY SOUTH YORKSHIRE – S66 8NW

The extensive remains of a small Cistercian abbey, in a beautiful setting. The soaring early Gothic transepts of its church were preserved as a 'Romantic eye-catcher' when Capability Brown drastically landscaped their surroundings from the 1760s, covering up other parts of the ruins. These now reveal one of the most complete ground plans of any English Cistercian monastery.

OPENING TIMES

1 Apr-30 Oct, daily	10am-5pm
31 Oct-31 Mar	Closed
Last entry 30 mins before closing	

VISIT US

Direction: 1½ miles S of Maltby, off A634

Train: Conisbrough 7 miles

Bus: Visit traveline.info for the latest bus timetables and routes

Tel: 01709 812739

NON-MEMBERS

Adult **£5.60** | Concession **£5.00**
Child **£3.40** | Family 2 Adults **£14.60**
Family 1 Adult **£9.00**

ACQ.1921   OVP

MAP PAGE 333 (5G)
OS MAP 111/120, 279: SK544898

Stott Park Bobbin Mill, Cumbria

WELCOME TO THE

NORTH WEST

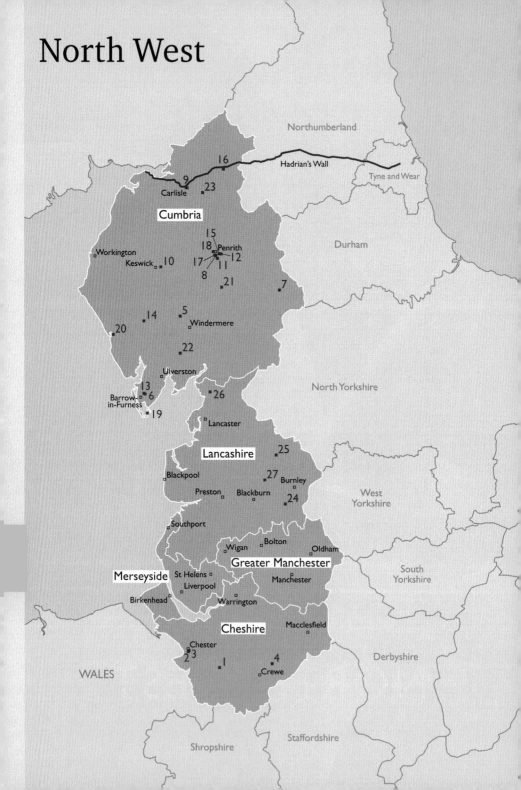

North West

Northumberland

Hadrian's Wall

Tyne and Wear

16

9
Carlisle
23

Cumbria

15
18
Penrith
Workington
17 12
Keswick 10 11
8
21
7

5
14
Windermere

20

22

Ulverston

13
Barrow- 6
in-Furness
19

26

Lancaster

Lancashire

25

Blackpool

27
Burnley
Preston Blackburn
24

Southport

Wigan Bolton
Oldham

Greater Manchester

Merseyside

St Helens
Liverpool Manchester

Birkenhead

Warrington

Cheshire

Macclesfield

Chester
2 3
1 4
Crewe

Durham

North Yorkshire

West Yorkshire

South Yorkshire

Derbyshire

WALES

Shropshire

Staffordshire

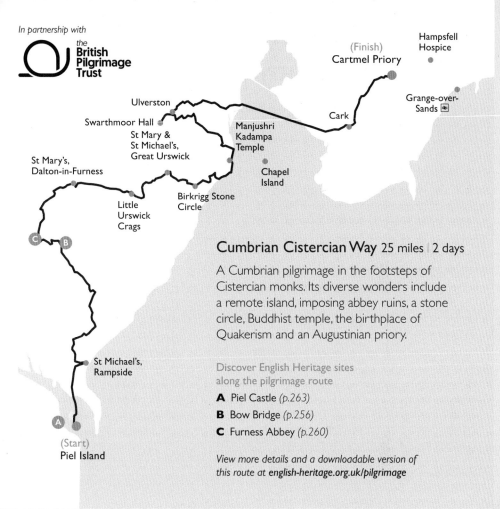

Hampsfell Hospice

(Finish)
Cartmel Priory

Grange-over-Sands

Ulverston

Cark

Swarthmoor Hall
St Mary & St Michael's, Great Urswick

Manjushri Kadampa Temple

St Mary's, Dalton-in-Furness

Chapel Island

Little Urswick Crags

Birkrigg Stone Circle

C **B**

Cumbrian Cistercian Way 25 miles | 2 days

A Cumbrian pilgrimage in the footsteps of Cistercian monks. Its diverse wonders include a remote island, imposing abbey ruins, a stone circle, Buddhist temple, the birthplace of Quakerism and an Augustinian priory.

St Michael's, Rampside

Discover English Heritage sites along the pilgrimage route

A Piel Castle *(p.263)*
B Bow Bridge *(p.256)*
C Furness Abbey *(p.260)*

A

(Start)
Piel Island

View more details and a downloadable version of this route at english-heritage.org.uk/pilgrimage

BEESTON CASTLE & WOODLAND PARK

CHESHIRE – CW6 9TX

Crowning a sandstone crag towering above the Cheshire Plain, Beeston Castle is among the most dramatically sited fortresses in England, offering some of the best views in the country. Long before the castle was built, the crag was a busy hive of human activity. Our recreated Bronze Age roundhouse brings its prehistoric past strikingly to life.

Based on Bronze Age houses discovered here on the site, the roundhouse was meticulously reconstructed by a team of over 60 volunteers with help from expert advisers. Using only tools and techniques available in the Bronze Age, they crafted the thatched house from Beeston crag oaks and local ash and hazel. The recreation also drew on evidence from across Europe, including Must Farm in the Cambridgeshire Fens, where archaeologists recently found evidence of not only the ground plans but also the roof structures and even the contents of Bronze Age houses. By no means a primitive shack – with a ground area of over fifty square metres, it's bigger than some modern homes – the roundhouse offers education groups immersive learning experiences in prehistoric crafts and building techniques. And for all visitors, it's a vivid evocation of life at Beeston 4,000 years ago.

Much later, in the 1220s, the 'Castle of the Rock' was begun here by Ranulf, Earl of Chester, one of the greatest barons in Henry III's England. It's approached via a ruined gatehouse in a multi-towered outer wall, defining a huge outer bailey climbing steadily up the hill to the castle's crowning glory, the inner bailey. Defended by a rock-cut ditch and a mighty double-towered gatehouse, this offers you truly astounding views across eight counties, from the Welsh Mountains to the Pennines. It also contains the famous castle well, over 100 metres (328 feet) deep and among the deepest in any English castle. According to legend, it's the hiding place of Richard II's treasure, allegedly guarded by demons.

Set in 40 acres of woodland, Beeston Castle is a paradise for walkers, nature lovers and adventurous children. A circular woodland walk winds around the base of the crag, through wildlife-thronged woods and past Beeston's sandstone caves (external viewing only). You can also reach the caves directly from the visitor centre, where the 'Castle of the Rock' display retells Beeston's 4,000-year story, including a famous Civil War siege.

The Sandstone Café offers hot and cold snacks and drinks. No indoor seating, but picnic tables are available outside.

OPENING TIMES

1 Apr-30 Oct, daily	10am-5pm
31 Oct-23 Dec, Sat-Sun	10am-4pm
2 Jan-10 Feb, Sat-Sun	10am-4pm
11-19 Feb, daily	10am-4pm
20 Feb-31 Mar, Wed-Sun	10am-4pm

Christmas Opening

24-25 Dec	Closed
26 Dec-1 Jan, daily	10am-4pm

Last entry 30 mins before closing

VISIT US

Address: Beeston Castle, Chapel Lane, Beeston, Cheshire CW6 9TX

Direction: Located 11 miles SE of Chester, on minor road off A49

Train: Chester 11 miles or Crewe 15 miles

Bus: Visit traveline.info for the latest bus timetables and routes

Tel: 01829 260464

Local Tourist Information:
Chester: 01244 402111

NON-MEMBERS

Adult £10.00 | Concession £9.00
Child £6.00 | Family 2 Adults £26.00
Family 1 Adult £16.00

Caution: steep ascent to inner bailey (no disabled access to the top of the hill). Steps and rough path to roundhouse. Boots or sturdy footwear recommended for woodland walk.

Parking: charges apply to non-members, free for Members with valid car sticker.

MAP PAGE 332 (6D)
OS MAP 117, 257/258: SJ537593

CHESTER CASTLE: AGRICOLA TOWER AND CASTLE WALLS

CHESHIRE – CH1 2DN

The original gateway to Chester Castle, this 12th-century tower houses a chapel with traces of wall paintings of c.1220, rediscovered in the 1980s.

OPENING TIMES

Please see website for event dates

VISIT US

Direction: Access via Assizes Court car park on Grosvenor St

Train: Chester 1 mile

Bus: Visit traveline.info for the latest bus timetables and routes

ACQ.1912 ♿ ⚠

Caution: steep stairs.

MAP PAGE 332 (6C)
OS MAP 117, 266: SJ405657

CHESTER ROMAN AMPHITHEATRE

CHESHIRE – CH1 1RE

The largest Roman amphitheatre in Britain, used by the 20th Legion, based at the fortress of 'Deva' (Chester). Excavations revealed two successive stone-built amphitheatres with wooden seating. The two buildings differed from all other British amphitheatres, underlining the importance of Roman Chester.

Managed by Cheshire West and Chester Council.

CHESTER ROMAN AMPHITHEATRE

OPENING TIMES

Any reasonable daylight hours

VISIT US

Direction: On Vicar's Lane, beyond Newgate, Chester

Train: Chester ¾ mile

Bus: Visit traveline.info for the latest bus timetables and routes

ACQ.1964 ♿ ⚠

Disabled access (no access to amphitheatre floor).

Caution: unguarded drops.

MAP PAGE 332 (6C)
OS MAP 117, 266: SJ408662

SANDBACH CROSSES

CHESHIRE – CW11 1AT

Dominating Sandbach market square, these are among the finest surviving Anglo-Saxon high crosses. Probably dating from the 9th century, and originally painted as well as elaborately carved.

OPENING TIMES

Any reasonable daylight hours

VISIT US

Direction: Market Sq, Sandbach

Train: Sandbach 1½ miles

Bus: Visit traveline.info for the latest bus timetables and routes

ACQ.1937 ♿

MAP PAGE 332 (6D)
OS MAP 118, 268: SJ759608

CUMBRIA

AMBLESIDE ROMAN FORT

CUMBRIA – LA22 0EN

Foundations of a 2nd- to 4th-century Roman fort, in a meadow beside Windermere. Possibly a supply base for Lake District patrols.

Managed by the National Trust.

OPENING TIMES

Any reasonable daylight hours

VISIT US

Direction: In Borrans Field, beside A5075 on south-western outskirts of Ambleside. 182 metres W of Waterhead car park

Train: Windermere 5 miles

Bus: Visit traveline.info for the latest bus timetables and routes

ACQ.1978 ⚠

Beware – cattle may be grazing.

No parking at site. Stout footwear advised.

Caution: unguarded drops.

MAP PAGE 334 (6D)
OS MAP 90, OL7: NY372034

BOW BRIDGE

CUMBRIA– LA13 0PL

This narrow 15th-century stone bridge across Mill Beck carried an old packhorse route to nearby Furness Abbey (see p.260).

OPENING TIMES

Any reasonable daylight hours

VISIT US

Direction: Located ½ mile N of Barrow-in-Furness, on minor road off A590; near Furness Abbey

Train: Barrow-in-Furness 1½ miles

Bus: Visit traveline.info for the latest bus timetables and routes

ACQ.1950 ⚠

Beware – livestock may be grazing on site.

Caution: sheer drop into water.

MAP PAGE 334 (7D)
OS MAP 96, OL6: SD224715

BROUGH CASTLE

CUMBRIA – CA17 4EJ

On a ridge commanding Stainmore Pass. Frequently the target of Scots raids, its towering keep dates from c. 1200. Like many other castles hereabouts, Brough was restored in the 17th century by Lady Anne Clifford, whose additions are still visible.

OPENING TIMES

1 Apr-30 Sep, daily	10am-5pm
1 Oct-31 Mar, daily	10am-4pm
24-26, 31 Dec & 1 Jan	Closed

VISIT US

Direction: 8 miles SE of Appleby

Train: Kirkby Stephen 10 miles

Bus: Visit traveline.info

ACQ. 1919 🎫 🅿 🚻 🖼 ⚠

Please note: approach may be muddy, stout footwear recommended.

Limited parking nearby. Please do not park on farm's access road.

Beware – livestock may be grazing on site.

New guidebook available late 2022.

Caution: steep slopes.

MAP PAGE 332 (1D)
OS MAP 91, OL19: NY791141

CASTLERIGG STONE CIRCLE
CUMBRIA – CA12 4RN

Among the most dramatically sited prehistoric stone circles in Britain, surrounded by a panorama of Lakeland fells. It's also one of the earliest circles, probably raised around 3000 BC. Thirty-three of its close-set stones still stand.

Managed by the National Trust.

OPENING TIMES

Any reasonable daylight hours

VISIT US

Direction: 1½ miles E of Keswick. Signposted from A66 and A591

Train: Penrith 16 miles

Bus: Visit traveline.info

ACQ.1883 🚻 🖼 ⚠

Limited parking in lay-by.

Beware – livestock may be grazing on site.

Sturdy footwear is recommended.

MAP PAGE 334 (5D)
OS MAP 89/90, OL4: NY291236

BROUGHAM CASTLE CUMBRIA – CA10 2AA

In a picturesque setting beside the River Eamont, near the site of a Roman fort, red sandstone Brougham Castle was founded in the early 13th century by Robert de Vieuxpont. His tall keep largely survives amid many later buildings added by the powerful Clifford family. These include the unusual double gatehouse and impressive 'Tower of League'. A formidable barrier against Scots invaders and a proclamation of baronial splendour, the castle welcomed Edward I in 1300. Falling into decay after James I's visit in 1617, Brougham was restored by the indomitable Lady Anne Clifford. She often visited with her travelling 'court', and died here in 1676.

There's a lot to explore at Brougham, and you can climb the spiral stairs to the keep top for panoramic views over the Eden Valley.

OPENING TIMES

1 Apr-30 Oct, daily	10am-5pm
31 Oct-31 Mar, Sat-Sun	10am-4pm
24-26 Dec & 1 Jan	Closed

Last entry 30 mins before closing

VISIT US

Direction: 1½ miles SE of Penrith, off A66

Train: Penrith 2 miles

Bus: Visit traveline.info for the latest bus timetables and routes

Tel: 01768 862488

Local Tourist Information:
Penrith: 01768 867466
Rheged: 01768 860034

NON-MEMBERS

Adult **£6.60** I Concession **£5.90**
Child **£4.00** I Family 2 Adults **£17.20**
Family 1 Adult **£10.60**

ACQ.1920 🍴 ♿ 🚻 🚩 🅿 🚶 🚹 🖼
🅿 🖼 🅾 OVP

Please note: car parking limited, in 'no through road' opposite castle entrance.

There is good wheelchair access to most of the site (excluding the keep).

New guidebook.

MAP PAGE 334 (5E)
OS MAP 90, OL5: NY537290

CARLISLE CASTLE

CUMBRIA – CA3 8UR

The storm-centre of many famous sieges, Carlisle Castle was for centuries the flashpoint of frontier warfare, as well as a notorious prison. Trace its long and sometimes grim history as you explore the powerful keep and view our vivid displays.

Carlisle Castle remains a dominating presence in the city it has watched over for nine centuries. You can witness its rich and varied story in a vivid exhibition celebrating Carlisle's fame as the most besieged town in Britain.

The medieval castle was built on the site of an important Roman fortress. The commanding keep was begun during the 12th century by King Henry I of England and completed by King David I of Scotland. It's a reminder that Carlisle Castle was for centuries a disputed frontier fortress, guarding the especially turbulent western end of the Anglo-Scottish border. It triumphantly repelled a siege by King Robert Bruce of Scotland in 1315, after a great Scots siege engine got stuck fast in mud.

The castle's violent history also included skirmishes with Elizabethan Border Reivers, a Civil War siege – the longest siege of a town in English history – and Bonnie Prince Charlie's Jacobite Rising of 1745-46. Carlisle was then the very last English fortress ever to suffer a siege. Overwhelmed by the Duke of Cumberland's Hanoverian army, its Jacobite defenders were imprisoned in the keep's dank basement. Today you can see the legendary 'licking stones', which they supposedly licked for moisture. Unique carvings on the keep's second floor were probably cut in the 1460-70s.

By the time Mary Queen of Scots was imprisoned here in 1568, Henry VIII's updating for heavy artillery had left its mark on the fortress, including the Half Moon Battery defending the Captain's Tower gatehouse. You can explore both the Tudor Battery and the 12th-century gatehouse, one of the best preserved in England.

Discover more highlights in 'Besieged', a display which includes examples of the weapons used during Carlisle's many sieges, a reconstruction graphic of the keep, a retelling of the daring rescue of a Border Reiver, and a 360-degree virtual tour of the castle.

Unusually, the medieval castle remained an operational fortress well into the 20th century. From 1873 to 1959 it was the regimental headquarters of Cumbria's Infantry Regiment, and today it hosts Cumbria's Museum of Military Life, which explores the regiment's 300-year history. English Heritage Members get free entry to the museum. There's a café in the museum, which also hosts a programme of temporary exhibitions. Separate opening times apply. Please visit cumbriasmuseumofmilitarylife.org for details.

🎬 *Outlander* (2014).

OPENING TIMES

1 Apr-30 Oct, daily	10am-5pm
31 Oct-10 Feb, Sat-Sun	10am-4pm
11-26 Feb, daily	10am-4pm
27 Feb-31 Mar, Sat-Sun	10am-4pm
24-26 Dec & 1 Jan	Closed

Last entry 30 mins before closing

VISIT US

Address: Carlisle Castle, Castle Way, Carlisle, Cumbria CA3 8UR

Direction: In Carlisle city centre. Follow Castle Street, past Carlisle Cathedral on left. At main road, take underpass to the castle

Train: Carlisle ½ mile

Bus: Visit traveline.info for the latest bus timetables and routes

Tel: 01228 591922

Local Tourist Information:
Carlisle: 01228 598596

NON-MEMBERS

Adult £11.60 | Concession £10.40
Child £6.90 | Family 2 Adults £30.10
Family 1 Adult £18.50

Ticket price includes entry to Cumbria's Museum of Military Life

ACQ.1963 OVP

Disabled access (limited).

Dogs on leads (restricted areas only).

Guided tours available to pre-book at a small extra charge.

Parking (disabled only, but signposted city centre car parks nearby).

Cumbria's Museum of Military Life café not managed by English Heritage.

MAP PAGE 334 (4D)
OS MAP 85, 315: NY396562

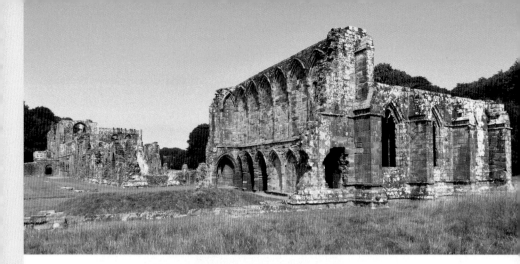

FURNESS ABBEY

CUMBRIA – LA13 0PJ

Among the north west's finest sights, the imposing remains of Furness Abbey are cradled in a lovely wooded valley known as the 'Vale of Nightshade'. These grand ruins inspired the painter Turner and the poet Wordsworth. Thanks to the recent completion of a major conservation programme, there's now even more to explore here.

Founded by Stephen of Blois, later King of England, Furness became the second richest Cistercian abbey in England. Its extensive red sandstone ruins proclaim its prosperity. Dating principally from the 12th and 13th centuries, they include the western tower and east end of the great church, with its presbytery – now free of scaffolding and internally accessible again after 14 years. You can also explore the chapter house, with its fine carved decoration, and almost the entire east range of the cloister. Follow the footpath up to the viewing platform for fantastic vistas over the abbey ruins.

The visitor centre exhibition reveals the abbey's history and a large collection of sculpture from the ruins, including striking effigies of knights. Treasures from an abbot's grave, including the rare silver-gilt 12th-century 'Furness Crozier' and a gemstone ring, are on permanent display.

We're very grateful to the Furness Abbey Fellowship for their support furnessabbeyfellowship.org/

OPENING TIMES

1 Apr-30 Oct, daily	10am-5pm
31 Oct-31 Mar, Sat-Sun	10am-4pm
24-26 Dec & 1 Jan	Closed

Last entry 30 mins before closing

VISIT US

Direction: Located 1½ miles N of Barrow-in-Furness, off A590

Train: Dalton and Roose 2 miles; Barrow-in-Furness 2 miles

Bus: Visit traveline.info for the latest bus timetables and routes

Tel: 01229 823420

NON-MEMBERS

Adult £7.80 | Concession £7.00
Child £4.70 | Family 2 Adults £20.30
Family 1 Adult £12.50

Dogs on leads (restricted areas only).

New guidebook.

MAP PAGE 334 (7D)
OS MAP 96, OL6: SD218717

CLIFTON HALL

CUMBRIA – CA10 2EA

The well preserved early Tudor tower of an otherwise vanished manor house, now surrounded by a busy working farmyard. Graphic panels reveal its history, and you can climb the spiral stairs to look into the kitchen and private chambers it contained, with a fine king-post roof.

OPENING TIMES

Any reasonable daylight hours

24-26 Dec & 1 Jan	Closed

Key available from farmhouse if tower is locked

VISIT US

Direction: In Clifton, 2 miles S of Penrith; signposted from A6 in village

Train: Penrith 2½ miles

Bus: Visit traveline.info

ACQ.1973 🐕 🐄 ⚠

No vehicular access. Please park in the village and walk to the site.

Beware – livestock may be grazing on site.

Farmyard may be muddy: stout footwear recommended.

Caution: steep stairs.

> MAP PAGE 334 (5E)
> OS MAP 90, OL5: NY530271

COUNTESS PILLAR, BROUGHAM

CUMBRIA – CA10 2AB

A monument erected in 1656 by Lady Anne Clifford of nearby Brougham Castle, to commemorate her final parting here from her mother, 40 years earlier. Sundials are carved on three faces, and on the low stone beside it money was given to the poor on each anniversary of their parting.

OPENING TIMES

Any reasonable daylight hours

VISIT US

Direction: ¼ mile E of Brougham. An access route has also been created, which runs from the B6262

(to Brougham) and starts near the junction with the A66

Train: Penrith 2½ miles

Bus: Visit traveline.info

ACQ.1977 🐕 ⚠

Caution: site on a very busy main road. Parking on B6262, close to the junction with A66. Safe access by footpath.

> MAP PAGE 334 (5E)
> OS MAP 90, OL5: NY546289

HARDKNOTT ROMAN FORT   CUMBRIA – CA19 1TH

Among the remotest and most spectacularly sited Roman forts in England, guarding a Roman road across the high fells. Its complete perimeter walls, headquarters building and nearby bath house and 'sauna' are clearly visible. Managed by the National Trust.

OPENING TIMES

Any reasonable daylight hours

VISIT US

Direction: 9 miles NE of Ravenglass; at W end of Hardknott Pass, via short uphill path from unclassified road

Train: Dalegarth (Ravenglass & Eskdale) 3 miles or Ravenglass 10 miles

Bus: Visit traveline.info

ACQ.1949 🐕 🐄 P ⚠

Very limited parking in lay-by. More parking at Jubilee Bridge, ½ mile to west. Access hazardous in winter months or bad weather. Stout footwear essential.

Beware – livestock may be grazing on site.

Visitors are strongly advised to approach from the western (Eskdale) direction: the road from Ambleside over the Wrynose and Hardknott passes is hazardous in poor weather, with hairpin bends and 1-in-3 gradients. Not accessible by coaches.

Caution: steep slopes.

> MAP PAGE 334 (6D)
> OS MAP 89/90, OL6: NY218015

KING ARTHUR'S ROUND TABLE

CUMBRIA – CA10 2BX

Grassy banks of a late Neolithic earthwork henge, dating from c. 2000-1000 BC, but much later believed to be King Arthur's jousting arena. Mayburgh Henge is nearby.

OPENING TIMES

Any reasonable daylight hours

VISIT US

Direction: At Eamont Bridge, 1 mile S of Penrith. Signposted from A6 at S end of village

Train: Penrith 1½ miles

Bus: Visit traveline.info

ACQ.1884 🐕 🐄 ⚠

No parking at site. Park at Mayburgh Henge (400 metres away).

Strictly no dogs when cattle are on site. Dogs on leads at other times.

Beware – cattle may be grazing.

> MAP PAGE 334 (5E)
> OS MAP 90, OL5: NY523284

MAYBURGH HENGE

CUMBRIA – CA10 2BX

Among the biggest and most impressive prehistoric henges in northern England, dating from the late Neolithic period. Its enormous circular bank still stands over 3 metres (10 feet) high. King Arthur's Round Table is nearby.

OPENING TIMES

Any reasonable daylight hours

VISIT US

Direction: At Eamont Bridge, 1 mile S of Penrith. Signposted from A6 at S end of village

Train: Penrith 1½ miles

Bus: Visit traveline.info

ACQ.1884 🐕 🐄 ⚠

Limited parking (roadside only).

Strictly no dogs when cattle are on site. Dogs on leads at other times.

Beware – cattle may be grazing.

Caution: steep slopes.

Sturdy and waterproof footwear required.

> MAP PAGE 334 (5E)
> OS MAP 90, OL5: NY519284

LANERCOST PRIORY

CUMBRIA – CA8 2HQ

The tranquil setting of Augustinian Lanercost Priory belies an often troubled history.

Less than half a mile from Hadrian's Wall, it suffered frequent attacks during the long Anglo-Scottish wars. The mortally sick King Edward I rested here for five months in 1306-07, shortly before his death on his final campaign.

There is still a great deal for you to see in one of Cumbria's best-preserved monasteries. The east end of the noble 13th-century church survives to its full height and you can admire some recently conserved monuments within its dramatic triple tier of arches. The nave, with its lofty west front, is still in full use as the parish church.

Lanercost's cloisters include a beautiful vaulted 13th-century refectory undercroft. Converted into the Tudor mansion of the Dacre family, they also include the Dacre Tower, adapted from the monastic kitchen, and the Dacre Hall (used as the village hall, so not often open to the public). The Dacre Hall displays fragments of 16th-century wall painting and a splendid Jacobean chimneypiece, recently returned here.

Set beside an ancient vicarage and 'vicar's pele tower' (exterior viewing only), Lanercost Priory's extensive remains offer an unforgettable visit.

Nearby farm buildings have been converted into a tearoom. The parish church, Dacre Hall, tearoom and visitor centre are not managed by English Heritage.

When you're in the area, visit Hadrian's Wall (p.266).

OPENING TIMES

1 Apr-30 Oct, daily	10am-5pm
31 Oct-10 Feb, Sat-Sun	10am-4pm
11-19 Feb, daily	10am-4pm
20 Feb-31 Mar, Sat-Sun	10am-4pm
24-26 Dec & 1 Jan	Closed

Last entry 30 mins before closing

VISIT US

Direction: Off the minor road through Lanercost, next to the church; 2½ miles NE of Brampton

Train: Brampton 3 miles

Bus: Visit traveline.info for the latest bus timetables

Tel: 01697 73030

NON-MEMBERS

Peak (28 May-31 Aug, Sun-Thu)
Adult **£7.80** | Concession **£7.00** | Child **£4.70**
Family 2 Adults **£20.30** | Family 1 Adult **£12.50**

Standard (1 Apr-27 May and Sep-Oct, Sun-Thu; 28 May-31 Aug, Fri-Sat)
Adult **£7.20** | Concession **£6.50** | Child **£4.30**
Family 2 Adults **£18.70** | Family 1 Adult **£11.50**

Off-peak (1 Apr-27 May and Sep-Oct, Fri-Sat and Nov-Mar)
Adult **£6.60** | Concession **£5.90** | Child **£4.00**
Family 2 Adults **£17.20** | Family 1 Adult **£10.60**

ACQ.1930 🎫 P 📷 ⚠ OVP

Please note: no toilet facilties available at site.

Lanercost tearoom is open every day except 25 and 26 Dec. Tel: 01697 741267 cafelanercost.co.uk (not managed by English Heritage).

MAP PAGE 334 (4E) OS MAP 86, 315: NY556637

PENRITH CASTLE

CUMBRIA – CA11 7EA

Begun in the later 14th century and subsequently transformed into a luxurious residence by Richard, Duke of Gloucester (afterwards Richard III). Surviving in places to its full height.

OPENING TIMES

Park:

| Summer | 7.30am-9pm |
| Winter | 7.30am-4.30pm |

VISIT US

Direction: Opposite Penrith railway station

Train: Penrith (adjacent)

Bus: Visit traveline.info for the latest bus timetables and routes

ACQ. 1913 🐕 ⚠

Caution: steep slopes.

MAP PAGE 334 (5E)
OS MAP 90, OL5: NY513299

PIEL CASTLE

CUMBRIA – LA13 0QN

Accessible only via small boat ferry, this 14th-century fortress was built by Furness Abbey (p.260) as a refuge from pirates and Scots raiders. The massive keep dominates a little island in Barrow harbour. Lambert Simnel, Yorkist pretender to Henry VII's throne, landed here in 1487.

OPENING TIMES

Any reasonable daylight hours. Access by ferry boat not managed by English Heritage

PIEL CASTLE

VISIT US

Direction: Via ferry from Roa Island, accessible by road 3¼ miles SE of Barrow-in-Furness

By Small Boat: Piel Castle can only be accessed by boat, please check website for latest ferry information

Train: Barrow-in-Furness 4 miles

Bus: Visit traveline.info for the latest bus timetables and routes

ACQ. 1973 🐕 🚶 🚻 ♿ ⚠

Public house for refreshments (not managed by English Heritage).

New guidebook.

Caution: deep water, steep slopes.

MAP PAGE 334 (7D)
OS MAP 96, OL6: SD233636

RAVENGLASS ROMAN BATH HOUSE

CUMBRIA – CA18 1SR

Among the tallest surviving Roman structures in northern Britain, the walls of this bath house stand up to 4 metres (13 feet) high, complete with remains of plasterwork and elegant niches for statues. It served Ravenglass Roman fort, which guarded a useful harbour and was garrisoned by troops from Hadrian's fleet.

OPENING TIMES

Any reasonable daylight hours

Parts of the site may be cordoned off due to conservation works

VISIT US

Direction: ½ mile SE of Ravenglass station, via signposted footpath from village car park and then private road. No vehicular access or parking at site

Train: Ravenglass (adjacent)

Bus: Visit traveline.info for the latest bus timetables and routes

ACQ. 1980 🐕 ⚠

Caution: falling masonry.

MAP PAGE 334 (6C)
OS MAP 96, OL6: SD088959

SHAP ABBEY

CUMBRIA – CA10 3NB

The impressive full height 15th-century tower and other remains of a remote abbey of Premonstratensian 'white canons'. Information panels guide you round the abbey and illustrate daily monastic life.

OPENING TIMES

Any reasonable daylight hours

VISIT US

Direction: 1½ miles W of Shap, on the bank of the River Lowther

Train: Penrith 10 miles

Bus: Visit traveline.info

ACQ. 1948 ♿ 🐕 P ⚠

Disabled access (limited views from outside the site).

Steep access road may be hazardous in wintry weather.

Parking: charges apply to non-members, free for Members with valid car sticker.

Caution: sheer drop into water.

MAP PAGE 334 (5E)
OS MAP 90, OL5: NY548152

WETHERAL PRIORY GATEHOUSE

CUMBRIA – CA4 8ES

Well preserved early 16th-century gatehouse, the sole survivor of a small Benedictine priory. A miniature 'pele tower' containing two storeys of comfortable rooms, it later became a fortified vicarage, a defence against border raiders.

OPENING TIMES

1 Apr-30 Sep, daily	10am-5pm
1 Oct-31 Mar, daily	10am-4pm
24-26, 31 Dec & 1 Jan	Closed

VISIT US

Direction: Near Wetheral village; 6 miles E of Carlisle, on B6263

Train: Wetheral ½ mile

Bus: Visit traveline.info

ACQ. 1978 🐕 ⚠ Caution: steep stairs.

MAP PAGE 334 (4D)
OS MAP 86, 315: NY468541

STOTT PARK BOBBIN MILL

CUMBRIA – LA12 8AX

Experience the Industrial Revolution first-hand at unique Stott Park Bobbin Mill, where a woodland walk enhances your visit to this unusual and fascinating attraction.

Fully working Stott Park is an unmissable one-off. In a lovely woodland setting near Lake Windermere, it's the very last survivor of the hundred-odd Lake District mills which produced wooden bobbins for the Lancashire cotton industry. 'Bobbin boys' aged from 10 to 14 worked 16 hours a day here to produce up to 250,000 bobbins a week. Packed with clattering belt-driven machinery, it's presented just as it was in about 1880.

Still fully operational, the mill's pulsating line shaft and pulley wheels were powered first by water and then by a magnificent original steam engine. The refurbished cross-tubed boiler, providing steam for the engine, was reinstalled in 2019. It's powered up on bank holidays and special event days throughout the year.

Displays tell the stories of Stott Park's people, and a hands-on family trail with children's dressing-up clothes helps you imagine what it was like to work here. You can also explore the mill's woodland surroundings. A timber footbridge handmade by local craftsmen crosses the stream, leading to a 200 metre-long footpath through two acres of woodland, where trees were coppiced to provide wood for bobbins. It's carpeted with bluebells in late April and early May.

Demonstrations of the mill machinery, showing you how a raw piece of coppiced timber is transformed into a bobbin, take place throughout the day.

Please visit our website or call the site for details of special events throughout the year.

OPENING TIMES

1 Apr-30 Oct,	
Wed-Sun & Bank Hols	10am-5pm
31 Oct-31 Mar	Closed

Last entry 1 hour before closing

Please call for details of steam days

VISIT US

Direction: Located 1½ miles N of Newby Bridge, off A590

Train: Grange-over-Sands 8 miles; Lakeside Station (Lakeside & Haverthwaite railway) ¾ mile

Bus: Visit traveline.info for the latest bus timetables and routes

Boat: Windermere Lake Cruises from Ambleside or Bowness to Lakeside, then ¾ mile walk

Tel: 01539 531087

Local Tourist Information:
Hawkshead: 01539 436946

NON-MEMBERS

Adult £10.00 | Concession £9.00 | Child £6.00
Family 2 Adults £26.00 | Family 1 Adult £16.00

ACQ.1974 ⬛ ♿ ⚔ E ⬛ ♟ ♟ P ⬛ ⬛

⚠ OVP

Disabled access (ground floor only. Specific interpretation for visually impaired visitors).

Lower car park for disabled parking (short downhill path to mill). Upper car park for general parking.

Disabled visitors can be dropped off at the mill entrance (with level access to site) before cars are parked. Please phone site in advance to arrange.

Parking: charges apply to non-members, free for Members with valid English Heritage car sticker.

MAP PAGE 334 (6D)
OS MAP 96/97, OL7: SD372881

GOODSHAW CHAPEL

LANCASHIRE – BB4 8QB

English Heritage's only Nonconformist place of worship, this atmospheric Baptist chapel displays a complete set of Georgian box pews, galleries and pulpit.

OPENING TIMES

Please call the key keeper for details
Tel: 01706 227333

VISIT US

Direction: In Crawshawbooth, 2 miles N of Rawtenstall via A682 (in Goodshaw Ave – turning off A682 opp. Alderson & Horan). Chapel approx. 1½ miles from main road

Train: Burnley Manchester Road 4½ miles

Bus: Visit traveline.info for the latest bus timetables and routes

ACQ.1976

Caution: steep stairs.

MAP PAGE 332 (4D)
OS MAP 103, OL21: SD814261

SAWLEY ABBEY

LANCASHIRE – BB7 4NH

Riverside remains of a Cistercian abbey founded in 1148. Its monks briefly returned during the Pilgrimage of Grace, but the insurrection collapsed and their abbot was executed.

OPENING TIMES

1 Apr-30 Oct, daily	10am-5pm
31 Oct-31 Mar, daily	10am-4pm
24-26, 31 Dec & 1 Jan	Closed

VISIT US

Direction: Located at Sawley; 3½ miles N of Clitheroe, off A59

Train: Clitheroe 4 miles

Bus: Visit traveline.info for the latest bus timetables and routes

ACQ.1951

Caution: falling masonry.

MAP PAGE 332 (3D)
OS MAP 103, OL41: SD777464

WARTON OLD RECTORY

LANCASHIRE – LA5 9PH

A rare survival of a large 14th-century stone house with great hall and chambers. It served as a residence and courthouse for the wealthy and powerful rectors of Warton.

WARTON OLD RECTORY

OPENING TIMES

1 Apr-30 Sep, daily	10am-6pm
1 Oct-31 Mar, daily	10am-4pm
24-26, 31 Dec & 1 Jan	Closed

VISIT US

Direction: At Warton; 1 mile N of Carnforth, on minor road off A6

Train: Carnforth 1 mile

Bus: Visit traveline.info for the latest bus timetables and routes

ACQ.1969

MAP PAGE 332 (3C)
OS MAP 97, OL7: SD499723

WHALLEY ABBEY GATEHOUSE

LANCASHIRE – BB7 9TN

The 14th-century gatehouse of the nearby Cistercian abbey, the second wealthiest monastery in Lancashire, beside the River Calder. The first floor was probably a chapel.

OPENING TIMES

Any reasonable daylight hours. External viewing only

VISIT US

Direction: In Whalley; 6 miles NE of Blackburn, on minor road off A59

Train: Whalley ¼ mile

Bus: Visit traveline.info for the latest bus timetables and routes

ACQ.1971

MAP PAGE 332 (4D)
OS MAP 103, 287: SD729362

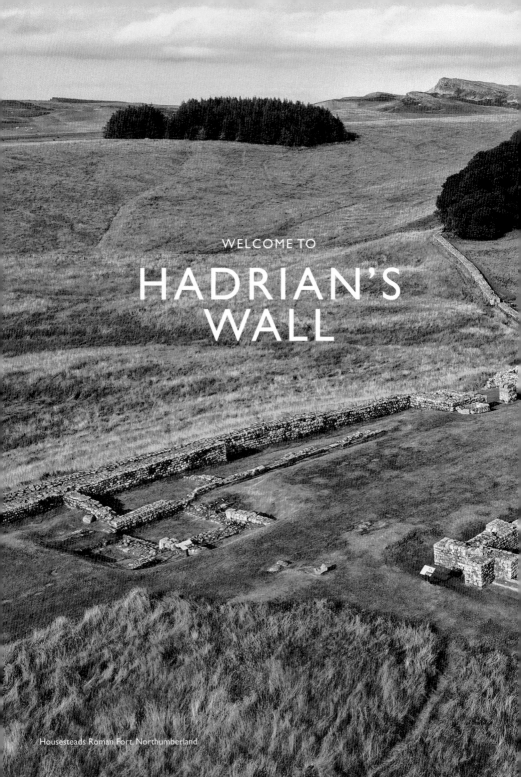

WELCOME TO

HADRIAN'S WALL

Housesteads Roman Fort, Northumberland

Hadrian's Wall 1900
AD 122-2022

2022 is the 1900th anniversary of the beginning of work on Hadrian's Wall in AD 122.

A year-long festival, funded by the North of Tyne Combined Authority, will celebrate the anniversary from Hadrian's birthday on the 24 January to Saturnalia on the 23 December 2022. English Heritage is one of many organisations, communities and individuals which form the Hadrian's Wall Partnership. During the festival we will be running events and activities to bring visitors and local communities closer to the people who lived and worked along the Wall from pre-Roman times to the present day.

Highlights will include a new exhibition at Corbridge Roman Town and an extended events programme at Birdoswald and Chesters Roman Forts.

Lanercost Priory is close by – see p.262

CUMBRIA

M74

2
1   3
7   8
4   6

A69

5.
Birdoswald
Roman Fort

CARLISLE

M6

Use this map to discover more of the Wall and make the most of your day

5 ···· 12	12 ···· 16	16 ···· 20
⊢—⊣ **12.5 miles***	⊢—⊣ **8 miles***	⊢—⊣ **8 miles***
🚗 25 mins	🚗 10 mins	🚗 15 mins
🚶 4 hrs	🚶 2 hrs 45 mins	🚶 2 hrs 30 mins
🚲 1 hr 15 mins	🚲 42 mins	🚲 45 mins

Hadrian's Wall
73 miles

Pilgrimage Walk

National Cycle Network route number

Main Roads

*All distances between sites are using most direct routes.

Hadrian's Wall Pilgrims' Way

23 miles | 2 days

From the 'Hooded Gods' of Housesteads, the Temple of Mithras and the well of water nymph Coventina, you then come to St Oswald's Church, Heavenfield, and Hexham Abbey, before ending your pilgrimage at Corbridge with its Roman Town and parish church incorporating re-used Roman masonry.

In partnership with

the **British Pilgrimage Trust**

Discover English Heritage sites along the pilgrimage route

A Housesteads Roman Fort *(p.272)*

B Carrawburgh Roman Fort and Temple of Mithras *(p.278)*

C Chesters Roman Fort & Museum *(p.274)*

D Corbridge Roman Town *(p.276)*

View more details and a downloadable version of this route at
english-heritage.org.uk/pilgrimage

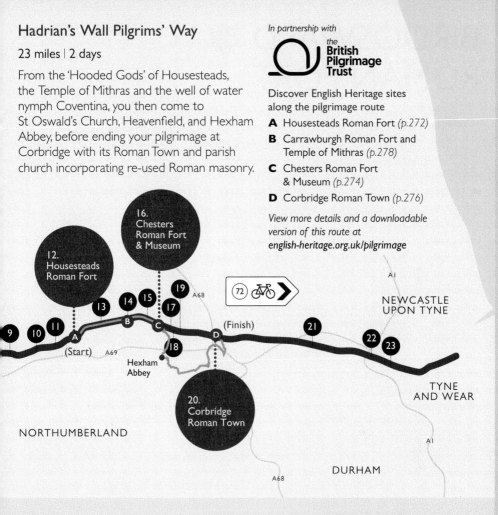

Caring for the Hadrian's Wall World Heritage Site and National Trail

When planning your holiday or visit, please remember to observe 'Every Footstep Counts' – the World Heritage Site's own country code. As you will appreciate, Hadrian's Wall is a fragile environment and the archaeology is easily damaged.

You can help us to protect this great Wonder of the World by ensuring you:

- Never walk on the Wall, as this may cause it to collapse.
- Always keep to the signed paths.
- Keep dogs on a lead and under close control.
- Use public transport whenever you can.

- Note that Hadrian's Wall Path National Trail is a footpath only. Please cycle on legal routes only, i.e. bridgeways, byways, roads and cyclepaths.
- Visit the organised paying sites, which are more robust and can accommodate visitors. Also please avoid walking alongside the Wall when the ground is very wet. The buried archaeology underfoot is particularly vulnerable to damage in the wet winter months between November and April.
- Avoid walking in a single file.
- Respect livestock and land.

BIRDOSWALD ROMAN FORT ⑤

CUMBRIA – CA8 7DD

A great place for a family day out, Birdoswald is an ideal base for discovering the Wall. Our award-winning displays – packed with interactives, family-friendly features and original artefacts – allow people of all ages to engage and explore together. They show you how and why the Wall was built, how it was used and defended, and what kind of people once lived here.

Among the most important Hadrian's Wall forts, Birdoswald was one of 16 major bases along the Wall. It has the best-preserved defences of any Wall fort. Known to the Romans as 'Banna', it was garrisoned by up to 1,000 Roman auxiliary soldiers – for most of its history a unit of Dacians, originally raised in what's now Romania, later joined by troops from northern Holland.

Just outside the fort, you'll find the longest continuous stretch of Hadrian's Wall visible today, a truly impressive sight. Once inside, imaginative displays introduce you not just to the Wall, but to the whole story of Roman Britain. You can create a model of the Wall with Lego bricks, use a crane to assemble an arch, take a digital quiz to discover what kind of Wall dweller you are, learn about signalling techniques and try out a periscope to get a soldier's-eye view over the original 5-metre (16.5-feet) height of the Wall. You'll also find out about the people who lived here for over three centuries; memorials and burial urns excavated near the site reveal the stories of soldiers and their wives and children. A great experience for children and adults alike, the displays are a must if you want to discover the full history of the Wall.

Innovative features also guide you round the whole of the fort. 'Viewfinders' help you explore vistas within and beyond the defences, and you can play Roman games and listen in to gossip from the commandant's house. Clues and puzzles lead families on the hunt for a spy, taking in the three main gates and the view over the ravine of the River Irthing.

You'll also discover another unique feature of Birdoswald; how it was continuously occupied for sixteen centuries after the collapse of Roman rule – by local post-Roman warlords, medieval and Elizabethan Borderers and the Victorian farmers who built the present picturesque turreted farmhouse.

Birdoswald is a family-friendly site. There's a generously sized room where visitors with younger children can park buggies, wash, hang coats and boots, play Wall-related games, get into a Roman tent and even try on a Roman toga.

Offering a café and an education room, Birdoswald also makes an ideal base for exploring the wild and beautiful surrounding countryside. The fort stands on the Hadrian's Wall Path National Trail, making it a perfect stopping place for ramblers and cyclists.

Archaeology Live: 11 Jun 2021-8 Jul 2022

This the second instalment of a major five-year archaeological excavation at Birdoswald Roman Fort. A collaboration between Historic England and Newcastle University, it continues to examine links between the fort and its adjacent settlements, its relationship with the Wall and the successive turf and stone Walls. Guided tours will provide fascinating insights, as more World Heritage Site secrets are unearthed. See website for details.

STAY WITH US

Wake up and go to bed in a Roman Fort. *The Bunkhouse* at Birdoswald is perfect for residential educational visits and large groups, sleeping up to 36 persons in 7 bedrooms.

See p.16 for details on staying at **Birdoswald** and our other holiday cottages.

OPENING TIMES

1 Apr-30 Oct, daily	10am-5pm
31 Oct-23 Dec, Sat-Sun	10am-4pm
2 Jan-10 Feb, Sat-Sun	10am-4pm
11-26 Feb, daily	10am-4pm
27 Feb-31 Mar, Wed-Sun	10am-4pm
Christmas Opening 24-25 Dec	Closed
26 Dec-1 Jan, daily	10am-4pm

Last entry 30 mins before closing

Café closes 4.45pm (summer) and 3.45pm (winter)

VISIT US

Address: Gilsland, Brampton, Cumbria CA8 7DD

Direction: 4 miles west of Greenhead off B6318. Signposted from A69 Carlisle – Hexham road at Brampton roundabout

Train: Haltwhistle 7 miles

Bus: Visit traveline.info for the latest bus timetables and routes

Tel: 01697 747602

Local Tourist Information: Haltwhistle: 01434 321863

NON-MEMBERS

Adult £10.00 | Concession £9.00 | Child £6.00
Family 2 Adults £26.00 | Family 1 Adult £16.00

Please note: short uphill walk from car park to fort.

Disabled access (to visitor centre, toilets, shop, tearoom and part of site. Disabled parking on site).

Parking: charges apply to non-members, free for Members with valid English Heritage car sticker.

MAP PAGE 334 (4E)   OS MAP 86, OL43: NY615663

HOUSESTEADS 🄓 ROMAN FORT

NORTHUMBERLAND – NE47 6NN

Set high on a hilltop with panoramic views, spectacularly sited Housesteads is the most complete example of a Roman fort anywhere in Britain – a must-see for all visitors to the Wall. Discover the stories of the fort and its people in the interactive exhibition, and find out how soldiers and their families lived on this wild northern frontier of the Roman Empire.

Among the most popular sites on Hadrian's Wall, this famous fort stands on the Whin Sill escarpment, flanked by dramatic stretches of the Wall. Hadrian's Wall Path runs just above it. The site museum houses an outstanding exhibition, vividly interpreting life here on the northern edge of the Roman Empire.

Begun in about AD 124 as one of 16 permanent forts supporting Hadrian's frontier system, Housesteads was known as Vercovicium. It was garrisoned by around 1,000 infantry from a unit originally raised in what's now eastern Belgium, and later reinforced by cavalry. The 5-acre fort displays the remains of gateways and a turreted wall: within are a host of clearly traceable buildings, including the commandant's house, hospital and the renowned multi-seater communal lavatories.

The Roman south gate was much later adapted into a 'bastle' farmhouse, fortified against the 'rank robbers hereabouts': the Border Reivers. Outside the fort wall are the excavated foundations of the Roman civilian settlement. One of the houses here produced evidence of a gruesome Roman double murder.

Visit the museum to witness the story of Housesteads and its people retold in a multimedia display. A short film traces the history of the fort and recreates its original appearance. Every aspect of Roman life here – what the soldiers wore, the tools and weapons they used, how they were cared for when sick, and deities they worshipped, including 'Hooded Gods' – is illuminated by displays. These feature many fascinating objects from the fort, most strikingly a winged Victory statue. Children can enjoy a dressing-up 'Discovery Box', and touchable replicas of Roman objects set at child-height, explained by Felix the Roman soldier. You can also follow Felix in the panels that guide you round the fort.

The fort and museum stand uphill from the car park (via a fairly strenuous 10-minute walk). The National Trust visitor centre by the car park offers a welcome and introduction to the site and an indoor café with outdoor seating for warm days.

Owned by the National Trust and managed by English Heritage.

OPENING TIMES

1 Apr-30 Oct, daily	10am-5pm
31 Oct-31 Mar, daily	10am-4pm
24-25 Dec	Closed

Last entry 45 mins before closing

VISIT US

Address: Housesteads Roman Fort, Haydon Bridge, Hexham, Northumberland NE47 6NN

Direction: Bardon Mill 4 miles

Bus: Visit traveline.info for the latest bus timetables and routes

Tel: 01434 344363

Local Tourist Information: Hexham: 01434 652220

NON-MEMBERS

Adult **£10.00** | Concession **£9.00** | Child **£6.00**
Family 2 Adults **£26.00** | Family 1 Adult **£16.00**

Free to National Trust members

Disabled access to the museum (companion recommended). Limited access to site. 750-metre walk up a steep gradient. Disabled parking available at the top of the hill. Please enquire at the visitor centre in the roadside car park to arrange disabled parking. Assistance dogs only in the museum.

Car park not operated by English Heritage (charge payable to Northumberland National Park).

MAP PAGE 335 (4F)
OS MAP 86/87, OL43: NY790688

CHESTERS ROMAN FORT AND MUSEUM ⑯

NORTHUMBERLAND – NE46 4EU

Set in the beautiful valley of the River Tyne, Chesters is the best-preserved Roman cavalry fort in Britain, with the finest surviving Roman bath-house complex and a unique Victorian-style museum.

Imaginative interpretation throughout the site, including a family trail, helps you explore the fort and its links with John Clayton, 'Saviour of the Wall'.

Known as Cilurnum, Chesters was positioned to defend the vulnerable section of Hadrian's Wall where it crossed the river. Around five hundred cavalry troops – the elite of the Roman auxiliary forces – were based here. From the late 2nd century the garrison was a regiment originating from Asturias in northern Spain.

Pictorial panels guide you round the many clearly marked features of the fort, including its four gates, a barrack block which cavalrymen shared with their horses, the headquarters building with its underground strongroom and the commanding officer's mansion with its private baths.

Armed with the 'Chesters Fort Takeover' trail leaflet, children can seek out the 'rubbing stones' concealed among the buildings, collecting tips to help them in their chosen roles of commander, trooper, guard, messenger, musician or commander's dog. Two viewfinders reveal how parts of the fort once appeared.

Between the fort and the river, the garrison's bath house survives to above head-height; the finest example of a military bath house in Britain. It's easy to imagine how the soldiers enjoyed this 'spa' complex of cold, warm and hot sauna baths, together with a big changing-room-cum-clubhouse, still equipped with niches, which probably housed bathers' clothes.

All this was rediscovered by John Clayton, the wealthy Victorian landowner whose mansion stands within sight of the west gate. His groundbreaking excavations here, and lifelong fascination with the Wall – sections of which he bought and safeguarded – played a crucial role in saving Hadrian's great frontier system for us to enjoy today.

His single-minded vision – and the help he got from family, friends and staff – is celebrated in the unique Clayton Museum, an absolute must-see for all visitors to Chesters. Packed with hundreds of fascinating finds from the central section of the Wall, it preserves its traditional Victorian layout and atmosphere. Sensitive reordering and creative storytelling, including Kindles disguised as Victorian books, help visitors to explore museum treasures – from statues of gods to a tiny dog figurine – at their chosen level of detail.

Take a break from your journey of discovery in the Chesters Tearoom with its indoor and outdoor seating. Check the website for details of an active events programme which runs throughout the summer.

OPENING TIMES

1 Apr-30 Oct, daily	10am-5pm
31 Oct-23 Dec, Sat-Sun	10am-4pm
2 Jan-17 Feb, Sat-Sun	10am-4pm
18-26 Feb, daily	10am-4pm
27 Feb-31 Mar, Wed-Sun	10am-4pm

Christmas Opening

24-25 Dec	Closed
26 Dec-1 Jan, daily	10am-4pm

Last entry 30 mins before closing

VISIT US

Address: Chollerford, Hexham, Northumberland NE46 4EU

Direction: ¼ mile W of Chollerford, on B6318

Train: Hexham 5½ miles

Bus: Visit traveline.info for the latest bus timetables and routes

Tel: 01434 681379

Local Tourist Information:
Hexham: 01434 652220

NON-MEMBERS

Adult **£10.00** | Concession **£9.00**
Child **£6.00** | Family 2 Adults **£26.00**
Family 1 Adult **£16.00**

Disabled access (companion recommended). Disabled parking and toilets.

Dogs on leads (restricted areas only).

Tearoom.

Parking: charges apply to non-members, free for Members with valid car sticker.

MAP PAGE 335 (4F)
OS MAP 87, OL43: NY912702

A new exhibition highlights evocative photographs of the Edwardian discovery of Roman Corbridge, helping you compare what the Edwardians found with what's visible at the site today. Find out more about the people who uncovered the most northerly town in Roman Britain and share their excitement about their remarkable discoveries.

20

CORBRIDGE ROMAN TOWN

—— NORTHUMBERLAND – NE45 5NT ——

For a really in-depth look at how people lived, worked and worshipped near Hadrian's Wall, Corbridge is the place to visit. Our extensive site museum offers you unique insights into Roman social life at Corbridge – the only place in Britain where you can walk the high street of a Roman town.

Beginning as a series of forts, Corbridge was founded well before Hadrian began his Wall, 2½ miles away. It developed into a prosperous town, the most northerly in the whole Roman Empire, providing goods and services for the Wall garrisons. You can still walk the original surface of its Roman main street, flanked by the impressive remains of granaries, mansions, markets and workshops.

Our museum showcases the most fascinating of our internationally important collection of site-finds, illuminating as never before the social and working life of a Roman town. You'll discover how Corbridge's people originated from all over the Roman Empire; thematically displayed weapons, jewellery and personal possessions mingle with grave finds and images of the town's many gods. A pictorial timeline traces Corbridge's development from its foundation until the collapse of Roman rule and the move to the site of the present town, clearly visible from the ruins.

Don't miss the Corbridge Lion sculpture, the poignant monuments to Corbridge's Roman children, or the intriguing Corbridge Hoard, one of the most important finds from Roman Britain.

OPENING TIMES

1 Apr-30 Oct, daily	10am-5pm
31 Oct-17 Feb, Sat-Sun	10am-4pm
18-26 Feb, daily	10am-4pm
27 Feb-31 Mar, Sat-Sun	10am-4pm
24-26 Dec & 1 Jan	Closed

Last entry 30 mins before closing

VISIT US

Direction: ½ mile NW of Corbridge, on minor road, then signposted

Train: Corbridge 1¼ miles

Bus: Visit traveline.info for the latest bus timetables and routes

Tel: 01434 632349

Local Tourist Information: Corbridge: 01434 632815

NON-MEMBERS

Adult £10.00 | Concession £9.00
Child £6.00 | Family 2 Adults £26.00
Family 1 Adult £16.00

ACQ.1933

Dogs on leads (restricted areas only).

Disabled access (parking, toilet, audio tour, access to the museum and perimeter of site).

Please note: we don't have a tearoom, but you'll find plenty of refreshment spots in Corbridge.

MAP PAGE 335 (4F)
OS MAP 87, OL43: NY982648

❶ HARE HILL

A short length of Wall still stands 2.7 metres (8ft 10in) high.

VISIT US

Direction: ¾ mile NE of Lanercost

 ACQ.1972 🐕

OS MAP 86, 43: NY564646

❷ BANKS EAST TURRET

Imposing and well-preserved turret with adjoining stretches of Hadrian's Wall.

VISIT US

Direction: On minor road E of Banks village; 3½ miles NE of Brampton

ACQ.1934 ♿🐕 P ⚠

Parking: charges apply to non-members, free for Members with valid car sticker.

OS MAP 86, 315: NY575647

❸ PIKE HILL SIGNAL TOWER

The remains of one of a network of signal towers predating Hadrian's Wall, Pike Hill was later joined to the Wall at an angle of 45 degrees.

VISIT US

Direction: On minor road E of Banks village

 ACQ.1971 🐕 P ⚠

Caution: steep slopes, unguarded drops.

OS MAP 86, 315: NY577648

❹ LEAHILL TURRET & PIPER SIKE TURRET

Turrets west of Birdoswald: Piper Sike has a cooking-hearth.

VISIT US

Direction: On minor road 2 miles W of Birdoswald Fort

ACQ.1952 🐕

OS MAP 86, OL43/315: NY586652

5 BIRDOSWALD ROMAN FORT

See feature on p.270

❻ HARROW'S SCAR MILECASTLE & WALL

A mile-long section of the Wall, rebuilt in stone later in Hadrian's reign. It's linked to Birdoswald Roman Fort (see p.270).

VISIT US

Direction: ¼ mile E of Birdoswald, on minor road off B6318

 ACQ.1946 🐕 🐄 P

Parking at Birdoswald.

OS MAP 86, OL43: NY620664

DON'T FORGET

Remember to take your membership card.

❼ WILLOWFORD WALL, TURRETS AND BRIDGE

A fine 914-metre (2,999-foot) stretch of Wall, including two turrets and impressive bridge remains beside the River Irthing. Linked by a bridge to Birdoswald Roman Fort (see p.270).

VISIT US

Direction: W of minor road, ¾ mile W of Gilsland

ACQ.1946 🐕 🐄 ⚠

Beware – livestock may be grazing on site.
Caution: deep water, steep slopes.

OS MAP 86, OL43: NY627664

❽ POLTROSS BURN MILECASTLE

One of the best-preserved milecastles on Hadrian's Wall, Poltross includes an oven, a stair to the rampart walk, and the remains of its north gateway. Known locally as 'the King's Stables'.

VISIT US

Direction: On minor road E of Banks village. Immediately SW of Gilsland village, by old railway station

ACQ.1938 🐕 P ⚠

Parking (follow brown signs).
Caution: deep water.

OS MAP 86, OL43: NY634662

❙❙ FOR UPDATES ON HADRIAN'S WALL, DON'T FORGET TO FOLLOW US ON FACEBOOK AND TWITTER.

9 WALLTOWN CRAGS

One of the best places of all to see the Wall, dramatically snaking and diving along the crags of the Whin Sill.

VISIT US

Direction: 1 mile NE of Greenhead, off B6318

 ACQ.1939 🐎 🐄 P ⚠

Parking not operated by English Heritage. Parking charge applies (payable to Northumberland National Park).

Caution: steep slopes, unguarded drops.

OS MAP 86/87, 43: NY674663

10 CAWFIELDS MILECASTLE

A fine stretch of Hadrian's Wall on a steep slope, with turrets and an impressive milecastle, probably built by the Second Legion.

VISIT US

Direction: 1¼ miles N of Haltwhistle, off B6318

ACQ.1960 🐎 🐄 🚶 🚻 P ⚠

Parking not operated by English Heritage. Parking charge applies (payable to Northumberland National Park).

Caution: unguarded drops.

OS MAP 86/87, OL43: NY716667

See Hadrian's Wall by bus with the AD122 service (subject to change, see traveline.info for details).

11 WINSHIELDS WALL

The highest point on the Wall, in rugged country with spectacular views.

VISIT US

Direction: W of Steel Rigg car park; on minor road off B6318

ACQ.1937 🐎 🐄 ⚠

Caution: unguarded drops.

OS MAP 86/87, 43: NY742676

12 HOUSESTEADS ROMAN FORT
See feature on p.272

13 SEWINGSHIELDS WALL

A length of Wall with milecastle remains, impressively sited along the Whin Sill. It commands fine views of many prehistoric and later earthworks to the north.

VISIT US

Direction: N of B6318; 1½ miles E of Housesteads Fort

ACQ.1946 🐎 ⚠

Caution: steep slopes.

OS MAP 86/87, OL43: NY805702

14 CARRAWBURGH ROMAN FORT AND TEMPLE OF MITHRAS

Built around AD 122, the fort housed a garrison of about 500 soldiers – first from France, later from Belgium – responsible for defending the frontier of the Roman Empire. It occupies an area of 3.5 acres on a natural terrace, overlooking the Northumberland National Park. Just below the fort hides a little stone temple to the eastern soldiers' god Mithras, with facsimiles of altars found during excavation.

VISIT US

Direction: 3¾ miles W of Chollerford, on B6318

ACQ.2020 Carrawburgh Roman Fort
ACQ.1953 Temple of Mithras 🐎 🐄 P

Parking not operated by English Heritage. Parking charge applies (payable to Northumberland National Park).

OS MAP 87, 43: NY859711

15 BLACK CARTS TURRET

A 460-metre (1,509-foot) length of Hadrian's Wall including one turret.

VISIT US

Direction: On Hadrian's Wall National Trail, about 20 minutes signposted walk from Chesters Roman Fort

ACQ.1970 ♿ 🐎 🐄 ⚠

Please note: no visitor parking available. Parking at Chesters Roman Fort (20 minute walk).

OS MAP 86, 315: NY575647

16 CHESTERS ROMAN FORT & MUSEUM
See feature on p.274

17 CHESTERS BRIDGE ABUTMENT

Close to Chesters Roman Fort are the remains of a bridge which carried Hadrian's Wall across the North Tyne. Visible on both river banks, but best viewed from the Roman fort.

VISIT US
Direction: ½ mile S of Low Brunton, on A6079

ACQ.1946

Site is liable to flooding.

Caution: deep water, steep slopes.

OS MAP 87, 43: NY914701

18 BRUNTON TURRET

Wall section and a surviving piece of turret 2.5 metres (8ft 2in) high, built by men of the Twentieth Legion.

VISIT US
Direction: ¼ mile S of Low Brunton, off A6079

ACQ.1947

OS MAP 87, OL43: NY922698

19 PLANETREES ROMAN WALL

A 15-metre (49-foot) length of narrow Wall on broad foundations, reflecting a change of policy concerning the thickness of the Wall during construction.

VISIT US
Direction: 1 mile SE of Chollerford on B6318

ACQ.1945

OS MAP 87, OL43: NY929696

20 CORBRIDGE ROMAN TOWN
See feature on p.276

21 HEDDON-ON-THE-WALL

A consolidated stretch of Wall, up to 2 metres (6ft 6in) thick in places.

VISIT US
Direction: Immediately E of Heddon village, S of A69

ACQ.1935

OS MAP 88, 316: NZ137669

OUR EVENTS

Check out our year-long programme of events.

english-heritage.org.uk/events

22 DENTON HALL TURRET

The foundations of a turret and a 65-metre (213-foot) length of Wall.

VISIT US
Direction: 4 miles W of Newcastle upon Tyne city centre, located immediately SE of A69

ACQ.1934

OS MAP 88, 316: NZ198655

23 BENWELL ROMAN TEMPLE

The remains of a small temple to the native god 'Antenociticus', in the 'vicus' (civilian settlement), which stood outside Benwell Fort.

VISIT US
Direction: Temple located immediately SE of A69, at Benwell in Broomridge Ave; Vallum Crossing in Denhill Park

ACQ.1936

OS MAP 88, 316: NZ217647

BENWELL VALLUM CROSSING

A stone-built causeway, where the road from the south crossed the Vallum earthwork on its way to Benwell Fort.

ACQ.1934

Viewing only – no access to the Vallum.

OS MAP 88, 316: NZ216646

FOR UPDATES ON HADRIAN'S WALL, DON'T FORGET TO FOLLOW US ON FACEBOOK AND TWITTER.

HADRIAN'S WALL 279

Belsay Hall, Castle and Gardens, Northumberland

WELCOME TO THE

NORTH EAST

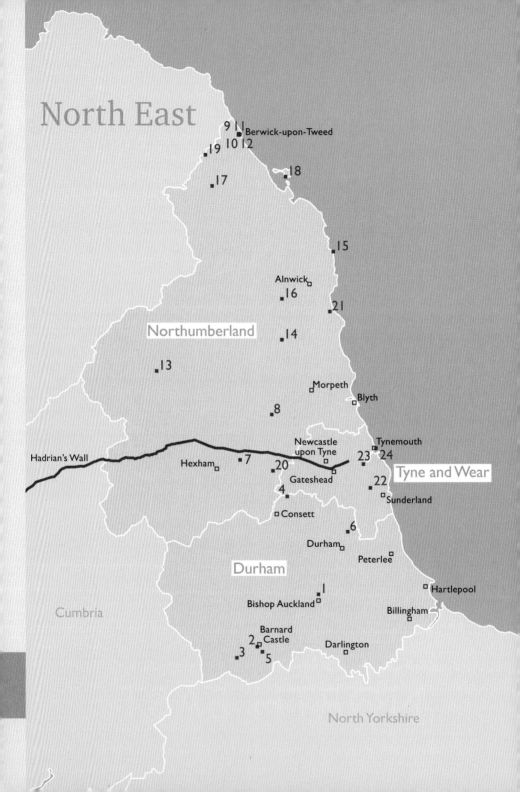

Finchale Camino Inglés

22 miles | 3 days

St Godric was the first English pilgrim to reach Santiago. Start at his Finchale Priory, a short step from Durham Cathedral, then walk the Weardale valley and end at Escomb Saxon Church. This route is a recognised English addition to the Camino de Santiago, which passes through the port city of A Coruña, where medieval pilgrims arrived from England.

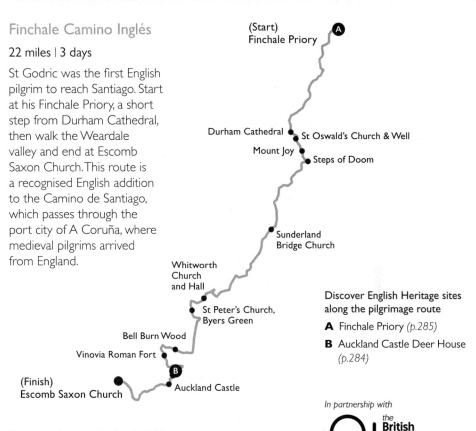

(Start) Finchale Priory **A**

Durham Cathedral • St Oswald's Church & Well

Mount Joy • Steps of Doom

Sunderland Bridge Church

Whitworth Church and Hall

St Peter's Church, Byers Green

Bell Burn Wood

Vinovia Roman Fort

B

(Finish) Escomb Saxon Church

Auckland Castle

Discover English Heritage sites along the pilgrimage route

A Finchale Priory *(p.285)*

B Auckland Castle Deer House *(p.284)*

In partnership with

the
British Pilgrimage Trust

View more details and a downloadable version of this route at **english-heritage.org.uk/pilgrimage**

DURHAM

AUCKLAND CASTLE DEER HOUSE
DURHAM – DL14 7QJ

A Gothic Revival 'eye-catcher' of 1760. A deer shelter with facilities for picnics and enjoying the view.

Managed by The Auckland Project.

OPENING TIMES
Park

1 Apr-30 Sep, daily	10am-6pm
1 Oct-31 Mar, daily	10am-4pm
24-26 Dec & 1 Jan	Closed

VISIT US
Direction: Located in Auckland Park, Bishop Auckland; N of town centre on A68

Train: Bishop Auckland 1 mile

Bus: Visit traveline.info for the latest bus timetables and routes

ACQ.1952 🐾 🐾 🚹

Parking (pay and display in town centre).

MAP PAGE 335 (5G)
OS MAP 93, 305: NZ216304

BARNARD CASTLE
DURHAM – DL12 8PR

Spectacularly set high above the River Tees, on the fringe of an attractive market town, this imposing fortress takes its name from its 12th-century founder, Bernard de Balliol. Later developed by Richard III.

OPENING TIMES

1 Apr-30 Oct, daily	10am-5pm
31 Oct-31 Mar, Sat-Sun	10am-4pm
24-26 Dec & 1 Jan	Closed

Last entry 30 mins before closing

VISIT US
Direction: In Barnard Castle town

Bus: Visit traveline.info for the latest bus timetables and routes

Tel: 01833 638212

NON-MEMBERS
Adult **£7.80** | Concession **£7.00**
Child **£4.70** | Family 2 Adults **£20.30**
Family 1 Adult **£12.50**

ACQ.1952 ♿ 🐾 ♻ 🖥 🚹 🚹 🎒 🎁

⚠ OVP

Parking (pay and display in town centre).

MAP PAGE 335 (5F)
OS MAP 92, OL31: NZ049165

BOWES CASTLE
DURHAM – DL12 9LG

Impressive ruins of Henry II's 12th-century keep, on the site of a Roman fort guarding strategic Stainmore Pass over the Pennines.

OPENING TIMES
Any reasonable daylight hours

VISIT US
Direction: In Bowes Village off A66; 4 miles W of Barnard Castle town

Bus: Visit traveline.info for the latest bus timetables and routes

ACQ.1931 🐾 ⚠

Caution: steep slopes.

MAP PAGE 335 (6F)
OS MAP 92, OL30/31: NY992135

DERWENTCOTE STEEL FURNACE
DURHAM – NE17 7RS

Built in the 1730s, Derwentcote is the last surviving cementation steel-making furnace in Britain. It produced high-grade steel for springs and cutting tools.

A circular walk through the Derwent Valley starts and finishes in the site car park. For more about the mill's surroundings, see landofoakandiron.org.uk

OPENING TIMES
Any reasonable daylight hours
Grounds only – no access to furnace

24-26 Dec & 1 Jan	Closed

DERWENTCOTE STEEL FURNACE

Woodland walk from site (stout footwear recommended). Please see English Heritage website and landofoakandiron.org.uk for up-to-date information about tours and events

VISIT US

Direction: 10 miles SW of Newcastle, on A694; between Rowland's Gill and Hamsterley

Train: MetroCentre, Gateshead, 7 miles

Bus: Visit traveline.info for the latest bus timetables and routes

ACQ.1985 🐕 P ⚠

Dogs on leads (restricted areas only).

Parking across main road from site.

Caution: deep water, steep slopes.

MAP PAGE 335 (4G)
OS MAP 88, 307: NZ130566

EGGLESTONE ABBEY
DURHAM – DL12 9TN

Ruins of a Premonstratensian monastery, picturesquely sited by the River Tees. Remains include parts of the 13th-century church and living quarters.

Egglestone Abbey can be reached by a short walk from Barnard Castle (p.284).

OPENING TIMES

1 Apr 2022- 31 Mar 2023, daily	10am-6pm
24-26, 31 Dec & 1 Jan	Closed

VISIT US

Direction: 1 mile S of Barnard Castle, on a minor road off B6277

Bus: Visit traveline.info for the latest bus timetables and routes

ACQ.1925 ♿ 🐕 P 🅿 ⚠

Parking: charges apply to non-members, free for Members with valid car sticker.

Caution: falling masonry.

MAP PAGE 335 (5G)
OS MAP 92, OL31: NZ062151

FINCHALE PRIORY DURHAM – DH1 5SH

Extensive ruins of a 13th-century priory, on the site of the hermitage of retired merchant adventurer St Godric. Beautifully positioned by the River Wear, with riverside walks nearby.

OPENING TIMES

1 Apr-30 Sep, daily	10am-5pm
1 Oct-31 Mar, daily	10am-4pm
24-26, 31 Dec & 1 Jan	Closed

VISIT US

Direction: 3 miles NE of Durham; on minor road off A167

Train: Durham 5 miles

Bus: Visit traveline.info for the latest bus timetables and routes

ACQ.1916 🐕 💻 🧍 🚻 🍃 P ⚠

Car park (charged, not English Heritage).

Caution: falling masonry, hidden drops.

MAP PAGE 335 (4G)
OS MAP 88, 308: NZ296471

NORTHUMBERLAND

AYDON CASTLE NORTHUMBERLAND – NE45 5PJ

An outstandingly complete defensible medieval manor house in a secluded and beautiful woodland setting, very near Hadrian's Wall. By 1315 Aydon had been fortified against the Scots. The 'castle' served as a farmhouse until 1966, yet remains remarkably unchanged. Explore the fully roofed hall and chambers, mount the battlements and picnic in the orchard.

A short drive from Corbridge Roman Town (p.276) and Chesters Roman Fort (p.274), and under a mile from Hadrian's Wall Trail.

🎬 *Ivanhoe* (1997); *Elizabeth* (1998).

OPENING TIMES

1 Apr-30 Oct, Wed-Sun & Bank Hols	10am-5pm
31 Oct-31 Mar	Closed
Last entry 30 mins before closing	

VISIT US

Direction: 3 mile NE of Corbridge, on minor road off B6321 or A68

Train: Corbridge 4 miles

Bus: Visit traveline.info for the latest bus timetables and routes

Tel: 01434 632450

NON-MEMBERS

Adult **£6.60** | Concession **£5.90** Child **£4.00** | Family 2 Adults **£17.20** Family 1 Adult **£10.60**

ACQ.1966 ♿ 🐕 🚹 💻 🧍 🚻 P 🅿 📷 ⚠ OVP

Disabled access (ground floor only).

Dogs on leads (restricted areas only).

Short walk from car park.

Accessible parking outside castle gate.

Parking: charges apply to non-members, free for Members with valid car sticker.

MAP PAGE 335 (4F)
OS MAP 87, 316: NZ001663

The northernmost town in England, strongly fortified Berwick-upon-Tweed was the key to the long-disputed Anglo-Scottish border. Our sites here trace many centuries of conflict and crisis.

BERWICK-UPON-TWEED BARRACKS NORTHUMBERLAND – TD15 1DF

Begun in 1717, Ravensdowne Barracks were among the first purpose-built English barracks. Look out for the 'candle smoke drawings', doodled by soldiers in the 1720s-60s.

They house an exhibition about the life of the British infantryman from the Civil War to 1914-18, plus the King's Own Scottish Borderers Regimental Museum and Berwick Museum and Art Gallery.

OPENING TIMES

1 Apr-24 Jul, Wed-Sun	10am-5pm
25 Jul-4 Sep, daily	10am-5pm
5 Sep-30 Oct, Wed-Sun	10am-5pm
31 Oct-31 Mar	Closed

Last entry 30 mins before closing
Opening times may vary

VISIT US

Direction: On the Parade, off Church Street in town centre

Train: Berwick-upon-Tweed ¼ mile

Bus: Visit traveline.info for the latest bus timetables and routes

Tel: 01289 304493

NON-MEMBERS

Adult £6.60 | Concession £5.90
Child £4.00 | Family 2 Adults £17.20
Family 1 Adult £10.60

ACQ. 1981 🔲🔲🔲🔲 E 🔲🔲🔲🔲
🔲🔲🔲 OVP

The barrack square is accessible to wheelchairs, but the museums are not.

Parking: pay and display in town.

MAP PAGE 335 (1F)
OS MAP 75, 346: NU001531

BERWICK-UPON-TWEED CASTLE
NORTHUMBERLAND – TD15 1DF

Riverside ruins of a medieval castle rebuilt by Edward I in 1296-98. Crucial in border warfare, this once-important castle changed hands between English and Scots several times before being superseded by the Ramparts.

OPENING TIMES

Any reasonable daylight hours

VISIT US

Direction: Accessible from riverside near Berwick-upon-Tweed railway station

Train: Berwick-upon-Tweed (adjacent)

Bus: Visit traveline.info for the latest bus timetables and routes

ACQ. 1931 🔲🔲⚠ Caution: deep water.

Parking: pay and display in town.

Please do not climb on the walls.

MAP PAGE 335 (1F)
OS MAP 75, 346: NT993534

BERWICK-UPON-TWEED MAIN GUARD
NORTHUMBERLAND – TD15 1HN

Georgian military guardhouse, displaying permanent and changing exhibitions about Berwick's history.

Managed by Berwick-upon-Tweed Civic Society.

OPENING TIMES

Please check website for details

VISIT US

Direction: Adjacent to Ramparts in Palace Street

Train: Berwick-upon-Tweed ¼ mile

Bus: Visit traveline.info for the latest bus timetables and routes

ACQ. 1981 🔲 E 🔲

Two steps to entrance.

Parking: pay and display in town.

MAP PAGE 335 (1F)
OS MAP 75, 346: NU000525

BERWICK-UPON-TWEED RAMPARTS
NORTHUMBERLAND – TD15 1DF

Surviving largely intact, Berwick's immensely impressive artillery ramparts make it one of the most important fortified towns in Europe. Begun in 1558 and updated to counter later threats, they surround the whole historic town, and you can walk their entire circuit.

A leaflet and map is available locally, or on our website.

OPENING TIMES

Any reasonable daylight hours
Please note: Dangerous after dark

VISIT US

Direction: the ramparts surround the town (accessed at various points)

Train: Berwick-upon-Tweed (adjacent)

Bus: Visit traveline.info for the latest bus timetables and routes

ACQ.1931 [♿] [🐕] [⚠]

Caution: dangerous steep hidden and unguarded drops. Proceed with great care. Please closely supervise children and keep dogs on leads.

Parking: pay and display in town.

MAP PAGE 335 (1F)
OS MAP 75, 346: NU003530

BLACK MIDDENS BASTLE HOUSE

NORTHUMBERLAND – NE48 1NE

A fortified farmhouse with thick walls and living quarters only accessible at first-floor level. Characteristic of the troubled 16th-century Anglo-Scottish borders.

OPENING TIMES

Any reasonable daylight hours

VISIT US

Direction: 180 metres N of minor road, 7 miles NW of Bellingham; or along a minor road from A68

Bus: Visit traveline.info for the latest bus timetables and routes

ACQ.1978 [🐕] [🐕] [⚠]

Caution: unguarded drops.

MAP PAGE 335 (3F)
OS MAP 80, OL42: NY773900

BRINKBURN PRIORY NORTHUMBERLAND – NE65 8AR

The beautiful church of Augustinian Brinkburn Priory, built in the Early English style, survives as completely roofed and restored in Victorian times. The church and adjoining Manor House are picturesquely set by the River Coquet, and reached by a scenic 10-minute walk from the car park.

OPENING TIMES

1 Apr-30 Sep, Wed-Sun & Bank Hols	10am-5pm
1-21 Oct, Sat-Sun	10am-4pm
22-30 Oct, Wed-Sun	10am-4pm
31 Oct-31 Mar	Closed

Last entry 30 mins before closing

VISIT US

Direction: 4½ miles SE of Rothbury, off B6344

Train: Morpeth 12 miles, Acklington 10 miles

Bus: Visit traveline.info for the latest bus timetables and routes

Tel: 01665 570628

NON-MEMBERS

Adult **£6.60** | Concession **£5.90**
Child **£4.00** | Family 2 Adults **£17.20**
Family 1 Adult **£10.60**

ACQ.1965 [♿] [🐕] [🍴] [P] [🚻] [🔲]
[⚠] [OVP]

MAP PAGE 335 (3G)
OS MAP 92, 325: NZ116983

BELSAY HALL, CASTLE AND GARDENS

NORTHUMBERLAND – NE20 0DX

Belsay has something for everyone. Twenty acres of outstanding gardens make a wonderful setting for a succession of fascinating buildings: a fine medieval castle, enlarged into a Jacobean mansion, and the elegant Greek Revival-style home that succeeded it.

The whole ensemble is the creation of the Middleton family over more than seven centuries. The castle, dominated by its massive 14th-century 'pele tower', was mainly built for defence, but also to impress, and you can still trace its elaborate medieval wall paintings. Later a Jacobean mansion wing was added, where the family lived until they moved into Belsay Hall.

Belsay Hall is an elegant Classical Greek Revival villa. Begun in 1807, it was designed by Sir Charles Monck (formerly Middleton), a man inspired by Ancient Greece and the buildings he'd seen on his honeymoon in Athens. Despite its austere façade, it had a comfortable interior, arranged round an amazing central 'Pillar Hall'. It's displayed without furnishings, so you can admire the fine craftsmanship of its construction.

The vast gardens provide a magnificent backdrop for the castle and hall. Grade I listed as among the best preserved examples of the 'Picturesque' style of gardens in Britain, they're also largely Sir Charles's work. Explore his romantic Quarry Garden, created where stone was cut for his hall, with ravines and sheer rock faces inspired by the quarries of Syracuse in Sicily. His grandson Sir Arthur Middleton, likewise a pioneering plantsman,

further embellished the quarry with exotic species, now in full maturity. He also added the Winter Garden, Yew Garden and Magnolia Terrace.

Don't miss our Victorian tearoom in the hall's original kitchen.

BELSAY AWAKES

Work continues on the Belsay Awakes project, supported by the National Lottery Heritage Fund. Due to launch in summer 2023, this includes extensive restoration of the gardens to the plans of designer Dan Pearson; new interpretation throughout the site, including a magical animation in the castle, featuring the Wild Man of Belsay; a Wild Man Trail for families and a Seasonal Trail for plant and wildlife enthusiasts; a new woodland play-and-learn area and outdoor classroom; the conservation of the hall roof, coach house and parts of the castle, and a new café.

Depending on the phase of work being undertaken, access to some parts of the site may be limited in 2022. Please see our website for regular updates.

OPENING TIMES

1 Apr-30 Oct, daily	10am-5pm
31 Oct-23 Dec, Sat-Sun	10am-4pm
2 Jan-10 Feb, Sat-Sun	10am-4pm
11-26 Feb, daily	10am-4pm
27 Feb-31 Mar, Sat-Sun	10am-4pm

Christmas Opening

24-25 Dec	Closed
26 Dec-1 Jan, daily	10am-4pm

Last entry 45 mins before closing

VISIT US

Address: Belsay Hall, Castle & Gardens, Belsay, Northumberland NE20 0DX

Direction: In Belsay; 14 miles NW of Newcastle, on A696

Train: Morpeth 10 miles

Bus: Visit traveline.info for the latest bus timetables and routes

Tel: 01661 881636

Local Tourist Information: Morpeth: 01670 500700

NON-MEMBERS

Adult **£12.80** | Concession **£11.50**
Child **£7.60** | Family 2 Adults **£33.20**
Family 1 Adult **£20.40**

Disabled access (grounds, tearoom and ground floor of hall and castle; toilets).

Dogs on leads (grounds only).

Tearoom (open daily Apr-Oct, weekends Nov-Mar).

New guidebook.

MAP PAGE 335 (3G)
OS MAP 88, 316: NZ086785

DUNSTANBURGH CASTLE

Take a bracing coastal walk to Dunstanburgh Castle, one of the most dramatically sited fortresses in England.

Defending a headland jutting from the rugged Northumberland coast, the castle was begun in 1313 by Earl Thomas of Lancaster, cousin and leading baronial enemy of Edward II. He built on a grand scale, perhaps to underline his rivalry with the Crown. The castle's most striking feature is the great double-towered gatehouse. It imitated the new royal castles – such as Harlech – built in Wales.

When his rebellion faltered in 1322, Lancaster may have hoped to take refuge in his remote fortress. But before reaching it, he was defeated, captured and beheaded. Later the castle was inherited by John of Gaunt, Richard II's powerful but unpopular uncle. Gaunt strengthened it against Scots attacks during the 1380s, converting the gatehouse into a strong keep.

Dunstanburgh's strength made it a target for both sides during the Wars of the Roses, when it saw fierce fighting. It changed hands at least three times, once after a siege by 10,000 Yorkists in 1462.

Today it's a peaceful place, though still remote and reachable only on foot. You can explore its circuit of walls and strong towers, and look into the rocky cove it protected. This is a famous place for seabirds. Kittiwakes, fulmars and razorbills all nest on the cliffs in the spring and summer, and the grassland is home to ground-nesting birds like skylarks.

Owned by the National Trust, maintained and managed by English Heritage.

OPENING TIMES

1 Apr-30 Sep, daily	10am-5pm
1-30 Oct, daily	10am-4pm
31 Oct-23 Dec, Sat-Sun	10am-4pm
26 Dec-1 Jan, daily	10am-4pm
2 Jan-10 Feb, Sat-Sun	10am-4pm
11-26 Feb, daily	10am-4pm
27 Feb-31 Mar, Sat-Sun	10am-4pm
24-25 Dec	Closed

Last entry 1 hour before closing

VISIT US

Direction: 8 miles NE of Alnwick; on footpaths from Craster or Embleton – stunning 1½ mile coastal walk. **Please note:** Satnav NE66 3TW directs to Craster car park. If parking at Craster, please allow at least 3-4 hours overall for visit and walk to and from castle

Train: Alnmouth, 7 miles from Craster; Chathill (not Sun), 5 miles from Embleton; 7 miles from Castle

Bus: Visit traveline.info for the latest bus timetables and routes

Tel: 01665 576231

Local Tourist Information:
Craster: 01665 576007

NON-MEMBERS

Adult **£6.60** | Concession **£5.90** | Child **£4.00**
Family 2 Adults **£17.20** | Family 1 Adult **£10.60**

Free to National Trust members

ACQ 1929 | OVP

Parking (in Craster village; approx. 1½ mile walk. A charge is payable – not English Heritage).

Nearest toilets in Craster village car park.

MAP PAGE 335 (2G)
OS MAP 75, 332: NU257219

EDLINGHAM CASTLE

NORTHUMBERLAND – NE66 2BW

The tower and other remains of a fortified medieval manor house, in a remote and beautiful setting.

Managed by the Edlingham Community Association.

OPENING TIMES

Any reasonable daylight hours

VISIT US

Direction: Accessible via a short path from Edlingham church, on a minor road off B6341; 6 miles SW of Alnwick

Train: Alnmouth 9 miles

Bus: Visit traveline.info for the latest bus timetables and routes

ACQ.1975

Waterproof footwear recommended. Guide pamphlet available in church.

MAP PAGE 335 (2G)
OS MAP 81, 332: NU116092

NORHAM CASTLE

NORTHUMBERLAND – TD15 2JY

Besieged at least 13 times by the Scots, this important medieval border castle was called 'the most dangerous place in the country'.

Recaptured after falling to James IV in 1513, it was rebuilt as an artillery fortress.

NORHAM CASTLE

Download a free audio tour from the English Heritage website.

OPENING TIMES

1 Apr-30 Sep, daily	10am-6pm
1-30 Oct, daily	10am-4pm
31 Oct-31 Mar, Sat-Sun	10am-4pm
24-26, 31 Dec & 1 Jan	Closed

VISIT US

Direction: In Norham village; 6 miles SW of Berwick-upon-Tweed, on minor road off B6470 (from A698)

Train: Berwick-upon-Tweed 7½ miles

Bus: Visit traveline.info for the latest bus timetables and routes

ACQ.1923

Disabled access (excluding keep).

Caution: steep slopes, unguarded drops.

MAP PAGE 335 (1F)
OS MAP 74/75, 335: NT906476

ETAL CASTLE NORTHUMBERLAND – TD12 4TN

Etal Castle was begun in the early 14th century as a tower house, in a strategic position by a ford on the Anglo-Scottish border. Vulnerable to raiders, it was soon reinforced by a curtain wall with corner towers and a gatehouse.

In 1513 the castle was suddenly thrust into the forefront of history, when King James IV of Scotland invaded with the largest Scots army ever to attack England. He quickly captured Etal Castle, but was soon afterwards defeated at the nearby Battle of Flodden, the greatest-ever English victory over the Scots. King James was killed along with nine Scots earls, fourteen lords, and thousands of his men.

You can also visit the nearby Flodden battlefield.

OPENING TIMES

1 Apr-30 Oct, daily	10am-5pm
31 Oct-31 Mar	Closed

Last entry 30 mins before closing

VISIT US

Direction: In Etal village, 10 miles SW of Berwick-upon-Tweed

Train: Berwick-upon-Tweed 10½ miles

Bus: Visit traveline.info for the latest bus timetables and routes

Tel: 01890 820332

NON-MEMBERS

See website for entry requirements

ACQ.1975

Toilets (in car park).

MAP PAGE 335 (1F)
OS MAP 74/75, 339: NT925393

LINDISFARNE PRIORY

NORTHUMBERLAND – TD15 2RX

You'll never forget a visit to the serene and remote Holy Island of Lindisfarne. It's been drawing visitors for over thirteen centuries, and still retains powerful memories of the monks and saints of Anglo-Saxon and medieval Northumbria. Enjoy the island's wildlife and wonderful coastal views, and discover stories of miracles, Viking raids, wandering monks and mariners in our colourful displays.

Founded by the Irish monk St Aidan in AD 635 and still a place of pilgrimage today, Lindisfarne Priory was one of the most important centres of early Christianity in Anglo-Saxon England. The dramatic approach to the island across the causeway only emphasises the tranquil appeal of this supremely atmospheric place.

St Cuthbert is the most celebrated of the priory's many holy men. After ten years seeking peace as a hermit on lonely Inner Farne Island, he reluctantly became bishop before retiring to die on Inner Farne in 687. Eleven years after his burial at the monastery, his coffin was opened and his body found to be undecayed – a sure sign of sanctity. His remains were then transferred to a pilgrim shrine.

But the rich monastery was easy prey for raiders, suffering a devastating attack by Vikings in 793 – the first significant Viking raid in western Europe. In 875 the monks left, carrying Cuthbert's remains, which after long wanderings were enshrined in Durham Cathedral in 1104, where they still rest. Only after that time did Durham monks re-establish a priory on Lindisfarne. Today you can see the evocative ruins of the richly decorated priory church they built in c. 1150, with their famous 'rainbow arch' – a vault-rib of the now-vanished crossing tower.

The priory is also renowned for the Lindisfarne Gospels, among England's greatest artistic and religious treasures. They were produced here in the late 7th or early 8th century by Bishop Eadfrith.

The same Lindisfarne artists may well have produced the 14 extraordinary 'name stones' discovered around the site. Visit the site museum's extensive displays to explore the 'Inscribed in Stone' feature, which celebrates these rare survivals of 8th-century craftsmanship, unique links with the vanished Saxon monastery.

Be sure to visit the neighbouring parish church of St Mary the Virgin to discover more about Lindisfarne's saints and people through the centuries.

STAY WITH US

Coastguard's Cottage on Lindisfarne sleeps six, with an accessible en-suite bedroom. Soak up the island's unique atmosphere, cut off from the mainland by the tides.

See p.16 for details on staying at **Lindisfarne** and our other holiday cottages.

OPENING TIMES

1 Apr-30 Oct, daily	10am-5pm
31 Oct-10 Feb, Sat-Sun	10am-4pm
11-26 Feb, daily	10am-4pm
27 Feb-31 Mar, Wed-Sun	10am-4pm

Christmas Opening
24-26 Dec & 1 Jan   Closed

Last entry 30 mins before closing. Opening times vary depending on the tides – please check website before visiting

Please note: the site museum will close from Nov 2022 until Mar 2023. The rest of the site remains open during normal winter hours. This is to allow work on a museum renewal project, launching along with other site enhancements in 2023.

The causeway floods at high tide so it is very important to check the tide times before crossing

VISIT US

Address: Lindisfarne Priory, Holy Island, Berwick-upon-Tweed, Northumberland TD15 2RX

Direction: On Holy Island, only reached at low tide across causeway; tide tables at each end, or from Tourist Information Centre

Train: Berwick-upon-Tweed 14 miles, via causeway

Bus: Visit traveline.info for the latest bus timetables and routes

Tel: 01289 389200

Tourist Information Centre: 01289 330733

NON-MEMBERS

Adult **£9.00** | Concession **£8.10**
Child **£5.40** | Family 2 Adults **£23.40**
Family 1 Adult **£14.40**

Dogs on leads (restricted areas only).

Parking and toilets in the village. Parking pay and display operated by Northumberland County Council.

Disabled access (limited in some areas of priory grounds).

MAP PAGE 335 (1G)
OS MAP 75, 340: NU126417

WARKWORTH CASTLE AND HERMITAGE

NORTHUMBERLAND – NE65 0UJ

Among the biggest, strongest and most impressive medieval fortresses in northern England, Warkworth Castle was the favourite home of the powerful and turbulent Percy family, Earls of Northumberland. Today you can explore its almost complete Great Tower and elaborate defences, and venture out to the atmospheric riverside hermitage.

Warkworth Castle straddles the neck of a tight loop in the River Coquet, guarding an attractive stone-built town. Its still-complete circuit of towered walls, including the powerful gatehouse and formidable Grey Mare's Tail Tower, took shape during the 13th century, and the fortress repelled a Scots siege in 1327.

But Warkworth attained its greatest glory under the Percy family, who wielded almost kingly power in the North during the later Middle Ages. The Percy lion badge proudly adorns the Great Tower, the castle's most outstandingly distinctive feature. Built on top of an earlier mound, this ingeniously planned 'keep' houses everything a medieval baron could desire. Ground-floor wine cellars; first-floor kitchens, great hall, chapel and great chamber and second-floor bedchambers are interconnected by completely separate systems of passages and stairways for servants and masters, so food and wine could appear in the lord's state rooms, without being seen on their way.

Cleverly lit by a central light well, this masterpiece of medieval design for gracious living is an intriguing place to explore. On selected days you can also view the second-floor 'Duke's Rooms', restored in the 1850s and equipped with antique-style Victorian furniture.

The Great Tower was built after 1377 for the first Percy Earl of Northumberland, who along with his famous son Harry 'Hotspur' – hero of many Border ballads – helped depose Richard II and set Henry IV on the throne, only to rebel against him in turn. Both were killed in battle, as were the second and third earls. Then the fourth earl remodelled Warkworth's courtyard, adding a complete new set of state rooms – entered via the still-impressive Lion Tower, bedecked with Percy heraldry – before himself being murdered by an angry mob in 1489.

A delightful riverside walk and a rowing boat ferry take you to a contrastingly tranquil feature of Warkworth, the supremely atmospheric 'Hermitage' hewn into a sandstone cliff (open selected days). Here a priest said prayers for the Percy family's souls. Within its tiny unlit chapel you can still trace worn carvings of a Nativity scene. Even tinier 'closets' provided views of the altar for worshippers, and yew trees grow amid the ruins of the priest's house. Take time to quietly experience this extraordinary survival from medieval England.

COMING SOON

From spring 2023, imaginative new interpretation, family activities and other features will help you explore the castle and the lives of the medieval people who lived and worked here. You'll discover how the medieval Warkworth household worked, from powerful Percy lords to the lowliest servants, and how the unique layout of the castle reflected its social hierarchy and daily life. You'll also find out more about the Percy family, 'Kings in the North', and the role their fortress played in the turbulent history of the 14th and 15th centuries.

OPENING TIMES

Castle
1 Apr-30 Oct, daily	10am-5pm
31 Oct-23 Dec, Sat-Sun	10am-4pm
2 Jan-17 Feb, Sat-Sun	10am-4pm
18-26 Feb, daily	10am-4pm
27 Feb-31 Mar, Wed-Sun	10am-4pm

Christmas Opening
24-25 Dec	Closed
26 Dec-1 Jan, daily	10am-4pm

Please see website for opening times of the Duke's Rooms

Hermitage
1 Apr-30 Jun, Sun-Mon & Bank Hols	11am-4pm
1 Jul-31 Aug, Fri-Mon	11am-4pm
1 Sep-30 Oct, Sun-Mon	11am-4pm
31 Oct-31 Mar	Closed

Last entry 30 mins before closing

VISIT US

Address: Castle Terrace, Warkworth, Northumberland NE65 0UJ

Direction: In Warkworth; 7½ miles S of Alnwick, on A1068. Access to Hermitage is via an approx. 15-minute riverside walk from the castle, including some slopes, and rowing boat ferry (included in entry charge). Staff will give directions. The Hermitage is reached by uneven steps, and unlit within

Train: Alnmouth 3½ miles

Bus: Visit traveline.info for the latest bus timetables and routes

Tel: 01665 711423

NON-MEMBERS

Castle
Adult £9.00 | Concession £8.10
Child £5.40 | Family 2 Adults £23.40
Family 1 Adult £14.10

Hermitage
Adult £5.60 | Concession £5.00
Child £3.40 | Family 2 Adults £14.60
Family 1 Adult £9.00

Castle and Hermitage Joint Ticket
Adult £12.80 | Concession £11.50
Child £7.60 | Family 2 Adults £33.20
Family 1 Adult £20.40

Disabled access: limited access in castle (steps to and within Great Tower). Disabled access to Hermitage is difficult.

Dogs on leads welcome in most areas.

Parking: charges apply to non-members, free for Members with valid car sticker.

MAP PAGE 335 (2G)
OS MAP 81, 332: NU247058

PRUDHOE CASTLE NORTHUMBERLAND – NE42 6NA

Guarding a strategic crossing of the River Tyne, impressive Prudhoe Castle was a vital bastion against Scots invaders. After resisting two Scots sieges during the 1170s – when King William the Lion lamented 'as long as Prudhoe stands, we shall never have peace' – it was given its tall keep, and later reinforced by towered walls. In the late 14th century it became a stronghold of the locally all-powerful Percy family, Earls of Northumberland.

You'll witness Prudhoe's great strength as you approach via the barbican, passing the picturesque mill pond and crossing the inner ditch to the formidable gatehouse. You can climb the steps to the atmospheric gatehouse chapel, explore the inner and outer baileys and look up at the towering keep. There's also a fine 'Regency Gothic' mansion within the walls, built by the Percys in the early 1800s as a 'gentleman's residence' for their land agent. Its elegant unfurnished rooms house family-friendly displays tracing the long history of this crucial fortress, continuously

occupied for over nine centuries. There's an array of site finds and a children's activity room with games.

Hadrian's Wall is a short drive away.

OPENING TIMES

1 Apr-30 Oct, Wed-Sun & Bank Hols	10am-5pm
31 Oct-31 Mar	Closed
Last entry 30 mins before closing	

VISIT US

Direction: In Prudhoe, on minor road off A695

Train: Prudhoe ¼ mile

Bus: Visit traveline.info for the latest bus timetables and routes

Tel: 01661 833459

NON-MEMBERS

Adult £7.80 | Concession £7.00
Child £4.70 | Family 2 Adults £20.30
Family 1 Adult £12.50

Dogs on leads (resricted areas only).

Toilets with disabled access on site.

MAP PAGE 335 (4G)
OS MAP 88, 316: NZ091634

HYLTON CASTLE
TYNE AND WEAR – SR5 3PA

The gatehouse-tower of a castle built by Sir William Hylton c. 1400. Supported by the National Lottery Heritage Fund, Hylton Castle Trust and Sunderland City Council have transformed the castle shell into a visitor attraction. Find out more at hyltoncastle.org.uk

OPENING TIMES

Please see website hyltoncastle.org.uk

VISIT US

Direction: 3¾ miles W of Sunderland

Metro: Seaburn (2½ miles)

Bus: Visit traveline.info

ACQ.1950 ⬚⬚⬚⬚⬚⬚⬚⬚⬚
P⬚⬚ Caution: CCTV at site.

MAP PAGE 335 (4H)
OS MAP 88, 308: NZ358588

ST PAUL'S MONASTERY, JARROW
TYNE AND WEAR – NE32 3DY

Home of the Venerable Bede, chronicler of early English Christianity. The Anglo-Saxon church, founded AD 685, partly survives.

OPENING TIMES

Monastery ruins: any reasonable daylight hours

VISIT US

Direction: In Jarrow, on minor road N of A185; follow signs for Bede's World

Metro: Bede ¾ miles

Bus: Visit traveline.info

Tel: 0191 489 7052

ACQ.1956 ⬚⬚ Caution: steep slopes.

MAP PAGE 335 (4G)
OS MAP 88, 316: NZ339652

TYNEMOUTH PRIORY AND CASTLE

—— TYNE AND WEAR – NE30 4BZ ——

Dramatic Tynemouth Priory and Castle is one of our most fascinating and varied coastal sites. Uniquely combining a medieval monastery and fortifications with 20th-century gun batteries and all-round seaward views, it crowns a rocky headland commanding the entrance to the River Tyne, the gateway to Newcastle.

A natural stronghold, the steep-sided headland housed an important Anglo-Saxon monastery, burial place of the sainted King Oswine of Northumbria. After this was destroyed by Vikings, a medieval monastery was founded on the site. It was later fortified against the Scots and became one of the largest defended areas in England.

You enter it through the powerful 14th-century monastic gatehouse, a miniature castle. Take in the interactive displays, where characters from Tynemouth's long and varied history help you explore the headland. The voice of Arthur Lloyd, a Second World War gunner, describes air raids, sinking ships and the primitive living conditions.

The spectacular ruins of the great 11th- to 13th-century monastic church, dominating the site, rise amid intriguing tombstones of Tynemouth mariners and artillerymen. At the east end is the priory's greatest treasure, the tiny 15th-century 'Percy Chantry' chapel, with its rose window and elaborately vaulted roof crowded with carved saints.

The fortress headland continued to guard the Tyne entrance right up until 1956. To experience life here during the two World Wars, venture down to explore the underground gun batteries, topped by a real long-range gun.

OPENING TIMES

1 Apr-30 Oct, daily	10am-5pm
31 Oct-17 Feb, Sat-Sun	10am-4pm
18-26 Feb, daily	10am-4pm
27 Feb-31 Mar, Sat-Sun	10am-4pm
24-26 Dec & 1 Jan	Closed

Last entry 30 mins before closing

Gun Battery: Access limited, please ask site staff for details

VISIT US

Direction: In Tynemouth, near North Pier

Metro: Tynemouth ½ mile

Bus: Visit traveline.info for the latest bus timetables and routes

Tel: 0191 257 1090

NON-MEMBERS

Adult **£7.80** | Concession **£7.00**
Child **£4.70** | Family 2 Adults **£20.30**
Family 1 Adult **£12.50**

ACQ.1969 🚹 ⚔ ❘ 🛡 ❘ 🏠 ❘ 🍴 🚶 🧍 ❘

📷 ⚠ OVP

Disabled access (priory only). Toilets with disabled access on site. Limited disabled parking available.

MAP PAGE 335 (4H)
OS MAP 88, 316: NZ373694

🖼 *King Gary* (2021).

Associated attractions in England

As well as free, unlimited entry to the hundreds of sites in our care, English Heritage membership also gives you free or discounted access to many associated attractions in England.

Visit **english-heritage.org.uk/ associated-attractions** for the full list and terms and conditions.

KEY

Discount applies to:

⊞ MEMBERS

🏠? NO. OF MEMBER'S CHILDREN

Please note: coloured square denotes Associated Attraction region

USE YOUR MEMBERSHIP TO GET DISCOUNTED ENTRY AT OVER 50 ATTRACTIONS.

PLEASE REMEMBER TO SHOW YOUR CARD AS PROOF OF MEMBERSHIP.

Terms and conditions may apply, so make sure you check the details on our website or call the individual property for more information.

Cutty Sark

25% DISCOUNT*

GREENWICH, LONDON – SE10 9HT

Visit the award-winning *Cutty Sark*. Delve into the ship's extraordinary history, meet characters from its past and discover what life was like on board the fastest ship of its day.

*Redemption by phone only – 020 8312 6608. Cannot be redeemed on group tickets. Valid on Adult, Child and Student/ Young Person tickets.

⊞ rmg.co.uk/cuttysark / 020 8312 6608

Strawberry Hill House & Garden

10% DISCOUNT*

TWICKENHAM, LONDON – TW1 4ST

Strawberry Hill House & Garden has been open to visitors for over 250 years. Created by Horace Walpole in the 18th century, Strawberry Hill is internationally famous as Britain's finest example of Georgian Gothic Revival architecture.

*Valid on house admission. Under 16s get free entry. Image © www.kilianosullivan.com

⊞ strawberryhillhouse.org.uk

Anne of Cleves House Museum

50% DISCOUNT*

LEWES, EAST SUSSEX – BN7 1JA

Discover how the Tudors and the Elizabethans lived, worked and relaxed at home. This 15th-century Wealden hall-house features authentically furnished rooms, traditional planted gardens and a local museum.

*Not valid on family tickets.

⊞ sussexpast.co.uk/attraction/anne-of-cleves-house-museum / 01273 474610

Blenheim Palace

30% DISCOUNT*

WOODSTOCK, OXFORDSHIRE – OX20 1UL

Home of the 12th Duke and Duchess of Marlborough and the birthplace of Sir Winston Churchill, Blenheim Palace is a World Heritage Site with over 300 years of history, 2,000 acres of parkland and formal gardens, and events, tours and exhibitions throughout the year.

*Receive 30% off a Palace, Park & Gardens ticket or Annual Pass when using the code EH30 online when pre-booking your tickets.

⊞ blenheimpalace.com / 01993 810530

Bletchley Park

20% DISCOUNT*

BLETCHLEY, BUCKINGHAMSHIRE – MK3 6EB

Bletchley Park, once the top-secret home of the Second World War codebreakers, is now a vibrant heritage attraction open daily to visitors. Experience the stories of the extraordinary achievements of the men and women who worked here.

*Offer excludes group tickets and learning tickets. Valid on general admission tickets. Free entry for Under 12s. Discounted family tickets available.

 ⊞ ⁉6 bletchleypark.org.uk / 01908 640404

Butser Ancient Farm

2 for 1 ENTRY*

HAMPSHIRE – PO8 0BG

Explore life in the past. Visit homes of the Stone Age, Bronze Age, Iron Age, Roman and Saxon periods, recreated as an experimental archaeology project in the beautiful South Downs.

*Cheapest ticket free. Not valid in conjunction with any other offer. Children require a purchased ticket and must be accompanied by an adult. Under 3s free. Please pre-book online. Excludes special events.

⊞ butserancientfarm.co.uk / 023 9259 8838

Canterbury Cathedral
20% DISCOUNT*

CANTERBURY, KENT – CT1 2EH

Founded by St Augustine in AD 597, Canterbury Cathedral is integral to England's story. Discover beautiful stonework, stained glass, Becket's Martyrdom and the Black Prince's tomb at this World Heritage Site.

*Not valid with other promotions or offers. Discount valid on visitor entry between 1 October and 31 March only.

▦ canterbury-cathedral.org / 01227 762862

Fishbourne Roman Palace
50% DISCOUNT*

FISHBOURNE, WEST SUSSEX – PO19 3QR

Explore the largest collection of early mosaic floors in Britain and recreated Roman garden. Join inspiring guided tours and look behind the scenes in the Collections Discovery Centre.

*Not valid on family tickets.

▦ sussexpast.co.uk/attraction/fishbourne-roman-palace-gardens / 01243 785859

Lewes Castle and Museum
50% DISCOUNT*

LEWES, EAST SUSSEX – BN7 1YE

Climb the zig-zag steps to the top of this early Norman castle for stunning panoramic views across Sussex, from the Downs to the coast. The adjoining Museum of Sussex Archaeology contains artefacts from prehistoric to medieval Sussex.

*Not valid on family tickets.

▦ sussexpast.co.uk/attraction/lewes-castle-museum / 01273 486290

Michelham Priory House & Gardens
50% DISCOUNT*

EAST SUSSEX – BN27 3QS

This picturesque island boasts a Tudor house and 14th-century medieval gatehouse with activities, displays of furniture and artefacts. Rooms include an interactive Victorian kitchen, Second World War evacuee's bedroom, Tudor kitchen, prior's room and undercroft.

*Not valid on family tickets.

▦ sussexpast.co.uk/attraction/michelham-priory-house-gardens / 01323 844224

USE YOUR MEMBERSHIP TO GET DISCOUNTED ENTRY AT OVER 50 ATTRACTIONS.
PLEASE REMEMBER TO SHOW YOUR CARD AS PROOF OF MEMBERSHIP.

Terms and conditions may apply, so make sure you check the details on our website or call the individual property for more information.

Oxford Castle & Prison

25% DISCOUNT*

OXFORD – OX1 1AY

Come and explore 1,000 years of history! Step back in time with our costumed tour guides and see fascinating stories come to life.

*Not available to redeem online. Discount can be redeemed by purchasing tickets from the gift shop with valid English Hertiage membership. Not valid in conjunction with any other offer, special ticketed events, Jailbreak and Murder Mystery experiences or Oxford History Walks. Standard Admission to the Guided Tour.

oxfordcastleandprison.co.uk **/** 01865 260666

The Royal Pavilion

20% DISCOUNT*

BRIGHTON, EAST SUSSEX – BN1 1EE

Discover the magnificent seaside residence of King George IV, where the Indian-style architecture contrasts with interiors inspired by China. Regency garden and gift shop.

*Not available for use with other promotions or for groups. Discounted tickets do not qualify for the annual pass, one time use only. Discount only valid on full adult admission.

brightonmuseums.org.uk **/** 0300 029 0900

Rycote Chapel

50% DISCOUNT*

OXFORDSHIRE – OX9 2PE

15th-century chapel with original furniture, including exquisitely carved and painted woodwork, and nearby restored Capability Brown ice house. Managed by the Rycote Buildings Charitable Foundation.

*No coaches. Excludes concessionary tickets. Offer valid on full price tickets.

visitsouthoxfordshire.co.uk **/** 01844 210210

Spinnaker Tower

20% DISCOUNT*

PORTSMOUTH, HAMPSHIRE – PO1 3TT

Experience the South Coast's most spectacular view, stretching up to 23 miles across the city, countryside and sea. Venture across the amazing glass Sky Walk, 100 metres above the harbour.

*Not available to redeem online. Not valid in conjunction with any other offer. Under 4s free. Not valid on special ticketed events, High Tea experiences, abseil experiences. Valid on Standard All Day Admission.

spinnakertower.co.uk **/** 023 9285 7520

Arthurian Centre/ The Vale of Avalon

20% DISCOUNT*

CAMELFORD, CORNWALL – PL32 9TT

Beautiful walks to the river Camel through historic landscape – King Arthur's legendary last battlefield, 6th-century scheduled monument, 13th-century longhouse, 18th-century and 'Muse' gardens, orchard; exhibition, tearoom and gifts.

*Cannot be used in conjunction with any other offer or promotion. Offer not valid for senior, student or other discounted rates.

⊞ 👪4 thevaleofavalon.co.uk / 01840 213947

Avon Valley Railway

50% DISCOUNT*

BITTON, SOUTH GLOUCESTERSHIRE – BS30 6HD

Step back in time and enjoy a ride on one of our steam or diesel hauled trains on weekends plus selected weekdays from April to September. Find us halfway between Bristol and Bath.

*Not valid on event days, dining trains or our Santa trains. Offer applies to standard steam or diesel operating days.

⊞ 👪4 avonvalleyrailway.org / 0117 932 5538

Dartington Hall Gardens

2 for 1 ENTRY*

DEVON – TQ9 6EL

Visit Dartington's historic gardens, with 26 acres of formal grounds and natural wilderness to explore. Plus a children's activity trail, shops, barn cinema, gallery, playground, restaurant and cafés.

*Valid on adult garden tickets. Redeem offer on arrival at the Welcome Centre. Free entry is given to the lowest value adult ticket.

⊞ dartington.org/gardens / 01803 847150

Pencarrow House & Gardens

2 for 1 ENTRY*

CORNWALL – PL30 3AG

Beautiful Georgian house and gardens, owned and loved by the Molesworth family for the last 500 years. Café, children's play area, gift and plant shop, free parking. Dogs welcome in the gardens.

*Not valid for special events. Open from April to October.

 ⊞ pencarrow.co.uk / 01208 841369

USE YOUR MEMBERSHIP TO GET DISCOUNTED ENTRY AT OVER 50 ATTRACTIONS.
PLEASE REMEMBER TO SHOW YOUR CARD AS PROOF OF MEMBERSHIP.

Terms and conditions may apply, so make sure you check the details on our website or call the individual property for more information.

PK Porthcurno – Museum of Global Communications

50% DISCOUNT*

CORNWALL – TR19 6JX

Visit a tranquil coastal valley in west Cornwall and discover the amazing story of our connected world, from the first undersea telegraph cables to the wonder of today's internet.

*When booking tickets online please select English Heritage Member to redeem the discount.

pkporthcurno.com / 01736 810966

Powderham Castle

20% DISCOUNT*

DEVON – EX6 8JQ

Over 600 years of history can be discovered within the walls of one of Devon's oldest family homes.

*Valid on Castle & Grounds tickets. Excludes grounds tickets, group tickets and memberships. This offer applies to standard public opening and may not be applicable to certain events.

 powderham.co.uk / 01626 890243

The Salisbury Museum

25% DISCOUNT*

SALISBURY, WILTSHIRE – SP1 2EN

Nationally important collections relating to Stonehenge and local archaeology. The museum is housed in a Grade I listed building in the Cathedral Close, where King James I stayed in 1610 and 1613.

*Day tickets only.

salisburymuseum.org.uk / 01722 332151

Shepton Mallet Prison

20% DISCOUNT*

SOMERSET – BA4 5LU

A recently decommissioned Victorian prison offering two-hour tours. Your guide will shine a light on the reality of life behind the high prison walls of this historic and fascinating building.

*Applies to guided tours only, subject to availability. Under 5s go free.

sheptonmalletprison.com / 01749 681862

Sherborne Castle & Gardens

£1.50 DISCOUNT*

DORSET – DT9 5NR

Built by Sir Walter Raleigh in 1594 and home to the Digby family since 1617. The castle contains magnificent staterooms and collections, Raleigh's kitchen and a museum. Breathtaking landscape gardens by Capability Brown.

*Discount valid on Castle and Gardens admission. Not valid on special events. Please check sherbornecastle.com for details.

 ⊞ 👫4 sherbornecastle.com / 01935 813182

Wiltshire Museum

25% DISCOUNT*

DEVIZES, WILTSHIRE – SN10 1NS

See gold from the time of Stonehenge in our award-winning Prehistory Galleries – a 'must see' when visiting Stonehenge and Avebury. Tells the story of Wiltshire across 13 galleries.

*Applies to standard entry only. Children are free.

 ⊞ wiltshiremuseum.org.uk / 01380 727369

Woodchester Mansion

2 for 1 ENTRY*

GLOUCESTERSHIRE – GL10 3TS

The Mansion is a unique unfinished neo-Gothic house. See how the building was constructed, discover why it was never completed, meet the bats and visit the café and gift shop.

*Not applicable on group admission. Offer valid on mansion tickets.

⊞ 👫6 woodchestermansion.org.uk / 01453 861541

Hedingham Castle

20% DISCOUNT*

ESSEX – CO9 3DJ

The 900-year-old keep of Hedingham Castle contains five floors of unique Norman architecture, set in 140 acres of ancient defensive ramparts, landscaped grounds and woodland.

*Not valid on event days. Please check website for opening times and details.

 ⊞ 👫6 hedinghamcastle.co.uk / 01787 460261

USE YOUR MEMBERSHIP TO GET DISCOUNTED ENTRY AT OVER 50 ATTRACTIONS.
PLEASE REMEMBER TO SHOW YOUR CARD AS PROOF OF MEMBERSHIP.

Terms and conditions may apply, so make sure you check the details on our website or call the individual property for more information.

Holkham Hall

20% DISCOUNT*

NORFOLK – NR23 1RH

Palladian stately home with stunning architecture, art and classical statuary. Discover more at the Holkham Stories Experience and Walled Garden. Explore our café, gift shop, ropes course and hire a bike.

***Not valid with any other offer or discount. Online booking is strongly recommended. Use discount code EH2022. Valid on 'Holkham Hall, Holkham Stories Experience and Walled Garden' or 'Holkham Stories Experience and Walled Garden' standard admission.**

holkham.co.uk / 01328 713111

Stow Maries Aerodrome

2 for 1 ENTRY*

ESSEX – CM3 6RN

A hidden gem, deep in rural Essex, this is the last remaining First World War aerodrome still functioning in Europe. Crammed with exhibitions and aircraft, housed in the original buildings with plenty of space – a must-see for any fan of aviation or 20th-century history.

***Excludes event days. Offer applies to regular admission.**

stowmaries.org.uk

King Richard III Visitor Centre

2 for 1 ENTRY*

LEICESTERSHIRE – LE1 5DB

Discover the incredible story of the king's life, death and discovery, and see the place where his remains lay undiscovered for over 500 years.

***Valid on full-priced admission. Excludes group, schools or family tickets. See website for full terms and conditions**

kriii.com / 0300 300 0900

National Civil War Centre

30% DISCOUNT*

NEWARK, NOTTINGHAMSHIRE – NG24 1JY

Explore one of the most fascinating times in British history: a remarkable story of superstitions, serious sibling rivalry and seismic change which has affected the country we live in today.

***Discount available on Adult, Senior, Student and Child tickets. Tickets can be booked online. Please select the ticket which applies to you, followed by English Heritage, from the ticket list.**

nationalcivilwarcentre.com / 01636 655765

Blists Hill Victorian Town

10% DISCOUNT*

SHROPSHIRE – TF7 5UD

Enjoy a family day at Ironbridge's recreated Victorian town. Discover more about life in 1900 from our costumed townsfolk. No cars, no TV, just tons of fun!

*Valid on single site and passport tickets. Excludes special events.

■ ⊞ 👪4 ironbridge.org.uk/explore/blists-hill-victorian-town / 01952 433424

British Motor Museum

£2 DISCOUNT*

WARWICKSHIRE – CV35 0BJ

Discover the world's largest collection of historic British cars. Experience the sights, sounds and stories of our motor industry. A great family day out.

*Discounts must be redeemed when purchasing tickets online using discount code: EH-BMM-VDE21. Cannot be used in conjunction with any other offer, group, family or education tickets or when purchasing an annual pass. Not valid on up to five special show days each year. Only valid against museum entry.

■ ⊞ 👪4 britishmotormuseum.co.uk/ / 01926 641188

Shakespeare's Schoolroom & Guildhall

20% DISCOUNT*

STRATFORD-UPON-AVON – CV37 6HB

Discover where William Shakespeare was educated and inspired to become the world's greatest playwright. Interactive fun for the whole family.

*Cannot be combined with other offers.

■ ⊞ 👪4 shakespearesschoolroom.org / 01789 203172

Shrewsbury Prison

20% DISCOUNT*

SHREWSBURY, SHROPSHIRE – SY1 2HP

A recently decommissioned Victorian prison offering two-hour tours led by an ex prison officer who will shine a light on the reality of life behind bars in this fascinating and historic building.

*Applies to guided tours only, subject to availability. Under 5s go free.

■ ⊞ shrewsburyprison.com / 01743 343100

USE YOUR MEMBERSHIP TO GET DISCOUNTED ENTRY AT OVER 50 ATTRACTIONS.
PLEASE REMEMBER TO SHOW YOUR CARD AS PROOF OF MEMBERSHIP.

Terms and conditions may apply, so make sure you check the details on our website or call the individual property for more information.

Warwick Castle

50% DISCOUNT*

WARWICK – CV34 6AH

Witness 1,100 years of history come vividly to life. Spectacular shows and attractions, spellbinding storytelling and exhilarating experiences make Warwick Castle one of the most exciting historic locations in Europe.

*Valid on Castle Entry. Excludes any secondary attraction or secondary product/service.

warwick-castle.com / 01926 406663

Barley Hall

15% DISCOUNT*

YORK – YO1 8AR

A stunning medieval townhouse, once home to the Priors of Nostell and a Lord Mayor. Lovingly restored to its original splendour, it is a true hidden gem of York.

*Apply the discount when you pre-book online by selecting the '15% off' option, or when you buy a ticket on admission. Pre-booking is recommended. Offer excludes joint tickets. Valid on adult, child and concession tickets.

barleyhall.co.uk / 01904 615505

Bolton Castle

10% DISCOUNT*

NORTH YORKSHIRE – DL8 4ET

Bolton Castle, one of the country's best-preserved late medieval castles, gives visitors a taste of what life was really like during medieval times and during Mary Queen of Scots' stay. With falconry, archery displays and wild boar feeding.

*Offer applies to Castle & Garden tickets. Please book tickets on arrival. Not valid on group bookings.

boltoncastle.co.uk / 01969 623981

DIG:
An Archaeological
Adventure

2 for 1 ENTRY*

YORK – YO1 8NN

From the creators of JORVIK Viking Centre, a hands-on archaeological experience giving kids the chance to discover the history of York.

* Pre-book by calling 01904 615505. Excludes Family tickets and joint attraction tickets. Valid on adult, child and concession tickets.

digyork.com / 01904 615505

Fountains Abbey & Studley Royal Water Garden

FREE ENTRY*

NORTH YORKSHIRE – HG4 3DY

Spectacular World Heritage Site including 12th-century abbey ruins and stunning Georgian water garden.

*Offer applies to normal admission to the whole estate. Not available to education or corporate members.

⬛ ⊞ 👫6 nationaltrust.org.uk/fountains-abbey / 01765 608888

The Green Howards Museum

2for1 ENTRY*

RICHMOND, NORTH YORKSHIRE – DL10 4QN

Friendship, adventure, service and sacrifice; the 300-year history of this illustrious regiment is told through the stories of the soldiers who served.

*Offer applies to adult and concession tickets. Under-16s free.

⬛ ⊞ 👫6 greenhowards.org.uk / 01748 826561

JORVIK Viking Centre

15% DISCOUNT*

YORK – YO1 9WT

Featuring the famous multi-sensory ride experience and the state-of-the-art galleries showcasing unique 1,000-year-old artefacts. Visit JORVIK Viking Centre to discover York's fascinating Viking heritage.

*You can apply the discount when you pre-book online by selecting the 'English Heritage' option, or when you buy a ticket on admission. Not available for family tickets or joint attraction tickets. Valid on adult, child and concession tickets.

⬛ ⊞ 👫6 jorvikvikingcentre.co.uk / 01904 615505

Merchant Adventurers' Hall

50% DISCOUNT

YORK – YO1 9XD

Built in 1357, discover the Merchant Adventurers' Hall, one of the finest Medieval guildhalls in the world. Home to York's entrepreneurs for 660 years and counting.

⬛ ⊞ 👫6 merchantshallyork.org / 01904 654818

USE YOUR MEMBERSHIP TO GET DISCOUNTED ENTRY AT OVER 50 ATTRACTIONS.
PLEASE REMEMBER TO SHOW YOUR CARD AS PROOF OF MEMBERSHIP.

Terms and conditions may apply, so make sure you check the details on our website or call the individual property for more information.

York Mansion House

25% DISCOUNT*

YORK – YO1 9QL

From the beautiful simplicity of the 18th-century kitchens to the magnificence of the state rooms, walk through centuries of society life and discover treasure, feasting and the lords of the city.

mansionhouseyork.com / 01904 553663

York's Chocolate Story

20% DISCOUNT*

YORK – YO1 7LD

Celebrate the rich culture of chocolate within York. Join our guided tour through 3,000 years of chocolate history and discover the heritage of York's iconic confectionery brands.

*Not valid on special event days. Please contact us at info@yorkschocolatestory.com to make your booking or check our FAQ page. We do accept walk-ups, however cannot guarantee tour availability.

yorkschocolatestory.com / 01904 527765

Lowther Castle & Gardens

20% DISCOUNT*

CUMBRIA – CA10 2HH

One of the most stunning visitor attractions in the north west, Lowther Castle has it all – drama, romance, style and stories. Castle ruins, gardens, historical exhibition, adventure playground, café and shop.

*Valid on adult Castle and Gardens day ticket. Cannot be applied to annual passes. Image © Val Corbett.

lowthercastle.org / 01931 712192

The Bowes Museum

10% DISCOUNT*

BARNARD CASTLE,
COUNTY DURHAM – DL12 8NP

Founded by Joséphine Bowes, the Museum houses a fascinating European fine and decorative art collection, with exciting exhibitions, fabulous food, gorgeous gifts and stunning parkland.

*Tickets must be pre-booked via our website using discount code EHeritage10. Not applicable when an additional cost is applied to special exhibitions and events. Excludes groups tickets. Valid on museum passes.

thebowesmuseum.org.uk / 01833 690606

Cadw

Caernarfon Castle

English Heritage Members can gain half-price admission to Cadw attractions during the first year of membership and free entry in subsequent years.

Beaumaris Castle, Anglesey LL58 8AP **T.** 01248 810361

Blaenavon Ironworks, Nr Pontypool, Torfaen NP4 9RQ **T.** 01495 792615

Cae'r Gors*, Rhosgadfan, Caernarfon LL54 7EY **T.** 01286 831715

Caerleon Roman Fortress, Caerleon, Newport NP18 1AE **T.** 01633 422518

Caernarfon Castle, Caernarfon, Gwynedd LL55 2AY **T.** 01286 677617

Caerphilly Castle, Caerphilly CF83 1JD **T.** 029 2088 3143

Carreg Cennen Castle, Nr Trapp, Carmarthenshire SA19 6UA **T.** 01558 822291

Castell Coch, Cardiff CF15 7JS **T.** 029 2081 0101

Chepstow Castle, Chepstow, Monmouthshire NP16 5EY **T.** 01291 624065

Cilgerran Castle, Nr Cardigan, Pembrokeshire SA43 2SF **T.** 01239 621339

Conwy Castle, Conwy LL32 8AY **T.** 01492 592358

Criccieth Castle, Criccieth, Gwynedd LL52 0DP **T.** 01766 522227

Denbigh Castle, Denbigh LL16 3NB **T.** 01745 813385

Dolwyddelan Castle, Dolwyddelan, Gwynedd LL25 0JD **T.** 01690 750366

Harlech Castle, Harlech, Gwynedd LL46 2YH **T.** 01766 780552

Kidwelly Castle, Kidwelly, Carmarthenshire SA17 5BQ **T.** 01554 890104

Lamphey Bishop's Palace*, Lamphey, Pembroke SA71 5NT **T.** 03000 256000

Laugharne Castle, Laugharne, Carmarthenshire SA33 4SA **T.** 01994 427906

Margam Stones Museum, Margam, Port Talbot SA13 2TA **T.** 01639 871184

Oxwich Castle, Oxwich, Swansea SA3 1ND **T.** 01792 390359

Plas Mawr, Conwy LL32 8DE **T.** 01492 573605

Raglan Castle, Raglan, Monmouthshire NP15 2BT **T.** 01291 690228

Rhuddlan Castle, Rhuddlan, Denbighshire LL18 5AD **T.** 01745 590777

*Entry to these sites is free.

Rug Chapel and Llangar Church, Corwen, Denbighshire LL21 9BT **T.** 01490 412025

Segontium Roman Fort*, Caernarfon, Gwynedd, LL55 2LN **T.** 01286 677617

St Davids Bishop's Palace, St Davids, Pembrokeshire SA62 6PE **T.** 01437 720517

St Dogmael's Abbey*, The Coach House, Shingrig, St. Dogmaels, Pembrokeshire SA43 3DX **T.** 01239 615389

Strata Florida Abbey, Pontrhydfendigaid, Ceredigion SY25 6ES **T.** 01974 831261

Tintern Abbey, Tintern, Monmouthshire NP16 6SE **T.** 01291 689251

Tretower Court and Castle, Tretower, Powys NP8 1RD **T.** 01874 730279

Valle Crucis Abbey, Nr Llangollen, Denbighshire LL20 8DD **T.** 01978 860326

Weobley Castle, Nr Llanrhidian, Swansea SA3 1HB **T.** 03000 256000

Cadw, Ty'r Afon

Welsh Government, Bedwas Road, Caerphilly CF83 8WT **T.** 03000 252239 **E.** cadw@gov.wales **W.** gov.wales/cadw

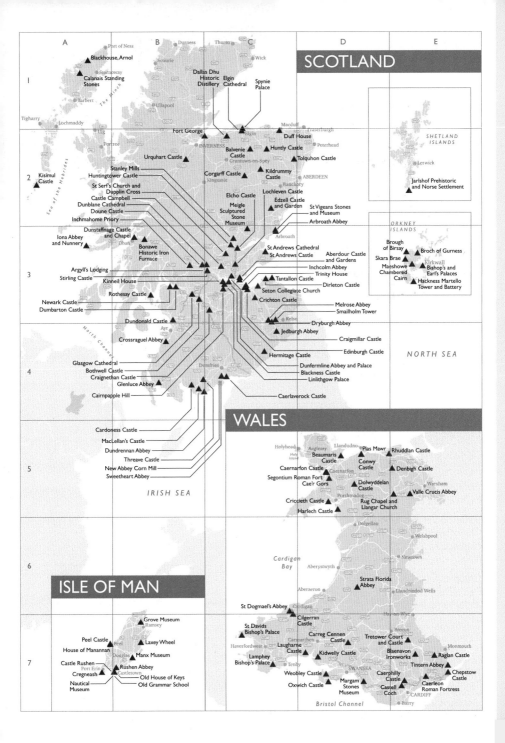

SCOTLAND

A · Port of Ness
Blackhouse, Arnol
Calanais Standing Stones
Stornoway
Scourie
Durness
Thurso
Wick
Dallas Dhu Historic Distillery
Elgin Cathedral
Spynie Palace

1

Tarbert
Ullapool

Tigharry
Lochmaddy
Macduff
Fraserburgh

SHETLAND ISLANDS

Lerwick

Kisimul Castle
Portree
Fort George
Elgin
INVERNESS
Duff House
Peterhead

Jarlshof Prehistoric and Norse Settlement

2

Urquhart Castle
Stanley Mills
Huntingtower Castle
St Serf's Church and Dupplin Cross
Castle Campbell
Dunblane Cathedral
Doune Castle
Inchmahome Priory
Balvenie Castle
Grantown-on-Spey
Corgarff Castle
Kingussie
Kildrummy Castle
ABERDEEN
Huntly Castle
Tolquhon Castle
Banchory
Elcho Castle
Lochleven Castle
Meigle Sculptured Stone Museum
Edzell Castle and Garden
St Vigeans Stones and Museum
Arbroath Abbey

ORKNEY ISLANDS

Brough of Birsay
Skara Brae
Maeshowe Chambered Cairn
Broch of Gurness
Kirkwall
Bishop's and Earl's Palaces
Hackness Martello Tower and Battery

3

Iona Abbey and Nunnery
Oban
Bonawe Historic Iron Furnace
Dunstaffnage Castle and Chapel
Argyll's Lodging
Stirling Castle
Kinneil House
Rothesay Castle
Newark Castle
Dumbarton Castle
Dundonald Castle
Ayr
Arbroath
St Andrews Cathedral
St Andrews Castle
Inchcolm Abbey
Trinity House
Tantallon Castle
Dirleton Castle
Seton Collegiate Church
Crichton Castle
Melrose Abbey
Smailholm Tower
Aberdour Castle and Gardens

NORTH SEA

4

Glasgow Cathedral
Bothwell Castle
Craignethan Castle
Glenluce Abbey
Cairnpapple Hill
Crossraguel Abbey
Dumfries
Kelso
Dryburgh Abbey
Jedburgh Abbey
Craigmillar Castle
Edinburgh Castle
Hermitage Castle
Dunfermline Abbey and Palace
Blackness Castle
Linlithgow Palace
Caerlaverock Castle

WALES

5

Cardoness Castle
MacLellan's Castle
Dundrennan Abbey
Threave Castle
New Abbey Corn Mill
Sweetheart Abbey

IRISH SEA

Holyhead
Anglesey
Holy Island
Llandudno
Beaumaris Castle
Plas Mawr
Rhuddlan Castle
Caernarfon Castle
Conwy Castle
Denbigh Castle
Segontium Roman Fort
Caernarfon
Cae'r Gors
Dolwyddelan Castle
Wrexham
Porthmadog
Criccieth Castle
Rug Chapel and Llangar Church
Valle Crucis Abbey
Harlech Castle

Dolgellau
Welshpool
Newtown

6

Cardigan Bay
Aberystwyth
Aberaeron
Strata Florida Abbey
Llandrindod Wells

ISLE OF MAN

St Dogmael's Abbey
Cardigan
Hay-on-Wye

7

Grove Museum
Ramsey
Peel Castle
Peel
Laxey Wheel
House of Manannan
Douglas
Manx Museum
Castle Rushen
Port Erin
Rushen Abbey
Cregneash
Castletown
Old House of Keys
Old Grammar School
Nautical Museum

St Davids Bishop's Palace
Haverfordwest
Carmarthen
Lamphey Bishop's Palace
Tenby
Cilgerran Castle
Laugharne Castle
Carreg Cennen Castle
Kidwelly Castle
Tretower Court and Castle
Brecon
Blaenavon Ironworks
Monmouth
Raglan Castle
SWANSEA
Weobley Castle
Oxwich Castle
Margam Stones Museum
Caerphilly Castle
Castell Coch
CARDIFF
Caerleon Roman Fortress
Tintern Abbey
Chepstow Castle

Bristol Channel
Barry

Historic Scotland

Urquhart Castle

English Heritage Members can gain half-price admission to Historic Scotland attractions during the first year of membership and free entry in subsequent years.

Pre-booking recommended. Please check Historic Scotland website for details. Valid membership cards must be shown at Historic Scotland sites for entry.

Aberdour Castle and Gardens, Aberdour, Fife
T. 01383 860519

Arbroath Abbey, Angus
T. 01241 878756

Argyll's Lodging, Stirling
T. 01786 450000 (Stirling Castle)

Balvenie Castle, Dufftown, Grampian
T. 01340 820121

The Bishop's and Earl's Palaces, Kirkwall, Orkney
T. 01856 871918

The Black House, Arnol, Lewis, Western Isles
T. 01851 710395

Blackness Castle, Firth of Forth, Edinburgh and Lothians
T. 01506 834807

Bonawe Historic Iron Furnace, Taynuilt, Argyll
T. 01866 822432

Bothwell Castle, Bothwell, Greater Glasgow
T. 01698 816894

Broch of Gurness, Aikerness, Orkney
T. 01856 751414

Brough of Birsay, NW of Kirkwall, Orkney
T. 01856 841815 (Skara Brae)

Caerlaverock Castle, Nr Dumfries, Dumfries and Galloway
T. 01387 770244

Cairnpapple Hill, Torphichen, Edinburgh and Lothians
T. 01506 634622

Cardoness Castle, Nr Gatehouse of Fleet, Dumfries and Galloway
T. 01557 814427

Castle Campbell and Gardens, Dollar Glen
T. 01259 742408

Corgarff Castle, Nr Strathdon, Grampian
T. 01975 651460

Craigmillar Castle, Edinburgh and Lothians
T. 0131 661 4445

Craignethan Castle, Lanark, Greater Glasgow
T. 01555 860364

Crichton Castle, Nr Pathhead, Edinburgh and Lothians
T. 01875 320017

Crossraguel Abbey, Nr Maybole, Greater Glasgow
T. 01655 883113

Dallas Dhu Historic Distillery, Nr Forres, Grampian
T. 01309 676548

Dirleton Castle and Gardens, Dirleton, East Lothian
T. 01620 850330

Doune Castle, Doune
T. 01786 841742

Dryburgh Abbey, Nr Melrose, Borders
T. 01835 822381

Duff House, Banff, Grampian
T. 01261 818181

Dumbarton Castle, Dumbarton, Greater Glasgow
T. 01389 732167

Dunblane Cathedral, Dunblane
T. 01786 823388

Dundonald Castle, Dundonald, Greater Glasgow
T. 01563 851489

Dundrennan Abbey, Nr Kirkcudbright, Dumfries and Galloway
T. 01557 500262

Dunfermline Abbey and Palace, Dunfermline, Fife
E. dunfermlineabbeyandpalace.vo@hes.scot

Dunstaffnage Castle and Chapel, Nr Oban, Argyll
T. 01631 562465

Edinburgh Castle, Edinburgh and Lothians
T. 0131 225 9846

Edzell Castle and Garden,
Edzell, Angus
T. 01356 648603

Elcho Castle, Nr Bridge of Earn,
Perthshire
T. 01738 639998

Elgin Cathedral, Elgin, Highlands
T. 01343 547171

Fort George, Nr Ardersier
village, Highlands
T. 01667 462834

Glasgow Cathedral, Glasgow
T. 0141 552 6891

Glenluce Abbey, Nr Glenluce,
Dumfries and Galloway
T. 01581 300541 (Sun to Tue)
01557 331856 (Wed to Sat)

Hackness Martello Tower and
Battery, Hoy, Orkney
T. 01856 701727

Hermitage Castle,
Nr Newcastleton, Borders
T. 01387 376222

Huntingtower Castle, Nr Perth,
Perthshire
T. 01738 627231

Huntly Castle, Huntly, Grampian
T. 01466 793191

Inchcolm Abbey,
Firth of Forth, Fife
T. 07836 265146

Inchmahome Priory,
Lake of Menteith, Central
T. 01877 385294/07836 313769

Iona Abbey and Nunnery,
Island of Iona, Argyll
T. 01681 700512

Jarlshof Prehistoric and Norse
Settlement, Sumburgh Head,
Shetland   **T.** 01950 460112
(1 Apr-30 Sep), 01856 841815
(1 Oct-31 Mar)

Jedburgh Abbey and Visitor
Centre, Jedburgh, Borders
T. 01835 863925

Kildrummy Castle, Nr Alford,
Grampian
T. 01975 571331

Kisimul Castle, Isle of Barra,
Western Isles
T. 01871 810313

Linlithgow Palace, Linlithgow,
West Lothian
T. 01506 842896

Lochleven Castle, Lochleven,
Perthshire
T. 01577 862670

MacLellan's Castle, Kirkcudbright,
Dumfries and Galloway
T. 01557 331856

Maeshowe Chambered Cairn,
Nr Kirkwall, Orkney
T. 01856 851266

Meigle Sculptured Stone
Museum, Meigle, Angus
T. 01828 640612

Melrose Abbey, Melrose, Borders
T. 01896 822562

New Abbey Corn Mill, New
Abbey, Dumfries and Galloway
T. 01387 850260

Newark Castle, Port Glasgow,
Greater Glasgow
T. 01475 741858

Rothesay Castle, Rothesay,
Isle of Bute
T. 01700 502691

St Andrews Castle,
St Andrews, Fife
T. 01334 477196

St Andrews Cathedral,
St Andrews, Fife
T. 01334 472563

St Serf's Church and Dupplin
Cross, Dunning, Perthshire
T. 01764 684497

St Vigeans Sculptured Stones,
Nr Arbroath, Angus
T. 01241 878756

Seton Collegiate Church,
Nr Cockenzie, East Lothian
T. 01875 813334

Skara Brae and Skaill House,
Nr Kirkwall, Orkney
T. 01856 841815

Stirling Castle

Aberdour Castle

Smailholm Tower, Near
Smailholm, Borders
T. 01573 460365

Spynie Palace, Nr Elgin,
Grampian   **T.** 01343 546358

Stanley Mills, North of Perth
T. 01738 828268

Stirling Castle, Stirling, Central
T. 01786 450000

Sweetheart Abbey, New Abbey,
Dumfries and Galloway
T. 01387 850397

Tantallon Castle, Nr North
Berwick, East Lothian
T. 01620 892727

Threave Castle, Nr Castle
Douglas, Dumfries and Galloway
T. 07711 223101

Tolquhon Castle, Nr Aberdeen,
Grampian
T. 01651 851286

Urquhart Castle, Drumnadrochit,
Highlands
T. 01456 450551

Historic Scotland

Historic Environment Scotland, Longmore House
Salisbury Place, Edinburgh EH9 1SH **T.** 0131 668 8999
E. members@hes.scot **W.** historicenvironment.scot

Castle Rushen © Manx National Heritage

Manx National Heritage

Manx National Heritage welcomes English Heritage Members with free* admission to all its heritage attractions on presentation of a valid membership card.

Isle of Man

East of the Island

Douglas
Manx Museum

South of the Island

Ballasalla
Rushen Abbey

Castletown
Castle Rushen
Nautical Museum
Old Grammar School
Old House of Keys

Cregneash
Cregneash Village

North of the Island

Ramsey
Grove Museum

Laxey
Laxey Wheel

West of the Island

Peel
House of Manannan
Peel Castle

Admission charges may apply for some special events. Travel connections between the Isle of Man heritage sites are available on Victorian Steam Railway, Manx Electric Railway and Bus Vannin.

*Free admission applies to the Member only and children aged 4 years and under.

Manx National Heritage

Kingswood Grove, Douglas, Isle of Man IMI 3LY
T. 01624 648000 W. manxnationalheritage.im

IRELAND

	A	B	C	D	E
1					
2	ATLANTIC OCEAN			NORTHERN IRELAND	North Channel
3			REPUBLIC OF IRELAND		
4					IRISH SEA
5					
6				St George's Channel	
7		CELTIC SEA			

North Channel

Dunfanaghy

Glebe House and Gallery ▲
Dungloe
Letterkenny

Donegal Castle ▲ Donegal

Donegal Bay

Céide Fields ▲

Sligo Abbey ▲
Sligo
Carrowmore Megalithic Cemetery ▲ ▲ Parke's Castle
Collooney

Crossmolina Ballina
Achill Island
Tobercurry
Ballyconnell Clones Castleblayney
Monaghan

Boyle Abbey ▲ Boyle
Swinford Carrick on Shannon Cavan
Westport Knock Castlerea
Ardee

Longford
Old Mellifont Abbey ▲ Battle of the Boyne Visitor Centre ▲
Edgeworthstown Kells Drogheda
Clifden Roscommon Brú na Bóinne Visitor Centre ▲
Aughnanure Castle ▲ Tuam Delvin Navan
Oughterard Mountbellew Ballymahon Hill of Tara ▲ Trim ▲ Trim Castle Lusk
Ionad Culturtha an Phiarsaigh ▲ Athlone Kinnegad Swords Malahide

Athenry Castle ▲ Athenry Ballinasloe Kilbeggan Farmleigh ▲ The Casino ▲
Galway Celbridge Dublin
Dún Aonghasa ▲ Galway Bay Clonmacnoise ▲ Castletown ▲ Dublin Castle ▲
Loughrea Kilmainham Gaol ▲ Dún Laoghaire
Aran Islands Portumna Castle and Gardens ▲ Naas
Gort Portumna Birr Kildare Bray

Emo Court ▲
Port Laoise
Roscrea Athy Glendalough Visitor Centre ▲
Ennis Friary ▲ Ennis Roscrea Heritage (Castle & Damer House) ▲ Wicklow
Nenagh
Kilkee Shannon Thurles Dunmore Cave ▲ Arklow
Killrush Foynes Limerick Kilkenny Kilkenny Castle ▲
Listowel Rock of Cashel ▲ Cashel Jerpoint Abbey ▲
Ardfert Cathedral ▲ Tralee Tipperary Enniscorthy
The Blasket Centre ▲ Cahir Castle ▲ Cahir Clonmel JFK Memorial Park & Arboretum ▲
Dingle Castleisland Swiss Cottage ▲ Wexford
Blasket Islands Killorglin Mallow Fermoy Waterford Reginald's Tower ▲ Rosslare Harbour
Killarney Lismore
Ross Castle ▲ Macroom Dungarvan
Derrynane House ▲ Kenmare Cork
Ilnacullin (Garnish Island) ▲ Bantry Dunmanway
Desmond Castle (French Prison) ▲ Kinsale
Charles Fort ▲
Clonakilty

St George's Channel

CELTIC SEA

Rock of Cashel

Aughnanure Castle

OPW Heritage Ireland

Free entry for English Heritage Members.

Ardfert Cathedral, Ardfert,
Tralee, Co Kerry
T. +353 (066) 713 4711

Athenry Castle, Athenry,
Co Galway
T. +353 (091) 844797

Aughnanure Castle,
Oughterard, Co Galway
T. +353 (091) 552214

Battle of the Boyne Visitor Centre,
Oldbridge, Co Meath
T. +353 (041) 980 9950

The Blasket Centre, Dún Chaoin,
Dingle Peninsula, Co Kerry
T. +353 (066) 915 6444/
(066) 915 6371

Boyle Abbey, Boyle,
Co Roscommon
T. +353 (071) 966 2604

Brú na Bóinne Visitor Centre,
(Newgrange and Knowth),
Donore, Co Meath
T. +353 (041) 988 0300

Cahir Castle, Castle Street,
Cahir, Co Tipperary
T. +353 (52) 7441011

Carrowmore Megalithic
Cemetery, Carrowmore, Co Sligo
T. +353 (071) 916 1534

Castletown, Celbridge,
Co Kildare
T. +353 (01) 628 8252

Céide Fields, Ballycastle,
Co Mayo
T. +353 (096) 43325

Charles Fort, Summer Cove,
Kinsale, Co Cork
T. +353 (021) 477 2263

Clonmacnoise, Shannonbridge,
Co Offaly
T. +353 (090) 967 4195

Derrynane House, National
Historic Park, Caherdaniel,
Co Kerry
T. +353 (066) 947 5113

Desmond Castle (French Prison),
Cork Street, Kinsale, Co Cork
T. +353 (021) 477 4855

Donegal Castle, Donegal Town,
Co Donegal
T. +353 (074) 972 2405

Dublin Castle, Dame Street,
Dublin 2
T. +353 (01) 645 8813

Dún Aonghasa, Kilmurvey,
Inishmore, Aran Islands,
Co Galway
T. +353 (099) 61008

Dunmore Cave, Castlecomer
Road, Kilkenny
T. +353 (056) 776 7726

Emo Court, Emo, Co Laois
T. +353 (057) 862 6573

Ennis Friary, Abbey Street,
Ennis, Co Clare
T. +353 (065) 682 9100

Farmleigh, Phoenix Park,
Castleknock, Dublin 15
T. +353 (01) 815 5900/815 5981

Glebe House and Gallery,
Churchill, Letterkenny,
Co Donegal
T. +353 (074) 913 7071

Glendalough Visitor Centre,
Glendalough, Co Wicklow
T. +353 404 45352/25

Hill of Tara, Navan, Co Meath
T./F. +353 (046) 902 5903

Ilnacullin (Garnish Island),
Glengarriff, Bantry, Co Cork
T. +353 (027) 63040

Ionad Culturtha an Phiarsaigh,
Conamara, Inbhear, Ros Muc,
Co Galway
T. +353 (091) 574292

Jerpoint Abbey, Thomastown,
Co Kilkenny
T. +353 (056) 772 4623

JFK Memorial Park & Arboretum,
New Ross, Co Wexford
T. +353 (051) 388171

Kilkenny Castle, Kilkenny City,
Co Kilkenny
T. +353 (056) 770 4100

Kilmainham Gaol, Inchicore Road,
Kilmainham, Dublin 8
T. +353 (01) 453 5984

Old Mellifont Abbey, Tullyallen,
Drogheda, Co Louth
T. +353 (41) 982 6459

Parke's Castle, Fivemile Bourne,
Co Leitrim
T. +353 (071) 916 4149

Portumna Castle and Gardens,
Portumna, Co Galway
T. +353 (090) 974 1658

Reginald's Tower, The Quay,
Waterford
T./F. +353 (051) 304220

Rock of Cashel, Cashel,
Co Tipperary
T. +353 (062) 61437

Roscrea Heritage (Castle &
Damer House), Roscrea,
Co Tipperary
T. +353 (0505) 21850

Ross Castle, Killarney, Co Kerry
T. +353 64 6635851

Sligo Abbey, Abbey Street,
Sligo, Co Sligo
T. +353 (071) 914 6406

Swiss Cottage, Kilcommon, Cahir,
Co Tipperary
T. +353 (052) 7441144

The Casino, Cherrymount
Crescent, off the Malahide Road,
Marino, Dublin 3
T. +353 (01) 833 1618

Trim Castle, Trim, Co Meath
T. +353 (046) 943 8619 or
+353 (046) 943 8964

Charles Fort

Kilmainham Gaol

Swiss Cottage

Trim Castle

We welcome visitors
from near and far and we
are particularly delighted
to welcome Members
of English Heritage and
holders of the Overseas
Visitor Pass – we look
forward to meeting you.

For more information about
our sites (including those
where admission is free)
please visit our website
heritageireland.ie

f Find us on Facebook

Heritage New Zealand Pouhere Taonga

Kororipo Heritage Park

English Heritage Members get free entry to all our properties.

Aotearoa New Zealand's peopled heritage reaches back centuries. Indigenous Māori named and claimed the landscape and left ancestral and sacred places including ancient rock art, fortified settlements, and large ornate wharenui (meeting houses) which are part of the contemporary landscape. The country's more recent heritage sites are tangible reminders of this South Pacific nation's connection to Great Britain as well its self-defining moments, from the Kerikeri Mission Station in Northland, to Kate Sheppard House in Ōtautahi Christchurch, to Hayes Engineering Works in the gold mining region of Central Otago. Heritage New Zealand Pouhere Taonga cares for 45 properties and sites where you can learn about the people and places that make New Zealand what it is today.

OUR SITES RANGE FROM IMPRESSIVE HOMESTEADS, TO CENTRES OF INDUSTRY AND INNOVATION, TO BATTLE SITES, AND MORE, INCLUDING:

Old St Paul's (Wellington) – where stunning stained glass windows help illuminate the glorious native timber interior of this 19th-century Gothic Revival church, a home away from home for US servicemen during the Second World War.

The Kerikeri Mission Station and Stone Store (Northland) – the Mission Station is New Zealand's oldest standing building, built in 1821-22, while the nearby Stone Store is one of the country's most photographed buildings.

Fyffe House (Kāikoura) – where a whale of a time is guaranteed, the property built as part of the early whaling industry and partly on whale vertebrae foundations.

Alberton and Highwic (Auckland) – impressive dwellings that were home to two prominent colonial businessmen.

Totara Estate (Ōamaru) – British dinner tables have featured our finest cuts of meat over many years, and Totara Estate is where New Zealand's billion dollar frozen meat industry began.

Heritage New Zealand Pouhere Taonga

More information on heritage sites to visit can be found on Heritage New Zealand's website **heritage.org.nz**. Our staff look forward to welcoming you. Please check opening hours on the website prior to your visit to avoid disappointment.

HERITAGE NEW ZEALAND POUHERE TAONGA

St Mary's, Mundon, Essex

Friends of Friendless Churches

Friends of Friendless Churches save disused but beautiful old places of worship of architectural and historical interest from demolition, decay and unsympathetic conversion.

Working across England and Wales, we are an independent, non-denominational charity which cares for over 60 redundant places of worship and has helped hundreds more.

We believe that an ancient and beautiful church fulfils its primary function merely by existing; we preserve these buildings for the local community and visitors to enjoy. Without us, all of these buildings would no longer be here, or open to the public.

We warmly welcome visitors to our churches, but do not claim sophistication in terms of parking, toilets, attendants or shops, and access may require contacting a keyholder. Our churches are places for quiet study and contemplation, preserved for posterity as beautiful historic buildings.

Maintaining and repairing churches is a considerable financial challenge. We rely on the generosity of our members and on the willingness of groups of local Friends to fundraise and to act as our eyes and ears.

Friends of Friendless Churches

T. 020 7236 3934 E. office@friendsoffriendlesschurches.org.uk W. friendsoffriendlesschurches.org.uk
Follow us on 📷 📘 🐦 Registered charity no: 1113097

St George's, Portland. © Churches Conservation Trust

Churches Conservation Trust

Open a church door to discover 1,000 years of England's history.

Whether Anglo-Saxon carvings, medieval stained glass, grand Victorian architecture or proximity to the stories of our past, our collection of historic churches provides wonder and beauty in places you know and in those you don't.

We are the national charity protecting historic churches at risk. We've saved more than 350 beautiful buildings, enjoyed by almost 2 million visitors a year. Scattered the length and breadth of England in town and country, and ranging from ancient, rustic buildings to others of great richness and splendour, each has been saved because it represents something remarkable.

With our help and with your support they are kept open and in use – living once again in the heart of their communities. Entry is free, so push open the door and 1,000 years of history awaits you.

Discover more and see what's on near you at visitchurches.org.uk

Churches Conservation Trust

Society Building, 8 All Saints Street, London N1 9RL
T. 0845 303 2760 E. enquiries@thecct.org.uk
W. visitchurches.org.uk Registered charity no: 258612

Coanwood Friends Meeting House, Northumberland

Todmorden Unitarian Church, West Yorkshire

Walpole Independent Old Chapel, Suffolk

Historic Chapels Trust

An important story of dissent and faith.

HISTORIC CHAPELS TRUST

Historic Chapels Trust rescues non-Anglican places of worship in England that are no longer in use by their congregations. We aim to hand them on to future generations in good condition, as the physical record of religious life and a vital strand of our history.

Since 1993 we have rescued a remarkable collection of Nonconformist chapels, meeting houses and Catholic churches. Together, they are the evidence of a remarkable story of dissent from the Established Church and of self-determination and autonomy by people of faith, courage and social vision.

Historic Chapels Trust gratefully acknowledges financial support from Historic England.

Visit our chapels and churches

All our sites are Listed Grade II* or Grade I. Some are important for their architecture, some as rare survivals, some for their history, some for what the architectural historian John Summerson described as 'endearing simplicity'. All of them are worth visiting.

To visit our chapels and churches, please arrange a time with our local keyholders at the site first. Details of how to find the buildings and our keyholders are on our website.

Events in our chapels

Many of our chapels can be hired for concerts or other events. Some provide interesting venues for marriages or commemorative events. If you are interested in using one of our buildings look for details on our website.

Historic Chapels Trust

Society Building, 8 All Saints St, London N1 9RL
T. 020 7481 0533 & 07741 016832 E. chapels@hct.org.uk & vcooling@thecct.org.uk
W. hct.org.uk UK Registered charity no: 1017321

BLOOM
&WILD

hf holidays

VINTAGE

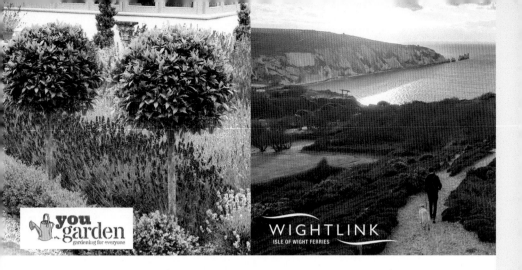

As a thank you for your support, we've teamed up with over 60 companies to provide discounts on a fantastic range of items, along with exclusive competitions, experiences and content. Whether you're looking for theatre tickets, home appliances, plants, wine, magazine subscriptions, clothing or holidays, you'll find an offer to help you save money.

Redeeming your rewards couldn't be easier. Simply visit the Members' Rewards section on our website and browse through the offers, which are grouped into food and drink, home and garden, family, travel, entertainment, lifestyle and outdoors. Then follow the instructions to claim your reward and start making great savings.

SUPPORT US AS YOU SAVE

There are so many benefits to shopping through Members' Rewards. In addition to giving you access to great money-saving deals that can be used to cover the cost of your membership, the revenue generated by these partnerships also helps to support our vital work to care for England's historic sites. This means you will be playing your part in helping us to make sure England's story survives to be enjoyed by future generations.

FIND OUT MORE

To see the full range of Members' Rewards on offer, visit **english-heritage.org.uk/rewards**

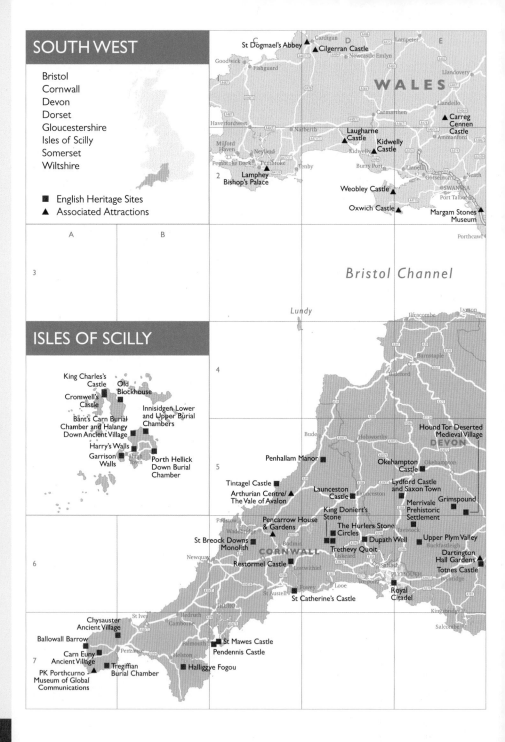

SOUTH WEST

Bristol
Cornwall
Devon
Dorset
Gloucestershire
Isles of Scilly
Somerset
Wiltshire

■ English Heritage Sites
▲ Associated Attractions

WALES

St Dogmael's Abbey ▲
▲ Cilgerran Castle
Cardigan
Lampeter
Goodwick
Fishguard
Newcastle Emlyn
Llandovery
Carmarthen
Llandeilo
▲ Carreg Cennen Castle
Haverfordwest
Narberth
Laugharne Castle ▲
Kidwelly Castle ■
Ammanford
Milford Haven
Neyland
Pembroke Dock
Pembroke
Tenby
Burry Port
Llanelli
Gorseinon
Neath
Lamphey Bishop's Palace ▲
Weobley Castle ▲
SWANSEA
Port Talbot
Oxwich Castle ▲
Margam Stones Museum
Porthcawl

Bristol Channel

Lundy
Ilfracombe
Lynton
Barnstaple
Bideford

Hound Tor Deserted Medieval Village ■
DEVON
Bude
Holsworthy
Penhallam Manor ■
Okehampton
Okehampton Castle ■
Lydford Castle and Saxon Town ■
Tintagel Castle ■
Arthurian Centre/ ▲ The Vale of Avalon
Launceston Castle ■
Merrivale Prehistoric Settlement ■
Grimspound ■
King Doniert's Stone ■
Pencarrow House & Gardens ▲
The Hurlers Stone Circles ■
Padstow
Wadebridge
St Breock Downs Monolith ■
CORNWALL
Bodmin
Dupath Well ■
Trethevy Quoit ■
Upper Plym Valley ■
Buckfastleigh
Newquay
Liskeard
Dartington Hall Gardens ▲
Restormel Castle ■
Lostwithiel
Saltash
Totnes Castle ■
PLYMOUTH
Ivybridge
St Austell
Fowey
Looe
Torpoint
Royal Citadel ■
St Catherine's Castle ■
Kingsbridge
Salcombe

ISLES OF SCILLY

King Charles's Castle ■
Old Blockhouse ■
Cromwell's Castle ■
Innisidgen Lower and Upper Burial Chambers ■
Bant's Carn Burial Chamber and Halangy Down Ancient Village ■
Harry's Walls ■
Garrison Walls ■
Hugh Town
Porth Hellick Down Burial Chamber ■

St Ives
Redruth
Camborne
Chysauster Ancient Village ■
Ballowall Barrow ■
Carn Euny Ancient Village ■
Penzance
Falmouth
Helston
St Mawes Castle ■
Pendennis Castle ■
PK Porthcurno Museum of Global Communications ▲
Tregiffian Burial Chamber ■
Halliggye Fogou ■
TRURO

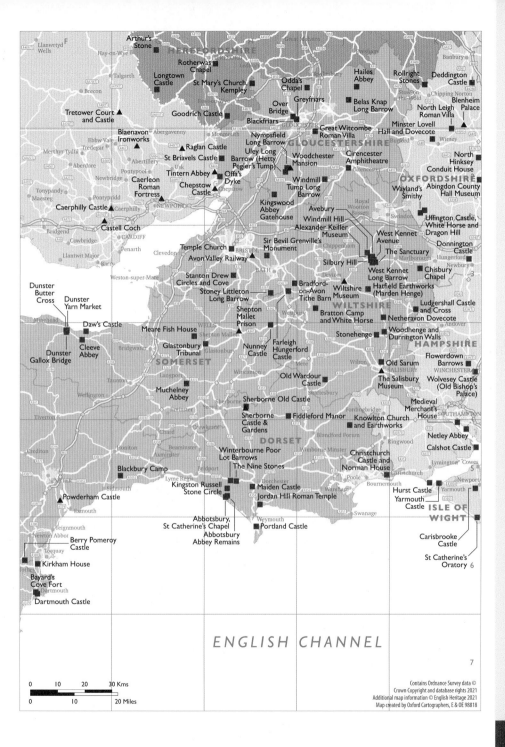

Llanwrtyd Wells
Hay-on-Wye
Arthur's Stone
Rotherwas Chapel
Longtown Castle
St Mary's Church, Kempley
Odda's Chapel
Hailes Abbey
Rollright Stones
Deddington Castle
Talgarth
Brecon
Over Bridge
Greyfriars
Belas Knap Long Barrow
North Leigh Roman Villa
Blenheim Palace
Banbury
Chipping Norton
Stow-on-the-Wold
Tretower Court and Castle
Goodrich Castle
Blackfriars
GLOUCESTER
Great Witcombe Roman Villa
Minster Lovell Hall and Dovecote
Witney
Blaenavon Ironworks
Abergavenny
Monmouth
Nympsfield Long Barrow
GLOUCESTERSHIRE
Ebbw Vale
Tredegar
Raglan Castle
Uley Long Barrow (Hetty Pegler's Tump)
Woodchester Mansion
Cirencester Amphitheatre
North Hinksey Conduit House
Merthyr Tydfil
Aberdare
Abertillery
St Briavels Castle
Windmill Tump Long Barrow
OXFORDSHIRE
Newbridge
Pontypool
Tintern Abbey
Offa's Dyke
Abingdon County Hall Museum
Tonypandy
Maesteg
Caerleon Roman Fortress
Chepstow Castle
Chepstow
Wayland's Smithy
Pontypridd
NEWPORT
Kingswood Abbey Gatehouse
Avebury
Uffington Castle, White Horse and Dragon Hill
Caerphilly Castle
Caerphilly
Windmill Hill
Alexander Keiller Museum
Swindon
Castell Coch
CARDIFF
West Kennet Avenue
Donnington Castle
Bridgend
Cowbridge
Sir Bevil Grenville's Monument
The Sanctuary
Newbury
Llantwit Major
Barry
Temple Church
BRISTOL
Silbury Hill
West Kennet Long Barrow
Chisbury Chapel
Weston-super-Mare
Avon Valley Railway
BATH
Stanton Drew Circles and Cove
Bradford-on-Avon
Wiltshire Museum
Hatfield Earthworks (Marden Henge)
Ludgershall Castle and Cross
Dunster Butter Cross
Dunster Yarn Market
Stoney Littleton Long Barrow
WILTSHIRE
Bratton Camp and White Horse
Netheravon Dovecote
Andover
Winehead
Daw's Castle
Shepton Mallet Prison
Stonehenge
Woodhenge and Durrington Walls
HAMPSHIRE
Meare Fish House
WELLS
Shepton Mallet
Dunster
Gallox Bridge
Cleeve Abbey
Glastonbury Tribunal
Bridgwater
Glastonbury
Nunney Castle
Farleigh Hungerford Castle
Old Sarum
SALISBURY
Flowerdown Barrows
WINCHESTER
SOMERSET
Wincanton
Mere
Wilton
The Salisbury Museum
Wolvesey Castle (Old Bishop's Palace)
Taunton
Langport
Old Wardour Castle
Muchelney Abbey
Sherborne
Shaftesbury
Medieval Merchant's House
SOUTHAMPTON
Wellington
Illminster
Sherborne Old Castle
Fordingbridge
Netley Abbey
Tiverton
Chard
Crewkerne
Sherborne Castle & Gardens
Fiddleford Manor
Knowlton Church and Earthworks
Blandford Forum
Calshot Castle
Crediton
Beaminster
Axminster
Bridport
Winterbourne Poor Lot Barrows
The Nine Stones
DORSET
Wimborne Minster
Christchurch Castle and Norman House
Ringwood
Netley Abbey
Cowes
Newport
EXETER
Honiton
Lyme Regis
Sidmouth
Blackbury Camp
Kingston Russell Stone Circle
Maiden Castle
Jordan Hill Roman Temple
Poole
Bournemouth
Christchurch
Wareham
Hurst Castle
Yarmouth
Yarmouth Castle
ISLE OF WIGHT
Powderham Castle
Exmouth
Abbotsbury, St Catherine's Chapel
Abbotsbury Abbey Remains
Weymouth
Portland Castle
Swanage
Carisbrooke Castle
Teignmouth
Newton Abbot
Berry Pomeroy Castle
St Catherine's Oratory
Torquay
Kirkham House
Bayard's Cove Fort
Dartmouth
Dartmouth Castle

ENGLISH CHANNEL

0   10   20   30 Kms
0   10   20 Miles

Contains Ordnance Survey data ©
Crown Copyright and database rights 2021
Additional map information © English Heritage 2021
Map created by Oxford Cartographers, E & OE 98818

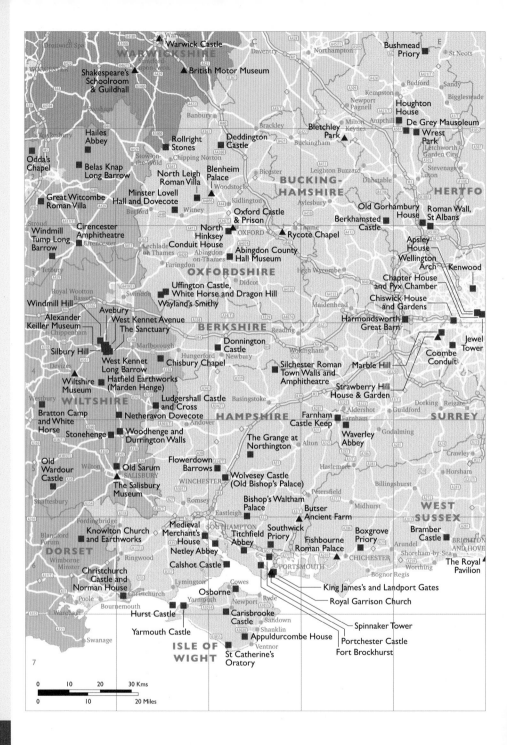

Warwick Castle
British Motor Museum
Shakespeare's Schoolroom & Guildhall
Hailes Abbey
Odda's Chapel
Belas Knap Long Barrow
Rollright Stones
Deddington Castle
Bushmead Priory
Houghton House
De Grey Mausoleum
Wrest Park
North Leigh Roman Villa
Blenheim Palace
BUCKING-HAMSHIRE
HERTFO
Great Witcombe Roman Villa
Minster Lovell Hall and Dovecote
Oxford Castle & Prison
Old Gorhambury House
Roman Wall, St Albans
Berkhamsted Castle
Windmill Tump Long Barrow
Cirencester Amphitheatre
North Hinksey Conduit House
OXFORD
Rycote Chapel
Apsley House
Wellington Arch
Kenwood
Lechlade on Thames
Abingdon County Hall Museum
Chapter House and Pyx Chamber
OXFORDSHIRE
Chiswick House and Gardens
Uffington Castle, White Horse and Dragon Hill
Wayland's Smithy
Harmondsworth Great Barn
Windmill Hill
Avebury
West Kennet Avenue
The Sanctuary
BERKSHIRE
Jewel Tower
Alexander Keiller Museum
Donnington Castle
Coombe Conduit
Silbury Hill
West Kennet Long Barrow
Chisbury Chapel
Silchester Roman Town Walls and Amphitheatre
Marble Hill
Strawberry Hill House & Garden
SURREY
Wiltshire Museum
Hatfield Earthworks (Marden Henge)
Ludgershall Castle and Cross
HAMPSHIRE
Farnham Castle Keep
Waverley Abbey
WILTSHIRE
Bratton Camp and White Horse
Netheravon Dovecote
The Grange at Northington
Stonehenge
Woodhenge and Durrington Walls
Flowerdown Barrows
Old Wardour Castle
Old Sarum
Wolvesey Castle (Old Bishop's Palace)
WINCHESTER
The Salisbury Museum
Bishop's Waltham Palace
Butser Ancient Farm
WEST SUSSEX
Knowlton Church and Earthworks
Medieval Merchant's House
Titchfield Abbey
Southwick Priory
Boxgrove Priory
Bramber Castle
DORSET
Netley Abbey
Fishbourne Roman Palace
BRIGHTON AND HOVE
Christchurch Castle and Norman House
Calshot Castle
PORTSMOUTH
CHICHESTER
The Royal Pavilion
Osborne
King James's and Landport Gates
Royal Garrison Church
Hurst Castle
Carisbrooke Castle
Spinnaker Tower
Yarmouth Castle
Appuldurcombe House
Portchester Castle
Fort Brockhurst
ISLE OF WIGHT
St Catherine's Oratory

0   10   20   30 Kms
0   10   20 Miles

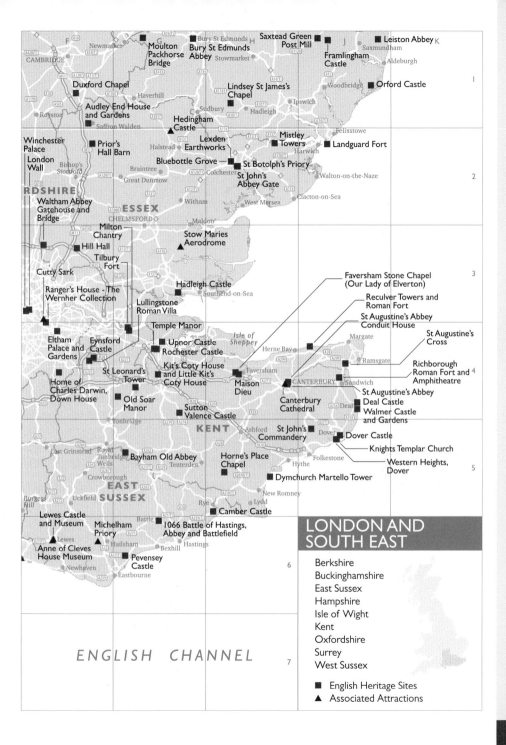

F · Newmarket · (A10)
CAMBRIDGE
Moulton Packhorse Bridge
G · Bury St Edmunds H
Bury St Edmunds Abbey · Stowmarket
Saxtead Green Post Mill
J · Saxmundham
Leiston Abbey K
Framlingham Castle
Aldeburgh

Duxford Chapel
Haverhill

Lindsey St James's Chapel
Woodbridge · Orford Castle

I

Audley End House and Gardens
Royston
Saffron Walden

Sudbury · Hadleigh
Ipswich

Hedingham Castle

Felixstowe

Winchester Palace
London Wall
Prior's Hall Barn
Bishop's Stortford
Lexden Earthworks
Halstead
Mistley Towers
Harwich
Landguard Fort

Bluebottle Grove
Braintree
Colchester
St Botolph's Priory
St John's Abbey Gate
Walton-on-the-Naze

2

Great Dunmow

West Mersea
Clacton-on-Sea

RDSHIRE
Waltham Abbey Gatehouse and Bridge
ESSEX
CHELMSFORD
Witham
Maldon

Milton Chantry
Hill Hall
Tilbury Fort
Stow Maries Aerodrome

3

Cutty Sark

Ranger's House - The Wernher Collection
Hadleigh Castle
Southend-on-Sea

Faversham Stone Chapel (Our Lady of Elverton)

Reculver Towers and Roman Fort

Lullingstone Roman Villa

St Augustine's Abbey Conduit House

Temple Manor
Isle of Sheppey

St Augustine's Cross

Eltham Palace and Gardens
Eynsford Castle
Upnor Castle
Rochester Castle
Herne Bay
Margate

Ramsgate

Richborough Roman Fort and Amphitheatre

4

St Leonard's Tower
Home of Charles Darwin, Down House
Kit's Coty House and Little Kit's Coty House
Faversham
Maison Dieu
CANTERBURY · Sandwich
St Augustine's Abbey

Old Soar Manor
Sutton Valence Castle
KENT
Canterbury Cathedral
Deal
Deal Castle
Walmer Castle and Gardens

tonbridge
Ashford
St John's Commandery
Dover
Dover Castle

East Grinstead
Royal Tunbridge Wells
Bayham Old Abbey
Tenterden
Horne's Place Chapel
Hythe
Folkestone
Knights Templar Church

Western Heights, Dover

5

Crowborough

Dymchurch Martello Tower

EAST
Uckfield SUSSEX
New Romney

Burgess Hill

Rye
Lydd
Camber Castle

Lewes Castle and Museum
Battle
Michelham Priory
1066 Battle of Hastings, Abbey and Battlefield

Lewes
Hailsham
Hastings

Anne of Cleves House Museum
Newhaven
Pevensey Castle
Bexhill
Eastbourne

6

ENGLISH CHANNEL

7

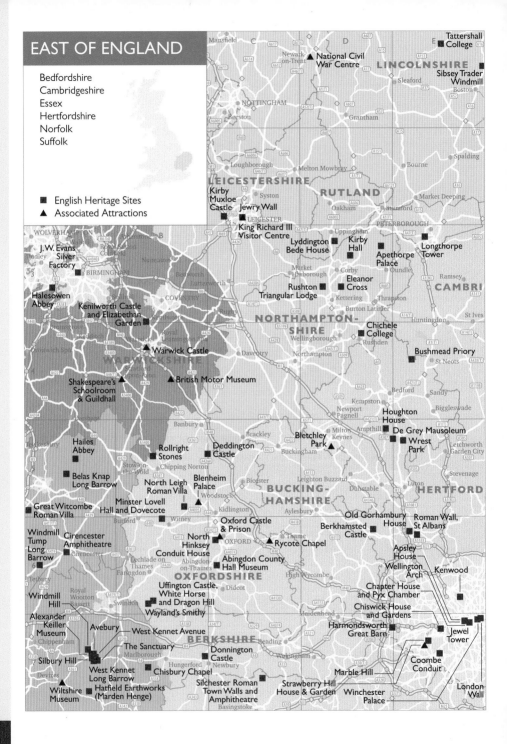

EAST OF ENGLAND

Bedfordshire
Cambridgeshire
Essex
Hertfordshire
Norfolk
Suffolk

■ English Heritage Sites
▲ Associated Attractions

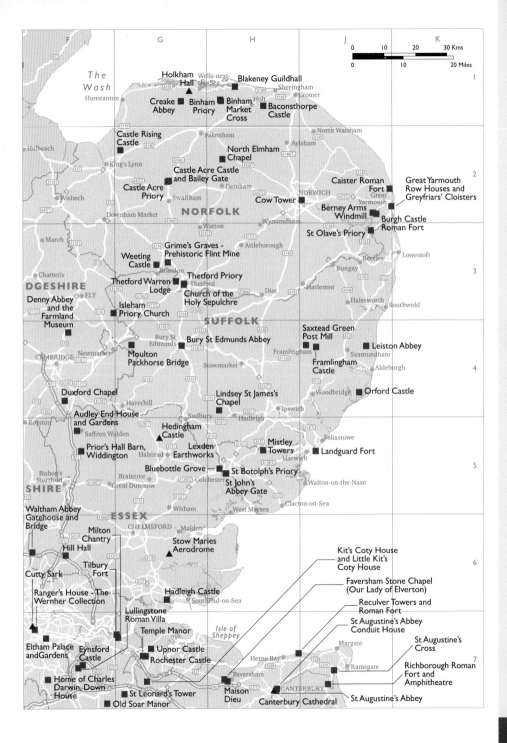

The Wash

Holkham Hall

Wells-next-the-Sea

Blakeney Guildhall

Sheringham

Cromer

Hunstanton

Holt

Creake Abbey

Binham Priory

Binham Market Cross

Baconsthorpe Castle

Holbeach

Castle Rising Castle

Fakenham

North Walsham

Aylsham

King's Lynn

North Elmham Chapel

Wisbech

Castle Acre Castle and Bailey Gate

Castle Acre Priory

Dereham

NORWICH

Caister Roman Fort

Great Yarmouth Row Houses and Greyfriars' Cloisters

Downham Market

Swaffham

Cow Tower

Great Yarmouth

Berney Arms Windmill

Burgh Castle Roman Fort

NORFOLK

Watton

Wymondham

March

St Olave's Priory

Lowestoft

Grime's Graves - Prehistoric Flint Mine

Attleborough

Beccles

Chatteris

Weeting Castle

Brandon

Bungay

Harleston

CAMBRIDGESHIRE

DENY Abbey and the Farmland Museum

Thetford Warren Lodge

Thetford Priory

Thetford

Diss

Halesworth

Southwold

Isleham Priory Church

Church of the Holy Sepulchre

SUFFOLK

Newmarket

Bury St Edmunds

Bury St Edmunds Abbey

Saxtead Green Post Mill

Leiston Abbey

CAMBRIDGE

Moulton Packhorse Bridge

Stowmarket

Framlingham

Saxmundham

Framlingham Castle

Aldeburgh

Duxford Chapel

Haverhill

Lindsey St James's Chapel

Woodbridge

Orford Castle

Ipswich

Royston

Audley End House and Gardens

Sudbury

Hadleigh

Saffron Walden

Hedingham Castle

Prior's Hall Barn, Widdington

Halstead

Lexden Earthworks

Felixstowe

Bishop's Stortford

Bluebottle Grove

Mistley Towers

Landguard Fort

Harwich

St Botolph's Priory

Braintree

Colchester

St John's Abbey Gate

Walton-on-the-Naze

Great Dunmow

Witham

West Mersea

Clacton-on-Sea

ESSEX

CHELMSFORD

Maldon

Waltham Abbey Gatehouse and Bridge

Milton Chantry

Hill Hall

Stow Maries Aerodrome

Tilbury Fort

Kit's Coty House and Little Kit's Coty House

Cutty Sark

Faversham Stone Chapel (Our Lady of Elverton)

Ranger's House - The Wernher Collection

Hadleigh Castle

Southend-on-Sea

Reculver Towers and Roman Fort

St Augustine's Abbey Conduit House

Lullingstone Roman Villa

Isle of Sheppey

Temple Manor

Margate

St Augustine's Cross

Eltham Palace and Gardens

Eynsford Castle

Upnor Castle

Rochester Castle

Herne Bay

Ramsgate

Richborough Roman Fort and Amphitheatre

Home of Charles Darwin, Down House

Faversham

CANTERBURY

St Leonard's Tower

Old Soar Manor

Maison Dieu

Canterbury Cathedral

St Augustine's Abbey

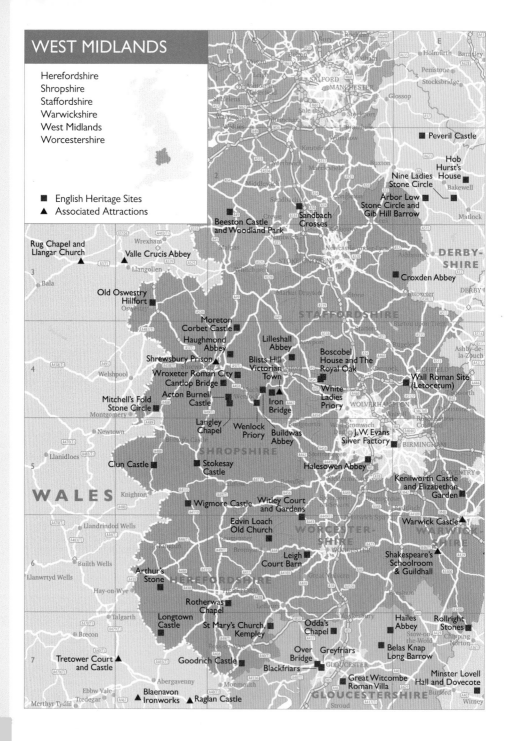

WEST MIDLANDS

Herefordshire
Shropshire
Staffordshire
Warwickshire
West Midlands
Worcestershire

■ English Heritage Sites
▲ Associated Attractions

Peveril Castle

Hob Hurst's House

Nine Ladies Stone Circle

Arbor Low Stone Circle and Gib Hill Barrow

Bakewell

Matlock

DERBY-SHIRE

DERBY

Croxden Abbey

Sandbach Crosses

Beeston Castle and Woodland Park

Rug Chapel and Llangar Church

Valle Crucis Abbey

Old Oswestry Hillfort

STAFFORDSHIRE

Moreton Corbet Castle

Haughmond Abbey

Lilleshall Abbey

Boscobel House and The Royal Oak

Shrewsbury Prison

Blists Hill Victorian Town

Wall Roman Site (Letocetum)

Wroxeter Roman City

Cantlop Bridge

Acton Burnell Castle

White Ladies Priory

Mitchell's Fold Stone Circle

Iron Bridge

WOLVERHAMPTON

Langley Chapel

Wenlock Priory

Buildwas Abbey

J.W. Evans Silver Factory

BIRMINGHAM

SHROPSHIRE

Clun Castle

Stokesay Castle

Halesowen Abbey

Kenilworth Castle and Elizabethan Garden

WALES

Wigmore Castle

Witley Court and Gardens

Warwick Castle

WARWICK-SHIRE

Edvin Loach Old Church

WORCESTER-SHIRE

Shakespeare's Schoolroom & Guildhall

Leigh Court Barn

Arthur's Stone

HEREFORDSHIRE

Rotherwas Chapel

Hailes Abbey

Rollright Stones

Longtown Castle

St Mary's Church, Kempley

Odda's Chapel

Belas Knap Long Barrow

Tretower Court and Castle

Goodrich Castle

Over Bridge

Greyfriars

Blackfriars

GLOUCESTER

Minster Lovell Hall and Dovecote

Blaenavon Ironworks

Raglan Castle

Great Witcombe Roman Villa

GLOUCESTERSHIRE

EAST MIDLANDS

Derbyshire
Leicestershire
Lincolnshire
Northamptonshire
Nottinghamshire
Rutland

■ English Heritage Sites
▲ Associated Attractions

Map labels:

Monk Bretton Priory
Adwick le Street
Scunthorpe
Grimsby
Cleethorpes
Brodsworth Hall and Gardens
Doncaster
NORTH EAST LINCOLNSHIRE
Brigg
Swinton
Conisbrough Castle
Gainsthorpe Medieval Village
Rotherham
Roche Abbey
Gainsborough
Market Rasen
SHEFFIELD
Mattersey Priory
Gainsborough Old Hall
Louth
Mablethorpe
Sutton Scarsdale Hall
Bolsover Cundy House
Worksop
Retford
NORTH SEA
Staveley
LINCOLN
Alford
Bolsover
Bolsover Castle
Rufford Abbey
Lincoln Medieval Bishops' Palace
Horncastle
Spilsby
Skegness
Mansfield
North Hykeham
Woodhall Spa
Bolingbroke Castle
Hardwick Old Hall
NOTTINGHAM-SHIRE
Tattershall College
Wingfield Manor
Newark-on-Trent
National Civil War Centre
LINCOLNSHIRE
Sibsey Trader Windmill
Ilkeston
Sleaford
The Wash
Beeston
NOTTINGHAM
Grantham
Boston
Hunstanton
Spalding
Holbeach
Castle Rising Castle
Ashby de la Zouch Castle
Loughborough
Melton Mowbray
Bourne
King's Lynn
Coalville
LEICESTERSHIRE
RUTLAND
Market Deeping
Wisbech
Downham Market
Syston
Oakham
Stamford
Jewry Wall
Kirby Muxloe Castle
LEICESTER
King Richard III Visitor Centre
Longthorpe Tower
PETERBOROUGH
March
Lyddington Bede House
Uppingham
Apethorpe Palace
Weeting Castle
Brandon
Kirby Hall
Market Harborough
Corby
Oundle
Ramsey
Chatteris
Rushton Triangular Lodge
Eleanor Cross
Kettering
Thrapston
CAMBRIDGESHIRE
Denny Abbey and the Farmland Museum
ELY
Isleham Priory Church
Burton Latimer
Huntingdon
St Ives
NORTHAMPTON-SHIRE
Chichele College
Wellingborough
Rushden
Daventry
Northampton
Bushmead Priory
St Neots
British Motor Museum
BEDFORD
Bedford
Sangy
Houghton House
Biggleswade
Newport Pagnell
Banbury
Brackley
Ampthill
De Grey Mausoleum
Bletchley Park
Milton Keynes
Wrest Park
Deddington Castle
Buckingham
Leighton Buzzard
North Leigh Roman Villa
Blenheim Palace
Bicester
Roman Wall, St Albans
BUCKING-HAMSHIRE
Woodstock
Kidlington
Aylesbury
Dunstable
Luton
Oxford Castle & Prison
Berkhamsted Castle
Old Gorhambury House
OXFORD
Thame
Berkhamsted
ST ALBANS

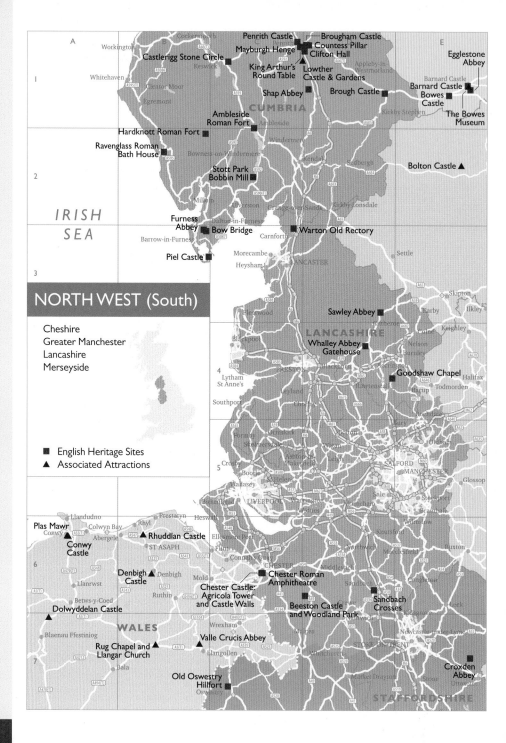

NORTH WEST (South)

Cheshire
Greater Manchester
Lancashire
Merseyside

■ English Heritage Sites
▲ Associated Attractions

A Workington
B Whitehaven
Cockermouth
Penrith Castle
Mayburgh Henge
Brougham Castle
Countess Pillar
Clifton Hall
E Egglestone Abbey
Castlerigg Stone Circle
Keswick
King Arthur's Round Table
Lowther Castle & Gardens
Shap Abbey
Brough Castle
Barnard Castle
Bowes Castle
The Bowes Museum
Cleator Moor
Egremont
CUMBRIA
Ambleside Roman Fort
Ambleside
Hardknott Roman Fort
Ravenglass Roman Bath House
Windermere
Bowness-on-Windermere
Kendal
Sedbergh
Bolton Castle ▲
Stott Park Bobbin Mill
Millom
Overston
Grange-over-Sands
Kirkby Lonsdale

IRISH SEA

Furness Abbey
Bow Bridge
Dalton-in-Furness
Carnforth
Warton Old Rectory
Barrow-in-Furness
Piel Castle
Morecambe
Heysham
LANCASTER
Settle
Skipton

Fleetwood
Sawley Abbey
Earby
Ilkley
Blackpool
LANCASHIRE
Whalley Abbey Gatehouse
Colne
Keighley
Nelson
Burnley
Goodshaw Chapel
Halifax
Lytham St Anne's
PRESTON
Blackburn
Accrington
Rawtenstall
Bacup
Todmorden
Southport
Leyland
Chorley
Rochdale

Ormskirk
Skelmersdale
Bolton
Bury
Oldham
Formby
Wigan
Leigh
SALFORD
MANCHESTER
Crosby
Ashton-in-Makerfield
Glossop
Bootle
St Helens
Sale
Stockport
Wallasey
Birkenhead
LIVERPOOL
Warrington
Widnes
Bramhall

Llandudno
Prestatyn
Heswall
Plas Mawr
Conwy
Colwyn Bay
Rhyl
Abergele
Rhuddlan Castle ▲
Ellesmere Port
Flint
Knutsford
Wilmslow
Conwy Castle
ST ASAPH
Connah's Quay
CHESTER
Northwich
Macclesfield
Buxton
Llanrwst
Denbigh Castle ▲
Denbigh
Mold
Chester Roman Amphitheatre
Middlewich
Sandbach
Congleton
Betws-y-Coed
Ruthin
Chester Castle: Agricola Tower and Castle Walls
Beeston Castle and Woodland Park
Sandbach Crosses
Dolwyddelan Castle
Nantwich
Leek
Blaenau Ffestiniog
Wrexham
Valle Crucis Abbey
WALES
Rug Chapel and Llangar Church
Llangollen
Whitchurch
Crewe
Newcastle-under-Lyme
STOKE-ON-TRENT
Croxden Abbey
Bala
Old Oswestry Hillfort
Oswestry
Market Drayton
Stone
Uttoxeter
STAFFORDSHIRE

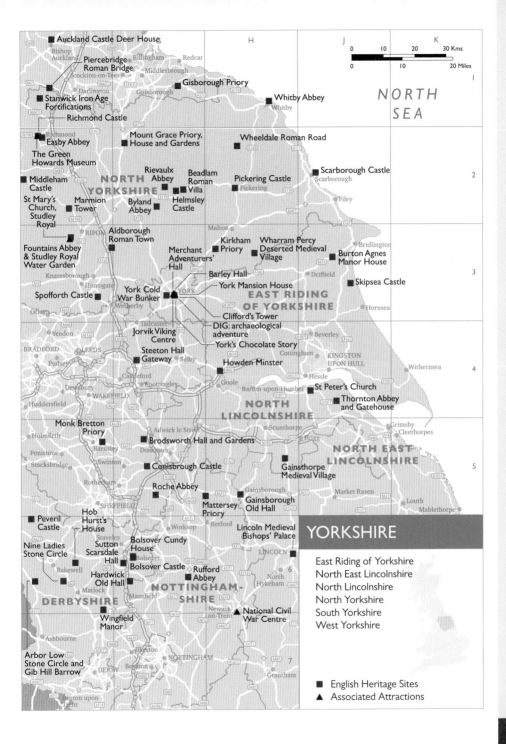

Auckland Castle Deer House
Bishop
Auckland
Piercebridge
Roman Bridge
Stockton-on-Tees
Billingham
Redcar
Middlesbrough
Darlington
Guisborough
Gisborough Priory
Stanwick Iron Age
Fortifications
Whitby Abbey
Whitby

NORTH
SEA

Richmond Castle
Richmond
Easby Abbey
The Green
Howards Museum
Mount Grace Priory,
House and Gardens
Wheeldale Roman Road

Middleham
Castle
NORTH
YORKSHIRE
Rievaulx
Abbey
Beadlam
Roman
Villa
Pickering Castle
Pickering
Scarborough Castle
Scarborough

2

St Mary's
Church,
Studley
Royal
Marmion
Tower
Byland
Abbey
Helmsley
Castle
Filey

RIPON
Aldborough
Roman Town
Malton

Fountains Abbey
& Studley Royal
Water Garden
Knaresborough
Merchant
Adventurers'
Hall
Kirkham
Priory
Wharram Percy
Deserted Medieval
Village
Bridlington
Burton Agnes
Manor House

3

Harrogate
Barley Hall
Driffield
Skipsea Castle

Spofforth Castle
York Cold
War Bunker
YORK
York Mansion House
EAST RIDING
OF YORKSHIRE
Hornsea

Otley
Wetherby
Clifford's Tower
DIG: archaeological
adventure
Beverley

Yeadon
Tadcaster
Jorvik Viking
Centre
York's Chocolate Story
Cottingham
KINGSTON
UPON HULL
Withernsea

BRADFORD
LEEDS
Steeton Hall
Gateway
Selby
Howden Minster
Hessle

Pudsey
Castleford
Knottingley
Goole
Barton-upon-Humber
St Peter's Church

Dewsbury
WAKEFIELD
NORTH
LINCOLNSHIRE
Thornton Abbey
and Gatehouse

Huddersfield
Grimsby
Cleethorpes

Monk Bretton
Priory
Adwick le Street
Scunthorpe
Brigg

Holmfirth
Barnsley
Brodsworth Hall and Gardens
NORTH EAST
LINCOLNSHIRE

5

Penistone
Swinton
Doncaster

Stocksbridge
Rotherham
Conisbrough Castle
Gainsthorpe
Medieval Village
Market Rasen
Louth

Roche Abbey
Gainsborough
Mablethorpe

SHEFFIELD
Mattersey
Priory
Gainsborough
Old Hall

Peveril
Castle
Hob
Hurst's
House
Worksop
Retford
Lincoln Medieval
Bishops' Palace
YORKSHIRE

Nine Ladies
Stone Circle
Staveley
Sutton
Scarsdale
Hall
Bolsover Cundy
House
Bolsover
LINCOLN
East Riding of Yorkshire

Bakewell
Bolsover Castle
Rufford
Abbey
North
Hykeham
6
North East Lincolnshire
North Lincolnshire

Hardwick
Old Hall
Matlock
NOTTINGHAM-
SHIRE
North Yorkshire
South Yorkshire

DERBYSHIRE
Mansfield
West Yorkshire

Wingfield
Manor
Newark-
on-Trent
National Civil
War Centre

Ashbourne
Ilkeston

Arbor Low
Stone Circle and
Gib Hill Barrow
NOTTINGHAM
Beeston
Grantham

DERBY

Burton upon
Trent

■ English Heritage Sites
▲ Associated Attractions

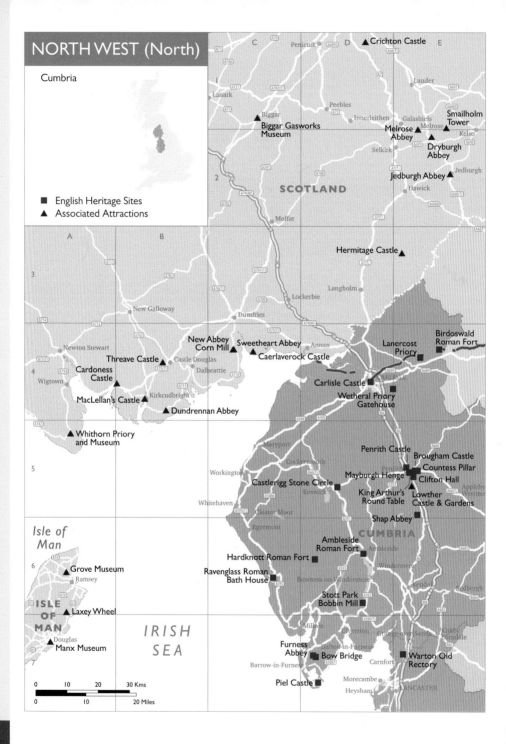

NORTH WEST (North)

Cumbria

■ English Heritage Sites
▲ Associated Attractions

SCOTLAND

Penicuik
▲ Crichton Castle
Lauder
Lanark
Biggar
▲ Biggar Gasworks Museum
Peebles
Innerleithen
Galashiels
Melrose ▲ Melrose
Melrose Abbey
Selkirk
▲ Smailholm Tower
Kelso
Dryburgh Abbey
Jedburgh Abbey ▲
Jedburgh
Hawick
Moffat

Hermitage Castle ▲

New Galloway
Lockerbie
Langholm
Dumfries
Annan

Newton Stewart
Threave Castle ▲
Cardoness Castle ▲
Castle Douglas
Dalbeattie
Kirkcudbright
Wigtown
MacLellan's Castle ▲
▲ Dundrennan Abbey
New Abbey Corn Mill ▲
Sweetheart Abbey ▲
Caerlaverock Castle ▲
Birdoswald Roman Fort ■
Lanercost Priory ■
Carlisle Castle ■
CARLISLE
Wetheral Priory Gatehouse ■

▲ Whithorn Priory and Museum

Maryport
Cockermouth
Workington
Keswick
Whitehaven
Cleator Moor
Egremont

Penrith Castle ■
Mayburgh Henge ■
Penrith
King Arthur's Round Table ■
Castlerigg Stone Circle ■
Shap Abbey ■
Brougham Castle ■
Countess Pillar ■
Clifton Hall ■
Lowther Castle & Gardens ▲
Appleby Westmo

Ambleside Roman Fort ■
Hardknott Roman Fort ■
Ravenglass Roman Bath House ■
Ambleside
Windermere
Bowness-on-Windermere
Kendal
Sedbergh

Isle of Man

▲ Grove Museum
Ramsey

ISLE OF MAN

▲ Laxey Wheel

Douglas
Manx Museum ▲

Stott Park Bobbin Mill ■
Millom
Ulverston
Dalton-in-Furness
Furness Abbey ■
Bow Bridge ■
Carnforth
Warton Old Rectory ■
Barrow-in-Furness
Piel Castle ■
Grange-over-Sands
Kirkby Lonsdale
Morecambe
Heysham
LANCASTER

IRISH SEA

0   10   20   30 Kms
0   10   20 Miles

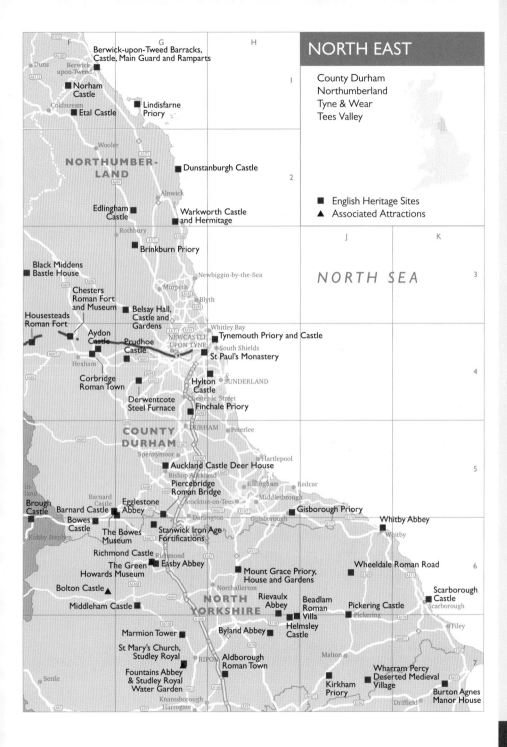

NORTH EAST

County Durham
Northumberland
Tyne & Wear
Tees Valley

■ English Heritage Sites
▲ Associated Attractions

NORTH SEA

Berwick-upon-Tweed Barracks, Castle, Main Guard and Ramparts

Duns
Berwick-upon-Tweed

■ Norham Castle

Coldstream
■ Etal Castle
■ Lindisfarne Priory

Wooler

NORTHUMBER-LAND

■ Dunstanburgh Castle

Alnwick

Edlingham Castle
■ Warkworth Castle and Hermitage

Rothbury
■ Brinkburn Priory

Black Middens
■ Bastle House

Newbiggin-by-the-Sea

Chesters Roman Fort and Museum
Morpeth

Housesteads Roman Fort
■ Belsay Hall, Castle and Gardens
Blyth

Whitley Bay

Aydon Castle
Prudhoe Castle
NEWCASTLE UPON TYNE
■ Tynemouth Priory and Castle
South Shields
■ St Paul's Monastery

Hexham

Corbridge Roman Town
■ Hylton Castle
SUNDERLAND
Chester-le-Street
■ Finchale Priory

Derwentcote Steel Furnace

COUNTY DURHAM
DURHAM
Peterlee

Spennymoor
Hartlepool

■ Auckland Castle Deer House
Bishop Auckland
■ Piercebridge Roman Bridge
Billingham
Redcar

Brough Castle
Barnard Castle
Egglestone Abbey
Stockton-on-Tees
Middlesbrough

■ Barnard Castle
Darlington
Guisborough
■ Gisborough Priory

Bowes Castle
Stanwick Iron Age Fortifications
■ Whitby Abbey

Kirkby Stephen
The Bowes Museum
Whitby

Richmond Castle
Richmond
■ Easby Abbey

The Green Howards Museum
■ Wheeldale Roman Road

Bolton Castle ▲
Northallerton
■ Mount Grace Priory, House and Gardens

Scarborough Castle

Middleham Castle
NORTH YORKSHIRE
Rievaulx Abbey
Beadlam Roman Villa
Pickering Castle
Scarborough

Marmion Tower
Byland Abbey
Helmsley Castle
Pickering
Filey

St Mary's Church, Studley Royal
Aldborough Roman Town
Malton

Fountains Abbey & Studley Royal Water Garden
RIPON
Kirkham Priory
■ Wharram Percy Deserted Medieval Village

Settle
Knaresborough
Harrogate
Driffield
Burton Agnes Manor House

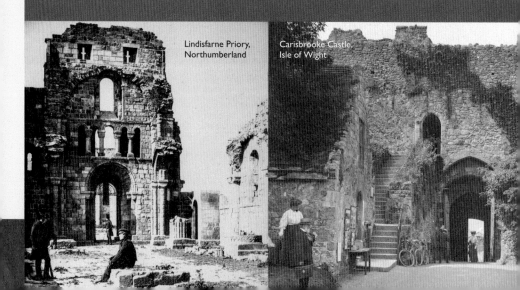

Stonehenge, Wiltshire

The history of
English Heritage

The extraordinary collection of buildings and monuments now in the care of English Heritage has its origins in the Ancient Monuments Protection Act of 1882, which brought dozens of monuments under the guardianship of the government.

Lindisfarne Priory,
Northumberland

Carisbrooke Castle,
Isle of Wight

Dover Castle, Kent

Eltham Palace, Greenwich

In 1913 an Act of Parliament was passed that gave the Office of Works new powers to schedule ancient monuments and create a collection of the most important buildings and sites. These were mostly prehistoric, Roman and medieval remains – at that time, country houses and industrial sites were not really regarded as heritage.

By 1933 there were 273 sites in the collection including **Stonehenge**, **Rievaulx Abbey**, **Carisbrooke Castle** and **Richborough Roman Fort**. The primary objective was of course conservation, but telling their stories was almost as important. All were open to the public and had guidebooks and explanatory signs. Some also sold postcards and even had tearooms.

After the Second World War the Ministry of Works (as the Office had become) started to collect industrial sites, and in 1949 it acquired its first country house, **Audley End** in Essex. The Ministry had its sights set on a number of other big houses, but the Treasury was nervous about the cost. After some debate, it was decided that the National Trust would take on country houses, and the Ministry would confine itself to older monuments.

This ruling did not stop the Ministry collecting. By 1970 there were 300 sites in England alone. Millions visited each year, making it by far the largest visitor attraction organisation in the country. Many of the sites now had museums and gift shops.

In 1983, the English collection was transferred to a new body called the Historic Buildings and Monuments Commission – soon re-christened English Heritage by its first chairman, Lord Montagu. It had two principal tasks. Firstly, it cared for the National Heritage Collection, and secondly, it ran the national system of heritage protection, including listing buildings, dealing with planning issues and giving grants.

In the following years, the collection became better run and more imaginatively displayed. The membership scheme was launched, and more buildings were acquired, including country houses like **Brodsworth Hall**. Membership grew, visitor numbers increased, and more people enjoyed the collections than ever before.

In 2015, the government agreed to separate English Heritage into two parts. English Heritage became a charity that looks after the collection and opens it to the public, and a government agency, Historic England, was created to champion the nation's wider heritage by running the listing system, dealing with planning matters and giving grants.

Since becoming a charity, English Heritage has brought the past to life for more people than ever before, attracting record numbers of visitors and more than a million Members. It has also carried out the largest conservation programme in its history and opened new exhibitions and experiences, including the award-winning footbridge at **Tintagel Castle**.

Brodsworth Hall and Gardens, South Yorkshire

Kenwood, Hampstead

Our global roots

England's history has been shaped by people from all over the world. The extraordinary time span of English Heritage sites gives us a unique perspective on the contribution to our culture and society of immigrants, traders, missionaries and invaders, and of our colonial past.

Hadrian's Wall

Abdul Karim
Royal Collection Trust
© Her Majesty
Queen Elizabeth II 2020

In prehistoric times transformational ideas about the building of great communal monuments like **West Kennet Long Barrow** (p.136) were introduced by settlers from mainland Europe. Another great monument – **Hadrian's Wall** (p.266) – was built and garrisoned by military units from throughout the Roman Empire, including Dacia (now Romania) and North Africa. Construction of the Wall began 1900 years ago; we'll be marking the anniversary with a spectacular new outdoor artwork and a packed programme of events. Roman forces had first arrived at **Richborough** (p.75) in AD 43. As the main entry point from mainland Europe, the site developed from a military supply base into a thriving port town and later a massive fort. This season we'll be telling its story in a new exhibition.

After the end of Roman rule, connections with the wider world were maintained. Excavations of the early medieval settlement at **Tintagel** (p.110) revealed North African oil jars, Spanish glassware and ceramics from Greece and Asia Minor.

The consolidation of Christianity as Britain's pre-eminent religion was led by Augustine, a monk from Rome. Hadrian, the 7th-century abbot of **St Augustine's Abbey** (p.79), Canterbury, who helped develop the Anglo-Saxon Church into an intellectual powerhouse, was born in North Africa. From the 5th to the 11th centuries Germanic peoples and Scandinavian Vikings settled here. And in 1066, of course, the Normans arrived, establishing their own lasting imprint on England's architecture and society.

From the 14th century trading networks spread across the globe, bringing new goods to English consumers such as silk and cotton, coffee, spices and sugar (in the late 14th century, the household at **Framlingham Castle** (p.172) consumed ginger, cinnamon, cloves, saffron and almonds, as well as quantities of French wine). But England's colonial success was partly built on the transatlantic slave trade. Between 1640 and 1807 Britain transported around 3 million enslaved Africans to its colonies in the Caribbean and Americas. At least 26 of our sites were linked to this economy, through plantation ownership, banking, commerce, industry or colonial administration. A new exhibition at **Brodsworth Hall** (p.246) explores these connections, with sculptures by carnival artist Carl Gabriel and award-winning poet Malika Booker.

Africans appeared in Britain from as early as the 3rd century AD as traders and soldiers; a lead figurine of a Black African warrior can be seen at **Wall Roman Site** (p.211), a staging post for Roman officials travelling on business. But the slave trade increased the proportion of Africans in England. Some aristocrats had Black servants like James Chappell at **Kirby Hall** (p.190). Dido Belle, the illegitimate daughter of a young Black woman and a Royal Naval officer was – more unusually – brought up by her great-uncle William Murray as part of his family at **Kenwood** (p.42). Many Black sailors served in Britain's Navy, and during conflict some prisoners of war were also Black, such as the French Caribbean soldiers incarcerated at **Portchester Castle** (p.62).

Britain's colonial interests lay not only across the Atlantic but also in India, Southeast Asia and the Pacific. Britain's empire expanded dramatically during Queen Victoria's reign. Although she did not travel beyond Ireland, she had 'a longing' to visit India. She commissioned portraits of people from a wide cross-section of Indian society, ages and occupations. This unique and extensive collection, painted by Rudolf Swoboda, is on display at **Osborne** (p.92). It includes a painting of Abdul Karim, a 24-year-old Muslim who taught the queen Hindi.

In London our colonial history may be traced through the statues, monuments (p.52) and blue plaques (p.50) in our care, from Christopher Columbus and Walter Ralegh to Robert Clive and General Gordon. These public memorials were erected when their subjects were viewed only as models of heroism, with little attention given to the lives of those under imperial rule.

Robert Clive and his officials, for example, plundered Bengal for profit and exacerbated a terrible famine through oppressive and inflexible policies. We are committed to telling the stories of those already commemorated in full; you can find out more on our website.

Our continuing research into the complex links between our sites, monuments and the wider world helps reveal the depth of connections that people in the past had with one another, and the multiplicity of people, cultures and ideas that have contributed to England's story. In some cases this may include confronting some painful truths about past actions. But by doing so we can learn more about our shared history – and its impact on our lives today.

Rievaulx Abbey, North Yorkshire

LGBTQ+ connections

The stories of LGBTQ+ people are entwined with the stories of our sites, and we're committed to exploring them as fully as possible. In this short piece we look at some of these stories, and explore why using modern labels can be restrictive when talking about people in the past.

Georgiana, Duchess of Devonshire (Courtesy National Gallery of Art, Washington)

Seely and Paget, who transformed Eltham Palace from Tudor palace to art deco mansion, referred to themselves as 'partners'. © Templewood Estate

We're proud that in 2021 the Queer Heritage and Collections Network – of which English Heritage is a founding partner – was recognised in the annual Museums + Heritage Awards.

For centuries many individuals have lived in ways which are different from accepted norms, but their stories are often hidden from view. The expression of same-sex love or gender nonconformity was often constrained by social attitudes, religious considerations or persecution under the laws of the time. This can limit our understanding of the true diversity of sexuality and gender in the history of England.

The terms we use today to describe a range of sexualities and gender identities – such as lesbian, gay, bisexual, transgender and queer – are comparatively recent inventions. For the most part, we don't know how people in the past would have described their sexuality or gender. We use the short form LGBTQ+ because we believe it comes closest to capturing the breadth of experiences and identities for those whose sexualities didn't fit within social norms.

In 1134, a young man called Aelred became a monk at **Rievaulx Abbey** (p.238) in Yorkshire. A talented author, theologian, preacher and diplomat, Aelred rose to become a loving and inspirational abbot. Some historians and theologians have found evidence in Aelred's writings to suggest that he was attracted to other men, although all the evidence indicates that he strictly adhered to his vow of chastity and abhorred any form of sexual contact between monks. LGBTQ+ Christians find inspiration in Aelred's writings, holding the saint in special esteem. Debate about his sexuality continues. You can learn more about Aelred in our exhibition at Rievaulx Abbey.

Historically, same-sex female attraction was not a criminal offence. Because it wasn't covered by law or otherwise socially recognised, evidence for lesbianism or female bisexuality is often difficult to find. In the 18th century, however, among fashionable women, a cult of same-sex 'romantic friendship' was accepted. One famous case was linked with **Chiswick House** (p.41) in London,

which in the later 18th century was home to Georgiana, Duchess of Devonshire. We know from her letters and from contemporary accounts that Georgiana formed passionate attachments to a number of women and in at least two cases her love was reciprocated, but we don't know how she would have described her sexuality: she also had a number of relationships with men.

The architects John Seely and Paul Paget were partners in life as well as in one of the most noteworthy architectural firms of the 20th century. They went into business together in 1922, when they were in their early twenties, and lived and worked together until Seely's death. Each referred to the other as 'the partner', and their friends and families used 'the partners' when speaking of them too. Their greatest architectural triumph was the transformation of **Eltham Palace** (p.38), a medieval palace on the outskirts of London, into an art deco mansion, completed in 1936.

Of the hundreds of people honoured with London blue plaques, many lived outside the accepted sexual norms of the time, from Oscar Wilde and Alan Turing to Virginia Woolf and Radclyffe Hall. Some were persecuted for it, and some helped to challenge public perceptions of gender and sexuality. All made significant contributions to our society, culture and shared history. The LGBTQ+ History hub on the English Heritage website offers insights into the histories of those honoured by blue plaques, and more.

The myriad lives which have been lived within the walls of English Heritage sites can never be fully known, as evidence of love, affection and relationships, especially those that existed outside the margins of acceptability, is often hidden or lost entirely. However, the indelible marks made by LGBTQ+ people in the past, whether they were able to live their lives openly or not, tell a story of defiance, strength and individuality.

Bridgerton
Ranger's
House,
Greenwich
Park

Sites on screen

Many of our historic sites have starred on screens both big and small – and not just in period dramas. In fact, in the past few years, they've been popular locations for some big-budget blockbuster movies.

Death of Stalin
Wrest Park, Bedfordshire

Mrs Brown
Osborne, Isle of Wight

Kid Who Would Be King
Tintagel Castle, Cornwall

Belle
Kenwood, Hampstead

The crew of *Avengers: Age of Ultron* (2015) took over several areas of **Dover Castle** during their shoot, and you can see the Secret Wartime Tunnels in the film's opening sequence. Rival mega-franchise *Transformers* used **Stonehenge** and **Rievaulx Abbey** as locations in 2017's *The Last Knight*. Arthurian myths and magic were brought into the 21st century at **Tintagel Castle** in *The Kid Who Would Be King* (2019), **Tilbury Fort** was a key location in 2017's *Wonder Woman*, and the grand Georgian shell of **Sutton Scarsdale Hall** stood in for the charred remains of Wayne Manor in 2016's *Batman vs Superman: Dawn of Justice*. **Waverley Abbey** has appeared in 2017's *The Mummy*, 2014's *Into the Woods* and 2016's *The Huntsman: Winter's War*.

Our sites made appearances in two 1990s hits. **Kenwood** appeared in *Notting Hill* (1999) as a location for a film-within-a-film, and *Robin Hood: Prince of Thieves* (1991) filmed on **Hadrian's Wall** and at **Old Wardour Castle**.

Book adaptations on screens both big and small often feature our sites. **Kirby Hall** stood in for *Mansfield Park* in a 1999 film version of Jane Austen's novel, which also filmed at **Kenwood**. **Wingfield Manor** doubled as the ruins of Thornfield Hall in a 2011 version of *Jane Eyre*, and a 2006 TV adaptation set Lowood School at **Bolsover Castle**. 2020's *Dracula* series featured **Whitby Abbey** and **Dover Castle**, while **Bradford-on-Avon Tithe Barn** appeared in *Wolf Hall* in

2015 and the 2018 series *Vanity Fair* filmed at **Marble Hill**. **Eltham Palace** was used in *Brideshead Revisited* (2008).

Our sites also pop up in films and shows focusing on the lives of notable people. *Belle* (2013) explored the story of **Kenwood** resident Dido Belle and filmed at the house. **Warkworth** and **Aydon castles** featured in *Elizabeth* (1998) and a 2019 film about *Mary Queen of Scots* was filmed at **Harmondsworth Great Barn**. *The Crown* (2016-) has used **Audley End House**, **Dover Castle** and **Eltham Palace**, with the latter doubling as a Hollywood dressing room in 2018's *Stan and Ollie*. Queen Victoria's **Osborne** appeared in 2017's *Victoria and Abdul*, 1997's *Mrs Brown* and the ITV series *Victoria*. **Brodsworth Hall** was also used in that series, as it was in *Darkest Hour* (2017).

More broadly, films and shows with period settings have made good use of our sites. **Wrest Park's** drawing room doubled as Moscow's Pillar Hall in Armando Iannucci's *Death of Stalin* (2017), and the house featured in TV series *Harlots* (2019-), *Belgravia* and *The Great* (both 2020). **Eltham Palace** was used in 2020's *Misbehaviour*, and **Tilbury Fort** appeared in *Tulip Fever* (2017), *Peterloo* (2018) and TV series *Taboo* (2017). Meanwhile **Ranger's House** doubled as the frontage of the home to the eponymous family in Netflix's *Bridgerton* (2020).

Look out for more of our sites on your screens in the year ahead.

Conisbrough Castle, South Yorkshire

Home of Charles Darwin, Down House, Kent

Sites in
literature

The places in our care have left their mark on England's literature, as well as on its history. Here's a selection of some of the novels, stories and poems inspired by our sites.

Whitby Abbey, North Yorkshire

Bram Stoker set key scenes of *Dracula* in the shadow of **Whitby Abbey**, described by Mina Murray in the novel 'as a most noble ruin, of immense size, and full of beautiful and romantic bits'. Stoker came across the name 'Dracula' (meaning 'son of the dragon') while reading about Romanian history in Whitby's public library.

Our medieval castles feature in various fictional takes on history, including **Warkworth Castle**, which appears as the Percy family's 'worm-eaten hold of ragged stone' in Shakespeare's *Henry IV*. Sir Walter Scott's *Ivanhoe* features **Conisbrough**

Stonehenge, Wiltshire

Kenilworth Castle and Elizabethan Garden, Warwickshire

and **Ashby de la Zouch** castles, and in *Kenilworth*, Scott uses the eponymous castle as a backdrop to explore rumours surrounding Robert Dudley and Elizabeth I. Scott also used **Peveril Castle** as a setting in *Peveril of the Peak*, while **Norham** and **Barnard** castles appear in his poems.

Geoffrey of Monmouth's far-fetched medieval bestseller *Historia Regum Britanniae* described how Merlin brought **Stonehenge** to Salisbury Plain from a mountain in Ireland. The stones are the setting for the climax of Thomas Hardy's *Tess of the D'Urbervilles* (1891), and William Wordsworth wrote about them in his poem 'Guilt and Sorrow': 'Pile of Stone-henge! So proud to hint yet keep/ Thy secrets…'.

The *Historia* also features **Tintagel Castle** as a mighty fortress in which Merlin casts a spell on Uther Pendragon to help him 'seduce' the lady of the castle. King Arthur is conceived as a result. Sir Thomas Malory and Alfred Lord Tennyson included the castle in their own retellings of the Arthurian legend – the latter describing it as 'half in sea, and high on land,/A crown of towers.' It also makes appearances in versions of the Tristan and Iseult legend written by Charles Swinburne, Thomas Hardy and Rosemary Sutcliff.

Sutcliff also set her *The Eagle of the Ninth* (1954) at **Hadrian's Wall**, describing it as 'a great gash of stonework, still raw with newness… leaping along

with the jagged contours of the land'. The Roman frontier famously inspired George R.R. Martin's huge ice wall in *Game of Thrones* (1996), and it is the grim setting for W.H. Auden's poem, 'Roman Wall Blues', in which a soldier complains: 'Over the heather the wet wind blows,/I've lice in my tunic and a cold in my nose'.

Some of our sites provided inspiration to writers, even if they didn't appear in the works themselves. John Hawley, the MP, merchant, mayor and privateer who built the first fortress at **Dartmouth Castle**, is thought to have inspired the character of 'the shipman' in Geoffrey Chaucer's *Canterbury Tales*. The complicated will of an 18th-century owner of **Brodsworth Hall** probably gave Charles Dickens the idea for the Jarndyce v Jarndyce case in *Bleak House*, and **Netley Abbey** may well have been Jane Austen's model for *Northanger Abbey*. In his famous diaries Samuel Pepys records drinking 'much good liquor' on one of his visits to **Audley End House**, which no doubt provided him with inspiration of sorts. For decades, **Down House** was Charles Darwin's home and laboratory, and today you can stand in the study where he wrote *On the Origin of Species* (1859).

We hope this literary list has given you some good ideas for your next day out, whether you're in search of inspiration or simply looking for a quiet place to sit down with a good book.

Glossary

Whether at a prehistoric monument or an art deco palace, you can understand more about our sites with these helpful explanations of just a few of the features you may come across when visiting.

PREHISTORIC SITES

Barrow
Artificial mound of earth, turf and/or stone, normally constructed to contain or conceal burials. Long barrows date from the early Neolithic period, round barrows mostly from the early Bronze Age.

Fogou *(pronounced foogoo)*
A stone-built tunnel, generally within a settlement, exclusively in west Cornwall and Scilly. Their purpose is still debated; suggestions have included storage, refuge from attack, and ritual.

Henge
Circular or sub-circular enclosure defined by a bank and (usually internal) ditch, with one or two (rarely more) entrances. Of ceremonial/ritual function, they contain a variety of internal features, sometimes including timber or stone circles. They date mainly from the late Neolithic period, 3000-2400 BC.

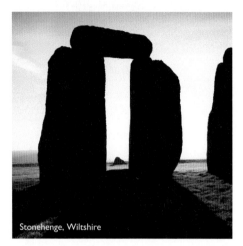
Stonehenge, Wiltshire

Sarsen
A large sandstone boulder. In the chalklands, these boulders were often used as standing stones. They get their name from 'Saracen' in the medieval sense of 'pagan, heathen'.

Trilithon
A structure composed of two large upright stones supporting a third, lintel stone.

ROMAN SITES

Basilica
A high-roofed rectangular hall used for legal and administrative purposes. It usually forms part of an important public building, such as the principia.

Hypocaust
An underfloor heating system found in expensive houses and bath-houses.

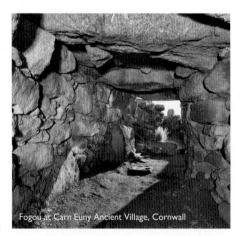
Fogou at Carn Euny Ancient Village, Cornwall

Housesteads Roman Fort, Northumberland

Inscription
Writing carved into stone. The Romans adorned buildings, memorial stones and religious objects with inscriptions.

Legionary
A citizen soldier of the Roman army. They were organised into legions of around 5,000 soldiers.

Principia
The command centre of a Roman fort, where the unit's standards and pay were kept.

Vicus
A settlement of military veterans, traders and civilians outside a Roman fort.

CASTLES

Barbican
An outward extension of a gateway, forming an enclosure outside the castle's main defences.

Scarborough Castle, North Yorkshire

Crenellation
The head of a castle wall, comprising higher sections (merlons) alternating with lower openings (crenels or embrasures).

Garderobe
A latrine, usually discharging into a cesspit or through an outlet into a moat or ditch.

Hoard or Hourd
Covered timber gallery overhanging the top of a wall, for the defence of the wall below.

Machicolation
An opening at the head of a wall or in a vaulted ceiling, allowing defenders to shoot weapons or drop stones onto attackers.

Dover Castle, Kent

MONASTERIES

Chapter House
The room in which the monks or nuns held daily meetings, including the reading of a chapter of the Rule of the monastic order.

Day Stair/Night Stair
Stairways leading from the dormitory for day and night-time use: the day stairs led to the cloister, the night stairs to the church.

Order
The international grouping to which each monastery or nunnery belonged, following a particular Rule (e.g. Benedictine, Cistercian, Carthusian).

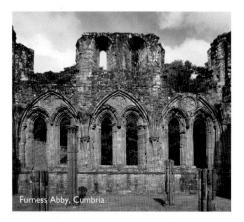
Furness Abby, Cumbria

Reredorter
A building containing the latrines, sometimes flushed by a channel of running water.

Warming house
The only room in a monastery where a communal fire was kept burning during the winter months.

COUNTRY HOUSES

Coach house
A structure, often close to the stables, in which coaches or carriages were kept under cover.

Drawing room
Derived from 'withdrawing room', space in the house used by the members of the family for recreational purposes after dinner or for receiving guests.

Osborne, Isle of Wight

Orangery
Building, either attached to the house or separate, for keeping orange and other citrus fruit trees warm over winter.

Portico
The centrepiece of a house's façade, usually forming a covered way over the entrance.

Scullery
Room within the service wing of a country house, in which meat and vegetables were washed and prepared, and crockery, cutlery and other utensils were cleaned.

Audley End House and Gardens, Essex

HISTORIC PARKS AND GARDENS

Grotto – An artificial rocky cave or a small garden building, sometimes decorated with shells.

Ha-ha – A dry ditch which divides the formal garden from the parkland without interrupting the view.

Parterre – A level space in a garden occupied by ornamental flowerbeds, often symmetrical in design.

Topiary – Trees or shrubs pruned and trained into shapes, particularly geometric, bird or animal forms.

Patte d'oie – A layout where several straight paths or avenues radiate from a single point. Patte d'oie means 'goose foot' in French.

Details of OS LandRanger and Explorer map references are provided for easy location of each property, with specific map numbers (LandRanger, Explorer) followed by the grid reference.

NB. Contains Ordnance Survey data © Crown Copyright and database rights 2016. Additional map information © English Heritage 2022. Map created by Oxford Cartographers Ltd.

MIX
Paper from responsible sources
FSC
www.fsc.org   FSC® C014496

English Heritage Handbook 2022/23

For English Heritage:
Luke Whitcomb, Louise Dando, Tom Dennis, Johanna Lovesey, Tersia Boorer, Richard Leatherdale, Tom Moriarty and Charles Kightly.

Design and Publishing:
Ledgard Jepson Ltd.
For Ledgard Jepson Ltd:
David Exley, Bev Turbitt, Andrea Rollinson, Liam Atkinson.

Cover Concept and Art Direction: Tony Dike (for English Heritage).

Cover Artwork: Luke Edward Hall.

Print: Produced by GGP Media GmbH, Pößneck, Germany.

Images: All images in this handbook are © English Heritage or © Historic England unless otherwise stated.

The following symbols indicate facilities available at the English Heritage properties listed in this handbook.

ACQ.1945	Date property came into the National Collection
♿	Adult changing facilities
🎧	Audio tours
👶	Baby changing facilities
🍴	Café
🎠	Children's play area
♿	Disabled access
🐕	Dogs allowed on leads
📖	Educational resources
🎭	Events
E	Exhibition
👪	Family learning resources
🎬	Film/TV location
❀	Gardens
📖	Guidebook available
🍽	Hire of properties for corporate and private events
🏠	Holiday cottage to let
🔔	Licensed for civil ceremonies
🐄	Livestock grazing on/around site
🚆	Local railway station
🚹🚺	Male/female toilet
🏛	Museum
🦮	Assistance dogs allowed only
OVP	OVP – admission free for Overseas Visitor Pass holders
♣	Park
P	Parking
🅰	Picnic area
🛍	Shop
☕	Tearoom
♿	Toilets with disabled access
⚠	Site may contain hazardous features

Please note: All of our sites have uneven surfaces due to their historic and/or outdoor nature so please wear appropriate footwear. Please observe site signage, barriers and staff instructions. Please supervise children closely. Metal detecting, smoking, fires, BBQs and unauthorised commercial photography and drones are prohibited at all our properties. Damage to our sites is a crime.